Simple and Fun Antennas for Hams

Authors
Chuck Hutchinson, K8CH
Dean Straw, N6BV

Production
Shelly Bloom, WB1ENT
Jodi Morin, KA1JPA
Joe Shea
Paul Lappen
Stephie Nelson, KA1IFB
Jayne Pratt Lovelace

Technical Illustrations
Dave Pingree, N1NAS
Michael Daniels

Cover Design
Sue Fagan

Contents

4 Antenna Masts and Supports

Projects:

5 HF Verticals

Projects:

6 More Simple and Fun Antennas for VHF and UHF

Projects:

7   More HF Dipoles

Projects:

8   Dual-Band VHF/UHF Antennas

Projects:

9   An HF Vertical That Needs No Radials—Try the HVD

Projects:

10   Yet More HF Dipoles

Projects:

11   More Facts About Feed Lines

12   A Potpourri of Antenna Ideas

Projects:

13   VHF Beam Antennas

Projects:

14   A Potpourri of Antenna Ideas

Towers

15   HF Beam Antennas

Projects:

16   Getting the Most Out of Your Antenna

Foreword

SIMPLE AND FUN ANTENNAS FOR HAMS

The title describes this book. It *is* all about antennas that are simple (neither complicated nor huge), that are fun, and that work.

For some time we've wanted to make a book like this one available to you: A book that doesn't get all tangled up in advanced theoretical concepts, but provides enough explanation for you to understand what you're reading; a book that is full of practical projects that you can build with confidence.

We put two of our best men on it: our *Antenna Book* editor, Dean Straw, N6BV, and the recently retired Chuck Hutchinson, K8CH. From their respective homes in urban California and rural Michigan they've worked to put *Simple and Fun Antennas for Hams* together just for you. At least they say that they worked. The evidence suggests that they actually enjoyed it.

I'm pleased with what they've done, and I believe that you will be too. Let us at ARRL HQ know what you think. We'd appreciate hearing from you about any errors that may have crept into the book or about suggestions on how we could make this book even more useful to you. A form for mailing your comments is included at the back of the book, or you can e-mail us at: **pubsfdbk@arrl.org.**

David Sumner, K1ZZ
Executive Vice President
Newington, Connecticut
February, 2002

IBM PC modeling data files for *Simple and Fun Antennas for Hams* are available on *ARRLWeb*: **http://www.arrl.org/notes/8624/**. These are input files for the modeling programs *EZNEC* (by W7EL) and *YW* (Yagi for Windows, available bundled with the 19th Edition of *The ARRL Antenna Book*.)

About the ARRL

The seed for Amateur Radio was planted in the 1890s, when Guglielmo Marconi began his experiments in wireless telegraphy. Soon he was joined by dozens, then hundreds, of others who were enthusiastic about sending and receiving messages through the air—some with a commercial interest, but others solely out of a love for this new communications medium. The United States Government began licensing Amateur Radio operators in 1912.

By 1914, there were thousands of Amateur Radio operators—hams—in the United States. Hiram Percy Maxim, a leading Hartford, Connecticut, inventor and industrialist, saw the need for an organization to band together this fledgling group of radio experimenters. In May 1914 he founded the American Radio Relay League (ARRL) to meet that need.

Today, ARRL with approximately 170,000 members is the largest organization of radio amateurs in the United States. The ARRL is a not-for-profit organization that:

- promotes interest in Amateur Radio communications and experimentation
- represents US radio amateurs in legislative matters, and
- maintains fraternalism and a high standard of conduct among Amateur Radio operators.

At ARRL headquarters in the Hartford suburb of Newington, the staff helps serve the needs of members. ARRL is also International Secretariat for the International Amateur Radio Union, which is made up of similar societies in 150 countries around the world.

ARRL publishes the monthly journal QST, as well as newsletters and many other publications covering all aspects of Amateur Radio. Its headquarters station, W1AW, transmits bulletins of interest to radio amateurs and Morse code practice sessions. The ARRL also coordinates an extensive field organization, which includes volunteers who provide technical information and other support services for radio amateurs as well as communications for public-service activities. In addition, ARRL represents US amateurs with the Federal Communications Commission and other government agencies in the US and abroad.

Membership in ARRL means much more than receiving QST each month. In addition to the services already described, ARRL offers membership services on a personal level, such as the ARRL Volunteer Examiner Coordinator Program and a QSL bureau.

Full ARRL membership (available only to licensed radio amateurs) gives you a voice in how the affairs of the organization are governed. ARRL policy is set by a Board of Directors (one from each of 15 Divisions). Each year, one-third of the ARRL Board of Directors stands for election by the full membership they represent. The day-to-day operation of ARRL HQ is managed by an Executive Vice President and his staff.

No matter what aspect of Amateur Radio attracts you, ARRL membership is relevant and important. There would be no Amateur Radio as we know it today were it not for the ARRL. We would be happy to welcome you as a member! (An Amateur Radio license is not required for Associate Membership.) For more information about ARRL and answers to any questions you may have about Amateur Radio, write or call:

ARRL—The national association for Amateur Radio
225 Main Street
Newington CT 06111-1494
Voice: 860-594-0200
Fax: 860-594-0259
E-mail: **hq@arrl.org**
Internet: **www.arrl.org/**

Prospective new amateurs call (toll-free):
800-32-NEW HAM (800-326-3942)
You can contact us also via e-mail at **newham@arrl.org**

1 Your First VHF Antenna

And the survey shows...that most of us are active on 2-meter FM. In fact, 2-meter FM is the most popular band and mode for US hams—it's where we tend to go for local contact.

Your experience is no doubt different, but apart from listening for and working DXpeditions and operating in contests, I spend most of my ham time monitoring or operating on the local (2-meter) ARES repeater. It's the place to be in bad weather or when I just want to talk to local ham friends.

It may surprise you to know that a large number of us hams only own a hand-held radio. All things considered, it shouldn't be a shock. They are reasonably priced and can be operated from just about anywhere.

When my wife (K8SYL) and I (K8CH) moved into our current house, we found ourselves a bit too far from the N8ZMT (Ionia County Michigan ARES) repeater for reliable communications with our hand-held transceiver. After a couple of weeks of checking into the ARES net while standing in the *right* place, I decided to build a better antenna for the hand-held. The idea is not original, but it is simple, easy and effective. Later, I'll share some thoughts on mounting the antenna.

THE SIMPLEST 2-METER GROUND PLANE

Thirty years ago, while working for Motorola, I heard a story that the engineering department had developed plans for a new product. It was a ground-plane antenna, and it had only two radials. Those plans lasted until the marketing department saw it. At marketing's insistence, the two radials

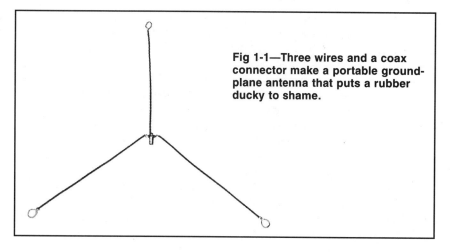

Fig 1-1—Three wires and a coax connector make a portable ground-plane antenna that puts a rubber ducky to shame.

became four. They said it made it look better and that it would be easier to sell.

Did it really happen that way? I don't know—that's not the point. The point of the story is that two radials really are enough. I'd used that concept to build antennas for HF in the past, but this time I needed a simple but effective 2-meter antenna, and it needed to provide some gain over the hand-held's rubber ducky antenna.

I didn't have to look to know that I had the necessary parts—about two feet of #12 Romex (house wire) and an SO-239 coax connector. I also had the solder, flux and soldering gun to connect the wires to the connector.

The antenna is illustrated in **Fig 1-1**. The sidebar (*How Ground-Plane Antennas Work*) explains a bit of the theory. Some of the following material may look familiar. It should because it has appeared in several recent editions of *The ARRL Antenna Book* and in *The ARRL Handbook*. Some newcomers, however, may not have seen

this design before, and I have also included some new, practical tips at the end of the chapter.

The W1VT Version of the Simplest Ground-Plane Antenna

A few years ago, my friend Zack Lau, W1VT, published an elegant implementation of this antenna in (July 1991) *QST*. You can follow Zack's directions to build your own antenna. You'll find that the methods are sound and you won't go wrong with his design. Here's Zack's article as it appeared in *QST*.

The rubber ducky antennas common on hand-held VHF and UHF transceivers work fine in many situations. That's no surprise, considering that repeaters generally reside high and in the clear so you and your hand-held don't have to! Sometimes, though, you need a more efficient antenna that's just as portable as a hand-held. Here's one: A simple *ground-plane* antenna you can build—for 146, 223 or 440 MHz—in no time flat. It features wire-end loops for safety (sharp, straight wires are hazardous) and convenience (its top loop lets you hang it off high objects for best performance).

What You Need to Build One

All you'll need are wire (single-conductor, #12 THHN), solder and a female coax jack for the connector series of your choice. Many hardware stores sell THHN wire—that is, *Thermoplastic High Heat Resistant Nylon* Coated, solid-copper house wire—by the foot. Get 7 feet of wire for a 146-MHz antenna, 5 feet of wire for a 223-MHz antenna, or 3 feet of wire for a 440-MHz antenna. [You can also strip the solid copper wire out of a piece of Romex 3-conductor cable, as I mentioned before.—K8CH.]

The only tools you need are a 100-W soldering iron or gun; a yardstick, long ruler or tape measure; a pair of wire cutters; a ½-inch-diameter form for bending the wire loops (a section of hardwood dowel or metal tubing works fine), and a file (for smoothing rough cut-wire edges and filing the coax jack for soldering).

You may also find a sharp knife useful for removing the THHN insulation.

Building It

To build a 146-MHz antenna, cut three 24⅝-inch pieces from the wire you bought. To build a 223-MHz antenna, cut three 17⅝-inch pieces. To build a 440-MHz antenna, cut three 10⅝-inch pieces.

The photos show how to build the antenna, but they may not communicate why the cut lengths I prescribe are somewhat longer than the finished antenna's wires. Here's why: The extra wire allows you to bend and shape the loops by hand. The half-inch-diameter loop form helps you form the loops easily.

Form an end loop on each wire as shown in **Fig 1-2**. Strip exactly 4 inches of insulation from the wire. Using your ½-inch-diameter form, bend the loop and close it—right up against the wire insulation—with a two-turn twist as shown in the bottommost example in Fig 1-2. Cut off the excess wire (about ½ inch). Solder the two-turn twist. Do this for each of the antenna's three wires.

Strip exactly 3 inches of insulation

from the unlooped end of one of your wires and follow the steps shown in **Fig 1-3**. Solder the wire to the connector center conductor. (Soldering the wire to a coaxial jack's center pin takes considerable heat. A 700 to 750° F iron with a large tip, used in a draft-free room, works best. Don't try to do the job with an iron that draws less than 100 watts.) Cut off the extra wire (about ½ inch).

Strip exactly 3 inches of insulation from the unlooped ends of the remaining two wires. Loop their stripped ends—right up to the insulation—through opposing mounting holes on the connector flange. Solder them to the connector. (You may need to file the connector flange to get it to take solder better.) Cut off the excess wire (about 2¼ inches per wire). This completes construction.

Adjusting the Antenna for Best Performance

Bend the antenna's two lower wires to form 120° angles with the vertical wire. (No, you don't need a protractor: Simply position the wires so they just about trisect a circle.) If you have no means of measuring SWR at your antenna's operating frequency, stop adjustment here and start enjoying your antenna! Every hand-held I know of should produce ample RF output into the impedance represented by the antenna and its feed line.

Adjusting the antenna for minimum SWR is worth doing if you have an SWR meter or reflected-power indicator that works at your frequency of interest. Connect the meter in line between your handheld and the antenna. Between short, identified test transmissions—on a simplex frequency—to check the SWR, adjust the angle between the lower wires and the vertical wire for minimum SWR (or reflected power). (You can also adjust the antenna by changing the length of its wires, but you shouldn't have to do this to obtain an acceptable SWR.) Before considering the job done, test the antenna in the clear to be sure your adjustments still play. (Nearby objects can detune an antenna.)

Plug and Play

As you use the ground-plane antenna, keep in mind that its coax connector's center wasn't made to bear

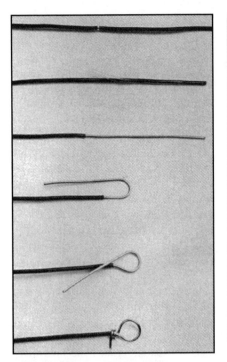

Fig 1-2—Making loops on the antenna wires requires that you remove exactly 4 inches of insulation from each. Stripping THHN insulation is easier if you remove its clear plastic jacket first.

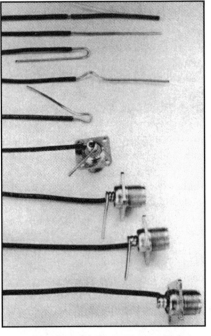

Fig 1-3—Remove exactly 3 inches of insulation to attach the vertical wire to the coax connector center pin. This photo shows an SO-239 (UHF-series) jack; Fig 1-1 shows a BNC jack. Use whatever your application requires.

weight and may break if stressed too much. Barring that, your ground-plane antenna should require no maintenance at all.

There you go: You may not have built a monument to radio science, but you've home-constructed a portable antenna that'll get much more mileage from your hand-held than its stock rubber ducky. Who said useful ham gear has to be hard or expensive to build?

THE K8CH PROTOTYPE VERSION OF THE SIMPLEST GROUND-PLANE ANTENNA

As you look at the W1VT antenna, you can see the strong mechanical connection between wire and connector. It's strong because this technique does not rely on solder for strength; it provides a strong durable mechanical connection.

When I built my own version, I wanted to make it simpler and easy to tune. For that reason, in the first prototype I did not wrap the vertical conductor around the connector. Rather, I merely placed the wire in the connector's center pin and soldered it. It's not as durable, but it works and should last a long time if the antenna is not subject to undue stress.

When I slit open the 2-foot length of Romex, I was left with three wires. One was a bare conductor, the other two were insulated—one black and one white. To make things look *right*, I stripped away all insulation.

To begin, I formed loops at the ends of the elements as described earlier. Before soldering the wraps, I removed any exposed sharp edges with a file. The loops are not an electrical necessity; rather they are there for safety and convenience. (Didn't your mother warn you about poking out your eye?) The loop at the top of the vertical element also provides a place to attach a short piece of string for mounting the antenna.

I built the prototype in my basement ham shack. As shown in **Fig 1-4**, my antenna ended up with all three elements 19-inches long. I started by attaching the two radials to the coax connector. I made each radial exactly 19-inches long. For the vertical element, I started with a length of 19³/₄ inches, which is a bit long to begin, and pruned it for a good SWR.

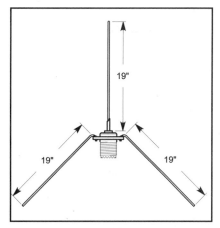

Fig 1-4—Final dimensions of the K8CH version of the simplest ground-plane antenna. If you are going to tune your antenna for best SWR, make the upright (vertical) element about an inch longer to begin. Prune about ¼ inch at a time.

I then adjusted the position of the lower wires for the best SWR.

I used a piece of nylon string to hang the antenna from an overhead joist in a clear part of the basement away from other objects. That evening, I checked into the county ARES net with the antenna still hanging in the basement. It worked! Yes, it works even better upstairs.

A NO-BEND VERSION OF THE SIMPLEST GROUND-PLANE ANTENNA

Soft-drawn copper wire bends easily. That's what you want for house wiring. It's not a benefit in an antenna that you want to hold a shape. What to do about it?

You could use copper-clad steel wire. It's strong and stiff and the kind of wire you might use to build an HF dipole. I didn't have any of this at hand, so I tried a different approach for my next version.

I visited a local tool shop that sells welding supplies. It cost me a dollar and a couple of pennies to leave the place. In my hand I had three 36-inch lengths of brazing rod.

Brazing rod is very stiff, a good conductor and easy to solder. Because it's stiff, don't try to make tight bends or wraps with it.

I formed the loops at the ends of my brazing-rod elements by wrapping

the wire around a socket from my ¼-inch-drive socket set. I used a pair of locking pliers to hold the end of the rod tight against the socket while forming the loop. Don't make a wrap at the end of the loop. Just close the circle and solder so that there are no open ends or sharp edges that might poke or snag.

I like the stiffness of the finished antenna. However, that stiffness makes it more difficult to work with the brazing rod. For most situations this is overkill. In other words, you'll probably do well with a copper-wire version. However, you might want to think about the alternatives that are available to you.

SUPPORTING THE ANTENNA INDOORS

One of the benefits of the simplest ground plane is that it has only two dimensions. That means that it's a lot easier to mount or conceal this antenna. Here are some ideas.

I mounted my antenna in a window and had satisfactory results. Donna Burch, W8QOY, tried mounting her 2-meter antenna in a window, but it didn't work well at all. When she mounted it against an inner wall in her apartment it worked fine. Evidently metal in her windows was the culprit. Later, I tried a number of different locations in my house and found best results with the antenna just hanging on a wall away from the windows. Eventually, the antenna ended up behind a wall hanging (a souvenir of Ecuador) where it is out of sight and yet performs well. You may want to experiment with various locations around your home.

Recently, Donna moved to another apartment complex. She mounted her old antenna in the center of a window—the traverse rod provides a handy support. The results were at best marginal. With help from a couple of friends, she tried her antenna in various locations around the apartment. Today, the antenna hangs by a short loop of string from a picture hook on an outer wall. She has a full-quieting signal into the county ARES repeater.

Curtain or traverse rods and picture hooks are obvious support candidates for this antenna. However, make sure you have no metal-to-metal contacts. There are two reasons for that. First, it will detune your antenna. (The

HOW GROUND-PLANE ANTENNAS WORK

Before trying to understand how a ground-plane antenna works, let's start with the most fundamental type of antenna of all—a *half-wave dipole*. You'll find a lot more information about dipoles in later chapters of this book.

Fig A1 shows a dipole mounted in its most common configuration—horizontally over ground. Overall, it is about a half wavelength long and is constructed using wire, separated by three insulators, with a feed line connected across the middle insulator. It should not come as a big surprise that this is known officially as a *horizontal half-wave dipole*.

You can also see that a half-wave dipole consists of two quarter-wave portions, leading to its dipole name, literally meaning "two poles." Incidentally, the Greek letter λ is a shorthand notation for "wavelength," something you'll see frequently throughout this book.

Fig A2 shows the same dipole, but it has now been mounted vertically over ground, where it is (surprise!) known as a *vertical half-wave dipole*. Continuing this evolutionary process, Fig A3 shows one half of the vertical dipole mounted just above the ground, with an "image antenna" extending down below the actual antenna. This theoretical configuration—where the image makes up the missing half of the vertical dipole—is often called a *monopole*, since it consists of "one pole" rather than the "two poles" of a dipole. Note that the feed line has been eliminated in this drawing for clarity. In practice, you would connect one conductor of the feed line to the wire at the top of the bottom insulator. The second conductor of the feed line would be connected to the ground itself.

Now, look at Fig A4, which shows the final evolutionary stage of our dipole. Here, the quarter-wave radiator has been raised some height above the ground

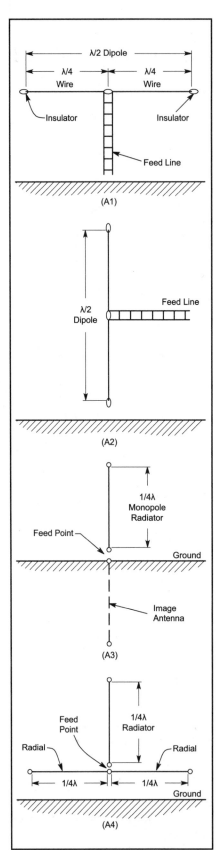

(A1)

(A2)

(A3)

(A4)

(say, mounted on a garage roof) and two quarter-wave *radials* have been connected to the bottom insulator and stretched out horizontally. These radials act as a surrogate ground, and since this surrogate is flat (like an "X-Y plane") this leads to the terminology *ground plane*. [OK, this may not be that obvious, but that's how such fancy names come about!]

As author K8CH points out in the text, the original ground-plane antenna used only two radials, but subsequent designs usually used four radials—simply because they looked more symmetrical and thus more pleasing to the eye. And that's how legends come about!

The sequence going from Fig A2 to Fig A4 illustrates the essential physical equivalence of these layouts. We'll get into this in some more detail in later chapters, but the electrical performance is a bit different for these two antennas. The feed-point impedance for a vertical half-wave dipole located close to the ground is somewhere in the vicinity of 90 Ω, while that for a quarter-wave ground-plane antenna is one half of that value. If you tilt the radials downwards you can raise the feed-point impedance to 50 Ω, for a 1:1 SWR for 50-Ω coax cable.
—*Dean Straw, N6BV*

Fig A—At A1, a typical half-wave horizontal dipole mounted above flat ground and fed in the center. At A2, the same dipole, but now turned vertical. At A3, the vertical half-wave dipole has been cut in half to make a quarter-wave radiator, mounted just above the ground. The "missing half" is made up by an "image antenna" mirrored in the plane of the ground. At A4, the progression continues to have a quarter-wave vertical radiator and two ground-plane radials, creating the "ground-plane antenna."

Fig 1-5—Technique for supporting the simplest ground-plane antenna by a nylon line. The support line runs through the antenna's top loop (at left) and is secured to the coax below the connector (at right). This minimizes strain on the antenna and coax connectors while providing solid support for the coax.

Fig 1-6—The antenna can be supported atop a length of PVC tubing. Simply run the coax feed line through the tubing and secure the tubing to an appropriate support. Notches cut in the top of the tubing allow the SO-239 connector to sit flat against the top of mast.

CAMOUFLAGE YOUR GROUND PLANE

Drapes can conceal an antenna from folks on the inside—or outside. In either case make sure that the antenna will not snag on drapes, curtains or blinds when they are operated normally.

You can apply spray paint to your antenna so that it blends with its surroundings. Make sure you don't paint the part of the coax connector where you connect your feed line.

Non-metallic adornments can be used to conceal the true function of your antenna if you want. However, you'll want to make sure that the effect is in harmony with your house and your personality. Feel free to use your imagination, but temper it with good sense and good taste.

SUPPORTING THE ANTENNA OUTDOORS

The simplest ground-plane antenna is not rugged enough for permanent outdoor mounting. There may be times, however, when you'd like to use it temporarily outdoors.

Perhaps the easiest solution is to toss a length of light nylon or Dacron

Fig 1-7—Photo of the PVC tubing mast lashed to a deck railing with a length of 3/16-inch Dacron line.

Fig 1-8—Photo of a short PVC mast lashed to a plastic outdoor chair. This will work, but a wind may tip it over if there is not sufficient weight in the chair.

metallic object in contact with the antenna becomes part of the antenna.)

Second, and more important, it can generate interference. An imperfect metal-to-metal contact can act as a diode, which will create harmonics. For those reasons, I prefer to use a short length of nylon twine to support my ground-plane antenna in the house.

Don't limit your experiments to window and wall mounting locations. You may realize satisfactory performance from your antenna by mounting it inside a closet or behind a piece of furniture. Just keep it away from metal objects.

line over a tree branch and support the antenna from that line. You need to remember that this is not a rugged antenna. For that same reason, I suggest that you run your line through the loop at the top of the antenna and extend it down the vertical wire tying it securely around the coax below the connector. The technique is illustrated in **Fig 1-5**.

If you use this technique, try to avoid hoisting the antenna past branches that could cause damage to the antenna. Also remember that the angle of the radials can make it more difficult to lower the antenna without damage than it was to raise it.

Using PVC Tubing for Mast

Another support technique, with which I've had good results, uses a length of PVC tubing to support this antenna. The idea, shown in **Fig 1-6**, is simple. The coax feed line for the antenna runs through a length of PVC tubing, and the antenna sits at the top of the tubing. The antenna is held in place by the weight of the coax.

I first used 1-inch schedule 40 PVC tubing for my mast because I had some left over from another project. You'll find that a PL-259 (UHF series) coax connector will pass through ¾-inch tubing and a BNC series connector will pass through ½-inch tubing. Nevertheless, I prefer the 1-inch tubing because it is stiffer.

I've used this support mast to operate from the front deck of our house. I lashed the PVC tubing to the deck as shown in **Fig 1-7**. Like the antenna itself, this PVC mast is best for temporary use in an outdoor setting.

No deck? You could try the idea shown in **Fig 1-8**. It works, but don't leave it without a weight in the seat. Without sufficient weight in the chair, this setup may become unstable and is apt to blow over in a breeze. You can probably come up with a better implementation of this idea, and I encourage you to try. You can find more ideas for simple masts in the chapter on antenna masts and supports.

2 Your First HF Antenna

Some folks may argue that the most effective HF antenna is a monoband Yagi. Others are always on the ready to champion the case for the quad. These are indeed fine beam antennas, and if price is not a barrier, it's hard to beat a beam. However, to mount that beam you'll probably need a tower with its base, guy wires and anchors. After that you'll want a rotator with its control cable and control box. Finally you'll need a sturdy mast to support your beam. The price tag for all that hardware can be daunting.

Perhaps that's why in an *ARRLWeb* survey that asked the question: "What antenna do you use *most* on HF?" Only about one in every four (1752) of the 6600 respondents reported that a Yagi or a quad is their most-used antenna. By contrast, nearly one third (2057) answered that it is a dipole that they most use on HF. The results are shown in the sidebar *What Antenna Do You Use Most on HF*.

HOW MUCH ANTENNA?

Do you *really* need big beams and tall towers to have fun on ham radio? Good question. Let's look at how little an antenna is necessary to have fun.

It was 1960, and I was making adjustments on my Heath Sixer (a low-power 6-meter AM transceiver). I had disconnected my home-built 2-element beam and was transmitting into the #47 pilot lamp that I used for a dummy load. (It takes less than 1 W to light a #47 lamp to full brilliance.) While I was making those adjustments, I heard a familiar voice calling back to me. It was Terry, K8SMC (now N8TO). Terry reported with a chuckle that I was "weaker than normal," but still perfect copy at his house 20 miles away. I didn't

think that was possible! Would you?

I might have made something more of that experience, but I didn't. Years later another man would explore and document how little it takes to communicate by Amateur Radio.

EVERYTHING WORKS

Thomas Schiller, N6BT, has studied antenna measurements, and has given a number of presentations on them. He is an active ham and enjoys DXing and contesting. Tom developed

Photo 1—A #47 pilot lamp draws 0.15 A at 6.3 V. One is shown here beside a US quarter.

the antenna design philosophy for and is co-founder of Force 12, Inc. He also wrote, "Everything Works," which appeared in July 2000 *QST*. This article by Tom is quite illuminating, and for that reason I've included most of it here for your enjoyment and enlightenment. I invite you to read the following and think about what Tom has to say.

Performance Envelope

How many times have we heard someone say, "My antenna really 'works'"? What does the word, "work" mean? The answer is, everything does work, to one degree or another. I hope that everyone will agree that this statement is absolutely true. How well it "works" is the issue and this is the "performance envelope" of the antenna system.

The first time I presented this idea was at the ARRL Pacific Division Convention in the fall of 1998. It was well received and I was encouraged to completely rewrite all of my material. My revised presentation was first viewed at the ARRL Southwestern Division Convention in the fall of 1999. It was further augmented and presented a couple weeks later to a packed double room audience at the ARRL Pacific Division Convention. There were more than a few eyebrows raised when I began with the digital slide; "Everything Works." It seemed to be out of character for me, because I always focus on efficiency.

I followed with an example of my first antenna, which enabled me to make contacts all over the West Coast on the 40-meter Novice band. I was WV6KUQ and the year was 1959. It was a very simple antenna, since it was the screen on my bedroom window. I made contacts, so I thought it was doing all right.

My high school science teacher, the late "Doc" Gmelin, W6ZRJ, tactfully informed me that it probably was not the best antenna and that it could be improved. He was the one who had given me my Novice test, became my Elmer and later was my high school physics teacher. At his suggestion, and with my Dad's assistance (both he and my Mom always encouraged and supported my adventures), we put up a Windom antenna. It was easy and did not require coax. The Windom certainly was not the greatest, but it was a tremendous improvement over the window screen. The performance envelope of the antenna system had been extended.

Witnessing the obvious improvement between the window screen and the Windom sparked my long-term interest in antennas. The performance difference between the two could best be summarized as, "Wow! This is going to be a lot more fun." The Windom antenna enabled me to make my first out-of-state QSO with a fellow Novice back in Delevan, Wisconsin. This was almost 2,000 miles away and we talked for more than 30 minutes. We then put up a vertical antenna for 40 meters made by attaching a large, insulated stranded wire on a wooden 2 × 4 frame. The ground system was a single ground rod (not very efficient, I later learned). This antenna enabled me to make my first DX QSO with JA2CMD. With my Dad's help again, we graduated to a 2-element, trapped tribander, which we managed to raise to 30 feet on a telescoping mast atop the roof. From my experience it was so impressive that I thought it must be the absolute best antenna possible.

This impression, of course, was incorrect. It was only the best one I had used so far. It was my personal, limited perception, certainly not an accurate assessment of the true situation. Strange as it might seem, it has taken years to realize that most everyone goes through this same learning process. Today, even with all the books on various antenna subjects, there remains a similar gap between perception and reality. My reality came into sharp focus in 1983.

Gary Caldwell, VA7RR (WA6VEF at the time), and I went to Saipan for the CQWW CW contest (AH0C). I had operated twice before from the southern end of the island utilizing the exist-

ing quad antennas of Byrd Brunemeier and Don Bower who worked for Far East Broadcasting Company (FEBC). After setting up the stations, we were asked if we would rather move to the north end of the island and use the FEBC short-wave broadcast antennas. These were located on Marpi Cliff, about 400 feet above the ocean. That decision took about two seconds.

We had brought along a typical trapped (new) tribander and a 30-foot mast. We also had about 1200 feet of coax. The antennas made available for us at FEBC's site were three TCI-611 curtains; designed for operation between 8-18 MHz (we used them on 40, 20, 15 and 10 meters). Each one cost about $300,000 (in 1982 dollars) and consisted of a pair of 240-foot towers with 61 phased dipoles between them. There was a passive reflector behind all the dipoles and a switching system to move the main lobe from side-to-side. These are huge antenna systems! We set up the stations in the main operations building and the slew controls were behind us on a large panel. These curtain antennas were specified to provide 21-dBi gain and a F/B ratio of 20 dB. The tribander was specified to provide about 8.5 dBd, or 10.6 dBi. It was a fascinating observation that to achieve an additional (theoretical) 10 dB over the trapped tribander required so much more hardware (and money).

I have kicked myself ever since for not having a tape recorder to share the experience of the difference between our trapped tribander and the curtains. We had been listening on the tribander while we did other things. The sun had already slipped below the rim of the Pacific Ocean when Gary suggested we hook up the curtain for 15 meters. It was late evening by the time we had attached a 4:1 coaxial balun to the large open-wire feed line heading out to one of the curtains. We were ready to do the classic "antenna A, antenna B" comparison, but the band was almost dead. We plugged the curtain feed line into an antenna selector, flipped the switch and were not ready for what we heard: the band came alive with all kinds of signals. It sounded more like midday. It was like turning on a light bulb in a dark room. We had an incredible QSO with HZIAB that is etched in our minds forever.

We made signal comparisons, both with 100 W to our antennas and with another station on Guam who was running 1 kW to a larger tribander. The difference between the antennas was unbelievable. HZIAB said both tribanders were 57 and the curtain was at least S9+40: an S-meter difference of about 50 dB.

Part of the signal level difference can be attributed to the location and the take-off angle of the cliff. Our 100 W to the tribander was the same as the kilowatt on Guam, so the cliff location made up the power difference, or about 10 dB; however, both our tribander and the curtain were looking over the same cliff. To try to satisfy everyone on this comparison, let us make an impossible assumption that the difference between the curtain and our tribander locations (in reference to the same cliff) accounts for 30 dB. The remaining difference is still 20 dB and must be attributed to the performance envelopes of the tribander and the curtain.

The true difference between the antennas was so far removed from the specifications that something did not make sense. Our performance envelope had been recalibrated to a limit that can be achieved only by a handful of antenna systems used in Amateur Radio. The challenge to understand the observed difference in performance envelopes led me to design, build, and evaluate hundreds of antennas. These efforts answered the questions about performance and also became the genesis and core of an antenna design philosophy, which has since been produced and marketed commercially.

The Illuminator Project

The performance envelope addresses the practical relationship between enjoyment of Amateur Radio and antenna performance. The entire station should be considered. However, the radios available today are all pretty good, so the antenna system is the major key. The primary effort in "The Illuminator" project was to quantify antennas (performance in dBi) and relate this to true performance. The basic chart relating performance to enjoyment is shown in **Fig 2-1**. It was developed with the assistance of many knowledgeable people, including typical amateurs, DXers, contesters and manufacturers.

The chart is intended to indicate the relationship between generalized antennas and expected enjoyment of Amateur Radio. It is certainly not a comprehensive representation of all antenna types and what can be accomplished. The ranges across the bottom of the chart, however, are pretty good indicators of antennas amateurs have used. The chart does not indicate take-off angle, which is very important for working DX, but not everyone is interested in working long distances. Fig 2-1 is used to represent relative increases in enjoyment of radio through improvements in antenna efficiency.

The center "Dipole in Clear" is a horizontal dipole in the clear at about $^1/_3$ - $^1/_2$ wavelength high. This is an efficient antenna and it is horizontally polarized, so it has ground reflection gain. It is directional (has a figure 8 pattern), which produces additional gain and assistance in reception (front to side ratio to reduce noise). A rotary dipole is quite impressive, especially on the low bands where apparent small changes can make large improvements. The most common dipole on the 80 and 40-meter bands is an inverted V type. After performing more than 30 tests, I've determined that an inverted V dipole will be 6-10 dB down from a horizontal dipole at the same apex height.

The range to the right of the chart in Fig 2-1 (not the extreme right of the chart) indicates 13 - 14 dBi gain, which is approximately 6 - 7 dB more than the dipole. This can be achieved by using a well-designed Yagi with a minimum boom length of around $^1/_2$ wavelength (35 feet on 20 meters). The extreme right of the chart is for systems with more gain. The largest HF arrays for amateurs rarely approach 20 dBi including ground reflection gain. The stack of six Force 12 C-3s (30 to 180 feet) on a 190-foot rotating tower at N7ML is in this range, as are the multi-element vertical dipole arrays on salt water that were used at 6Y2A and 4M7X.

The left-hand side of the Fig 2-1 chart refers to antennas that are very inefficient. As one moves from the center to the left of the chart (efficiency and gain decreasing), the ability to make QSOs, and hear what is going on, decreases rapidly. The extreme left side is pegged to a light bulb. Before approaching very poor performance (light bulb), we go through antennas that are either inefficient by design (intentionally or not), or by necessity (installation restrictions).

We should note the range across the bottom of the chart. My best estimate is that from –5 dBi to +13 dBi is the practical range of typical, installed (not in free space) amateur antennas. This represents inefficient verticals up to efficient Yagis at reasonable heights and is shown in the chart in **Fig 2-2**. Notice that this range is not all that large: 18 dB; and people with severe antenna restrictions will have a larger difference than 18 dB. If we take the center dipole, moving + or – a few dB makes a noticeable difference in the performance. Yagis and other horizontally polarized antennas receive a benefit from being over ground and will achieve ground reflection gain that can represent about 4 to 5.5 dB of the stated figures. Vertically polarized antennas do not benefit from ground reflection gain and usually lose energy because of the ground (unless it is over salt water).

It is important to keep in mind that this chart applies to both ends of the circuit. Oftentimes, a QSO is made because one end has an efficient system that has enough gain at the right angle(s) to overcome the shortcoming of the antenna at the other end and complete the path.

Once we are at a horizontal dipole (in the clear) performance level, we are doing very well and will experience a lot of fun and enjoyment in Amateur Radio. Below this envelope, we will be able to make QSOs, but our understanding of the activity on the air will be limited. If you think you are at this point, try something more efficient! Try something that "works better."

The charts are not intended to imply it is impossible to enjoy radio with something less than a dipole in the clear. Being able to hear anything and make QSOs can be enjoyable, but this will not necessarily move us along to share more of the enjoyment in radio. We should recognize the capability, the performance envelope, of our current antenna system and contemplate if there is another step we can take—just like my history, moving from one antenna to another and making discoveries.

How much "better" does the antenna have to be to make how much difference? The chart in **Fig 2-3** is a

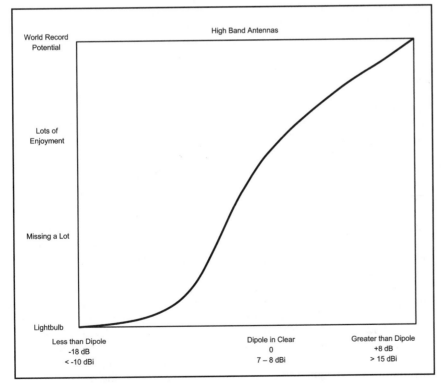

Fig 2-1—A chart relating "enjoyment" to HF antenna performance.

THE ILLUMINATOR ANTENNA

A light bulb. Did someone actually say the left-hand side of the performance chart in Fig 2-1 is a light bulb? Yes, it is. Can it actually "work"? Of course! As I stated in the beginning, everything does work. The difference is the performance envelope.

We gathered one day around a trio of laptop computers, a collection of coffee, soda and water, talking strategy for our contest team (6Y2A, 4M7X). The team leader, Kenny Silverman, K2KW shared some experiences he had many years ago using a light bulb. He was inside a building teaching code and using transceivers with light bulbs for dummy loads. He decided to move up into an amateur band and see what he could hear. Sure enough, he was able to make a couple QSOs on 20 meters. We all laughed at the incident and it was obvious an indoor light bulb had to be the worst antenna anyone could ever use.

In preparing Fig 2-1, we decided to select the light bulb for the left-hand side of the performance chart. *QST* Senior Assistant Technical Editor Dean Straw, N6BV, one of the contest team members and antenna collaborator for close to 25 years, agreed that the estimate of –18 dB to a dipole should be about right and proved to be so, at least on 10 meters. Note that the difference between a dipole and the world class performance antenna is much smaller than the difference between the light bulb and the dipole. I am my most staunch critic, so eventually it was time to test the light bulb (aka "The Illuminator") and see what it could do.

AN ILLUMINATING EXPERIENCE

A 150-W bulb was selected for the antenna and a TS-850S transceiver was used. The Illuminator, ah, antenna, um, dummy load was mounted on a porcelain base atop a wooden fence post at a height of about 4 feet. The light bulb is fed through a Force 12 B-1

A single Illuminator. Notice the balun attached to the side of the post.

current balun with 3-inch leads and the feed line was 9913 Flex, to minimize loss. The balun was used to insure the feed line would not radiate. The VSWR of the 150-W bulb was about 4:1 and the built-in tuner matched it easily. I later utilized an external tuner to make small changes as the filament heated up and changed impedance.

The first time The Illuminator was on the air was during the 2000 10-10 contest. I operated a total of about an hour. All of the contacts were in the Midwest United States. Experimentation showed that if a station moved the S-meter to S-3, I was fairly sure we could make the QSO. Many of the QSOs were made with one call, no repeats, and no comment about how weak the signal was. Interesting. It was obvious that the station on the other end was providing the majority of the necessary system gain to make the path. Nevertheless, it "worked." I remembered the many times I have heard how well an antenna "works," because of the number of countries that have been worked. All right, then,

maybe we can do even better.

The ARRL DX CW contest was coming. I have operated contests for more than 35 years, but I never felt so ill equipped to call someone. It was mid-morning on Saturday and the wind and rain made it impossible to work outside. I knew it was time to get on the air. I could hear several DX stations running pile-ups. The first station I decided to try was V47KP. I send my call at 36 WPM—he comes right back. One call. Perfect. It was just like using a "real antenna." Hey, that wasn't just my first DX with a light bulb, but a new distance record. My sporadic operating using The Illuminator antenna produced 14 countries on 10 meters the first day. I brought the log to the Paso Robles Amateur Radio Club potluck dinner that evening and Larry, W7CB, noticed I was missing Africa for Worked All Continents. Aha—another challenge!

I figured the best bet to work Africa would be if Jim Neiger, ZD8Z, was on because he is using very high gain antennas pointed at the US. The sun had begun to brighten the morning sky and I was tuning across the band with The Illuminator. By the way, the band is really quiet on this antenna. I hear someone. Sure enough, there he is. ZD8Z was having trouble maintaining his frequency and hearing through some European stations. His signal was less than S1 on the meter, so based on experience with The Illuminator, I knew I would have to wait for conditions to improve. About 90 minutes later the sun was fully up, and so was ZD8Z, reaching S3/S4 on peaks. It took a few calls, but we made it: the first Worked All Continents on a light bulb. Now I was really motivated, but there was more work to be done outside before the next rain. I decided that short rest periods were necessary every hour. With casual operating, the country count at the end of the contest was 28, with 41 stations worked.

To date, the farthest QSO on 10 meters was with ZD8Z . . . all with a barefoot powered light bulb from California. To peg The Illuminator to other antennas you might have experienced, there have been only two stations whose signals reached S6-S7 on the meter, which pushes at least S9+25 signal on a 5-element monoband Yagi. The typical signal level required for contact runs between S1 and S3 on the meter, measuring about S9+10 on the Yagi. Occasionally, success with signals reading less than S1 is possible and is most assuredly due to an effective antenna system and quiet location on the other end. The obvious moral here is that if you do not hear many strong signals, the antenna system is not very efficient.

SHEDDING LIGHT

Achieving Worked All Continents in a few hours with a light bulb clearly sheds light on the idea that "everything works." Putting the performance envelope in the spotlight is the important message of this experiment. Although I had fun using the light bulb, it certainly would not promote my interest in Amateur Radio if it were my only antenna. Adding a kilowatt amplifier would allow more QSOs to be made, but I would not hear any better. If I only had one (poor) antenna at my house, I would not be aware of the sea of activity on our bands. If I had two antennas, one would always work better and I would quickly discover the difference between their performance envelopes.

The more efficient your antenna, the more QSOs and enjoyment you'll receive from our wonderful hobby. Looking back to the Fig 2-2 chart, a dipole in the clear is a very good antenna and having an antenna with the gain of a 2-element Yagi gets us a long way to a potential world-class station.

While everything "works," some antennas certainly "work" much better than others.

—*Thomas H. Schiller, N6BT*

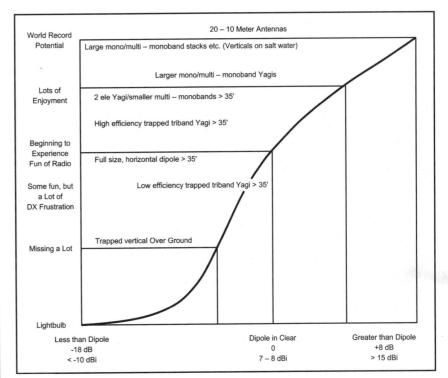

Fig 2-2—Comparing performance for specific antennas.

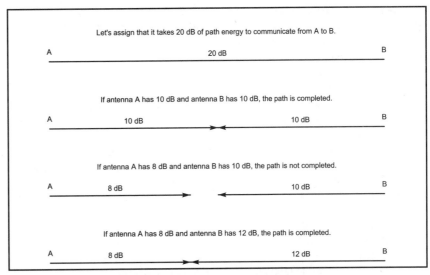

Fig 2-3—Comparing the gains necessary for success at both ends of the path.

hypothetical communications path and the relationship between the antennas at both ends.

Translating the charts into practical antenna systems, the following becomes apparent:

- More efficient antenna = expanded performance envelope
- More efficient antenna = longer operating window to make contacts
- More efficient antenna = more

enjoyment of radio

This concludes this section taken from the *QST* article by Tom Schiller, N6BT. You can read about Tom's experience with the light-bulb antenna in the sidebar *The Illuminator Antenna*.

THE HF DIPOLE

When you look at the graph in Fig 2-2, it's not hard to see that dipoles perform well. The ever-popular dipole is, in its simplest form, a wire fed at its center (see **Fig 2-4**). The name comes from the two poles (sides or halves) that make up the antenna.

As I began to write this chapter in the spring of 2001, my HF antennas are two dipoles. One is for 20-meters, and the other (a homemade trap dipole mounted at right angles to the first) covers 40, 20 and 10 meters. These are at 30 and 35 feet high respectively (see **Fig 2-5**). I don't expect to win any contests, but I have fun in contests. You might ask, "Do dipoles *really* work?" The answer is a resounding, "yes!"

How well does a dipole work?

I like to think of my dipoles as one-element Yagis. It's a reach, but if you stop and think about it, you might agree. As a matter of fact, my 20-meter dipole was once the driven element of a Yagi.

If you measure antenna performance on a dB per dollar scale, the dipole comes out a big winner. I asked my friend Trey Garlough, N5KO and HC8N, to share his experience with dipoles and low power. You'll find Trey's story in the sidebar.

Building a Dipole

You may choose to build your dipole as if it were a single-element Yagi. Construction techniques for such dipoles made with aluminum tubing are presented in the portions of this book that deal with Yagis. There are some performance advantages to this approach, since it allows you to rotate the antenna and thus "steer" the peaks and nulls. However, cost is not one of the advantages.

In this chapter, we're talking about dipoles made with wire. Specifically, we're going to talk about building a 40-meter dipole. But that's just for starters, because we'll next see how to add 15-meter coverage for very little cost. Finally, we'll add 20 meters to complete a three-band dipole arrangement. I think you'll like this project because it's inexpensive and it will give you coverage on three popular ham bands. And one of these bands ought to provide good propagation to somewhere just about any time you would care to operate. Before we start building, let's consider the components that comprise a dipole.

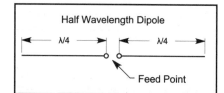

Fig 2-4—The dipole is one of the simplest antennas that hams use, and is also one of the most effective when you consider its low cost and the relatively small space it requires.

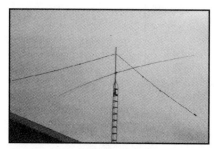

Fig 2-5—Dipoles at K8CH are supported by 30 feet of TV tower. The 20-meter dipole is the driven element from a Yagi. The trap dipole covers 40, 20 and 10 meters and was touched up in this photo so that you can see it more clearly.

Wire

Solid and stranded copper and copper-plated steel wire are the most popular choices for dipole construction. You should avoid soft copper wire, such as that used in house wiring, because it can stretch enough to detune your antenna. It is best to use #16 or larger (such as #14 or #12) for permanent antennas. I personally favor #14 copper-plated steel wire. I have also had excellent results when I've tightly twisted two strands of #18 copper-plated steel wire to make antennas.

I have used galvanized electric-fence wire with satisfactory results for a year or two. After that the zinc coating eroded and the underlying steel had begun to rust. At that point, the antenna did not work well. In other words, the price is attractive, but the results are not.

You can use insulated or uninsulated wire—it makes little difference. A dipole made with insulated wire will be somewhat shorter than one made with uninsulated wire. This effect is caused by the presence of the insula-

tion. You'll adjust the length of your dipole during installation and tuning, so this should not be a problem for you.

Insulated wire is thicker. For that reason, and depending on the color, it may be more visible than bare wire. Some wire rated for indoor use has a clear plastic coating over the insulation. This coating will deteriorate in direct sunlight, turn white and begin to shed. Within a year, it will look pretty scraggly—like it needs a shave.

When you purchase wire for your dipole be sure to buy a few feet extra. You'll need some wire to make the connections at the ends, and you'll also want to start with the antenna a bit long and trim it to length.

Insulators

Your dipole should have insulators at the center and at each end (see **Fig 2-6** and **2-7**). Mechanically these insulators need to handle the stresses of antenna and feed line plus wind and ice load. If you use trees for supports, you quickly discover that they move about in the wind. This flexing results in mechanical stress on your antenna, and the dipole insulators (as well as the wire) must be able to withstand those forces.

Electrically, the end insulators isolate the antenna from its supports. The potential at the dipole tips can be in the thousands of volts, so this is an important function.

At the dipole center, the voltage is relatively low. Here, you'll want to focus on mechanical considerations such as feed-line attachment and support.

There are a variety of commercially made insulators available on the market today. End insulators may be plain blocks with holes for your dipole wire and a support line. Center insulators cover a wide range of designs. You'll find them both plain and fancy. The plain variety have only holes for wire, and perhaps also for a support line. Others feature an SO-239 type connector. Some have a built-in balun. (See the Sidebar *To Balun or Not to Balun*.) They all work and you can choose the one that appeals to you the most. If you buy commercial insulators, I recommend that you buy the center insulator with the coax connector. It is more convenient and it is easier to weatherproof your installation.

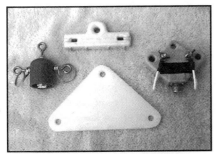

Fig 2-6—A collection of dipole center insulators. Three of them are commercially built units, and Mel Holloway, KD8LL, made the one at the bottom center. While all of these insulators have a hole or loop for a center support rope, this is not a necessary option.

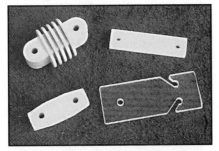

Fig 2-7—A collection of dipole end insulators. The unit at the lower right was built by K8CH for use with a portable QRP station. The angled slots allow for easy adjustment of the dipole leg lengths.

Of course, you can always choose to build your own. Plastic, glass or porcelain work well for insulators. You can also use varnished hardwood; however, you'll need to keep the wood sealed. I've had good results using electric-fence insulators and even plastic plumbing parts.

Feed Line

I suggest you use an RG-8 type coax for the dipole feed line. My personal preference is RG-213 with a noncontaminating jacket. This stuff will stand up to years of exposure to the elements and it has lower loss than smaller (such as RG-58) size coax. Nevertheless, for low power (less than 150 W), I sometimes use RG-58 for short runs. It's lighter and more flexible than RG-213 and that makes it nice for portable and temporary installations.

There are lower-loss coax types, but they usually require special care in

installation and are a little more likely to develop problems. That's why for HF I tend to stick with RG-213 or RG-58. Nevertheless, if your installation will require a long run of coax, you may want to consider an appropriate low-loss coax for your feed line. Dean Straw, N6BV has written more on these issues in Facts About Feed Lines, in Chapter 3.

Dimensions

Typical dipole lengths are given in **Table 2-1**. Height above ground and surrounding objects will have an effect on your dipole. If you can, you should start with slightly longer legs for your dipole and adjust those lengths for best SWR in your favorite part of the band. In other words, you should consider these lengths as being approximate.

Assembly

Before starting to construct our project, let's consider the appearance of the finished product, which you can see in **Fig 2-8**. The first step in building your 40-meter dipole is to gather the materials. Next, cut the wires a bit longer than indicated in the table.

Since our dipole project begins with a 40-meter dipole, we'll start with dimensions for that band. You'll need the extra length for tuning and to make the connections at the center and end insulators. Between 35 and 36 feet for each leg would be an appropriate starting point.

Make strong mechanical connections between the wires and the center insulator. These connections need to withstand the forces not only of antenna and feed line but also of wind, ice, etc. Do not rely on solder for mechanical strength.

Connect your feed line. If you purchased a commercially built center insulator with an integral coax connector, this part is easy. Just attach the coax to the connector. (See Chapter 3 on coaxial feed lines for directions on mounting connectors to coax.)

If your center insulator does not have a coax connector, you can connect your coax directly to the dipole wires. The coax center conductor goes to one side, and the shield connects to the other. Make solid mechanical connections and then solder for the electrical connection.

Table 2-1
Dipole Lengths

MHz	Overall Length Feet	Overall Length Inches	Leg Length Feet	Leg Length Inches
3.55	131	10	65	11
3.9	120	0	60	0
7.03	66	7	33	3.5
7.23	64	9	32	4.5
10.12	46	3	23	1.5
14.25	32	10	16	5
18.11	25	10	12	11
21.27	22	0	11	0
24.94	18	9	9	4.5
28.4	16	6	8	3
50.2	9	4	4	8

These figures are derived from the formula l = 468 ÷ Frequency (MHz). Where l is the overall length of the dipole.

Soldering can weaken the mechanical strength of wire—especially stranded or braided wire. The soldering process results in stiffening of what would otherwise be flexible wires so that continual bending in the wind will finally break them. Another soldering-related problem results from overheating the wires while soldering. This will result in a change of hardness in the portion of the wire that was overheated, and later when the wire flexes it is apt to break. For that reason, use only enough heat to melt the solder and to cause it to flow, wetting the wire.

Don't rely on twisting wires together to make your electrical contact. Copper oxidizes and a copper-to-copper oxide connection acts like a diode. That means that your antenna can become an interference generator if you do not make a good electrical

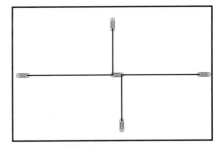

Fig 2-8—The three-band dipole has four legs. The longer legs are active on 40 and 15 meters, while the shorter legs provide 20-meter coverage. (See text.)

OPTIMIZING YOUR HAM RADIO FUN

Trey Garlough, N5KO (aka HC8N), is well known as one of the top contesters in the world. He's built and operated from superstations, and has been active from many exotic locations. [During my two most recent QSOs with him, Trey was in East Timor on one occasion and in the Galapagos Islands on the other. —Ed.] When he was very young, Trey's parents were active DXers. In his words:

They would work stations all over the world, then when the QSL cards arrived they would give me the envelopes and I would look up the country on the globe and paste the stamps into a little stamp book I had. They dropped out of ham radio by the time I was about seven years old, but it was too late—I was hooked. When I was in the third grade I decided that I was serious about becoming a radio ham, so one afternoon I learned the Morse code by memorizing a table in the World Book Encyclopedia that showed the dots and dashes. My favorite thing about Amateur Radio is getting on the air and working guys, because the magic of wireless lives on with every QSO.

Here's what Trey says about keeping the wonder and magic alive:

As a guy who has been involved in contesting for over 20 years, it is easy to be romanced by the idea that bigger is better. The essence of competition dictates that you are always trying to find an extra dB here and there. As you progress through the normal developmental cycle of a contest operator, trees give way to steel towers, wire antennas give way to rotary Yagis, and simple low-powered radios give way to complicated, feature-laden exciters driving auto-tune kilowatt amplifiers.

Recently I made a startling (to me) discovery: you don't need all that junk to have a good time operating ham radio. Actually it wasn't the first time I had made this discovery, only the most recent. Certainly there is great enjoyment in planning and building and improving your system, but inevitably the competitive-minded individual lets the system get so large and unruly that system maintenance snuffs out the sense of awe and wonder that wireless inspires.

Just as with all things, you eventually reach a point of diminishing returns. DXers and contest-ers measure this phenomenon in dB/dollar and QSOs/dollar. A more balanced ham might measure this in terms of fun achieved per hassle expended. In my discovery and rediscovery of the magic of "getting on the air and working guys," I have observed a few recurring themes.

100 watts is a nice round number

One hundred watts is a nice round number. It's 10 dB more than 10 watts and 10 dB less than 1000 watts, two extremely common power levels in use world-wide. Using modern commercial ham gear you can achieve 100 watts using a station that you can carry under one arm, such as a Kenwood TS-850, and Icom IC-706 or the 100-watt version of the Elecraft K-2.

To the 160 meter DXing enthusiast, this setup may not be enough. To the alpine hiker, this setup may be too much. But for the guy who does general-purpose operating and who likes to operate mobile or portable a few times a year this arrangement offers a very good fun/hassle ratio. Plus you can run a 100-watt radio for a long time on a car battery, and some-

---

connection. The nasty side of this is that your antenna system may still have a good SWR. For that reason, you'll want to solder your coax to the dipole wires.

Finally, connect the end insulators to the wires. These can be temporary connections until you've adjusted the wire lengths for best SWR in your favorite part of the band.

Installation

Dipole performance is best when the antenna is installed high, flat and in the clear. In other words, that's ideal. Nevertheless, most of us have to compromise when installing an antenna. For example, few of the many dipoles that I've installed, used and enjoyed over the last 40 years have been what you would call a *flattop*.

Don't be afraid to try the obvious or easy way—even if this means that your dipole will not be high, clear and flat. If it works well, you've got a winner. If it doesn't, try something else.

INVERTED-V (AKA "DROOPING") DIPOLE

In this popular configuration, the center of the dipole is supported and the ends are allowed to droop to a lower level. The plus side of an inverted V is that it requires only one tall support, and there is support for the feed line. On the negative side, you will pay a per-formance penalty for having the ends lower than the center. See the sidebar *How Inverted-V Antennas Work.*

In general, we can say that a flattop dipole is good. If you raise the center (to form an inverted V), you can expect somewhat better results. Finally if you could raise the center—and ends, you'd get the best results. Bottom line: Mount your dipole center as high as you reasonably can and do your best at get-ting the ends up as well.

Support

If you haven't already, you'll need to select your dipole supports. Trees are perennial favorites, but don't forget that they move in the wind—especially the upper branches. That movement will result in considerable stress to an antenna mounted in those branches. You can read more about this topic in the chapter on Antenna Masts and Supports.

times this is handy.

The half-wave dipole is the best antenna

The full-size half-wave dipole is the world's most underrated antenna, followed by the full-size quarter-wave vertical. Almost every antenna any ham puts up is a variation on one of these.

A friend of mine who lives in an antenna-restricted neighborhood is always fiddling around looking for the magic antenna for his location. One day he was putting up an 80-meter antenna that looked like a bird feeder and he told me "the magazine ad says this antenna works as well as a half-wave dipole" — an impressive claim indeed. The way I see it no matter how much loading you put on a three-foot-long 80-meter antenna, it's not going to work as well as a full-size half-wave dipole or a full-size quarter-wave vertical.

Be realistic

I don't fault my neighbor for his investigative spirit, but I think 80 meters was not a realistic band for him to start with in his quest to get on the air. A stealth full-size 20-meter ground plane dangling from a tree turned out to be an excellent performer.

Why are some guys so weak?

Many times from the Americas I have listened to signals on 40 meters on a good night and heard many a 599+40 European station followed by a barely audible European station and I have wondered how this is possible. I figure that a guy with 100 watts and a dipole might be 20 dB down from a guy with a big Yagi and a big amplifier, so that makes him 599+20. And his dipole might really be an Inverted V at 50 feet, so maybe he is only 599+10 now. And maybe he is really only running 5 watts, so he is now 589.

I am convinced that two experienced operators each running 100 watts and a trap vertical should be able to maintain almost daily contact with each other. They may not be able to communicate for hours on end, but they should be able to squeeze out a bit of communication every day if they choose the right time of day.

If you can work every station you can hear, then you are not hearing well enough

The biggest obstacle to most urban and suburban ham activity is man-made noise. This is one reason why mobile and hilltop portable operation is so popular worldwide. Many times a mobile station in a quiet location will outperform a fixed station with high power and Yagis because the mobile station can get away from the withering fusillade of power pole buzz.

Wireless is fun

My most recent rediscovery of the simple pleasure of wireless was inspired by a Field Day style operation from a tent on a hilltop in the Galapagos Islands using a TS-850 and an Inverted V hanging from a 25-foot pole that was temporarily lashed to a guava tree. I was in a quiet location well away from power line noise. What an eye-opening experience! It was so strange sitting there with the small radio with its built in tuner, the laptop and a single antenna, and using a spool of rope as a chair. It was a great reminder that all the additional baggage of towers and Yagis and rotors and amplifiers is at times an *enhancement* of the wireless experience, but it is not the *essence* of the wireless experience. —Trey Garlough, N5KO/HC8N

Tuning

Temporarily install your 40-meter dipole and check the SWR. To tune your dipole, shorten the antenna legs to raise the resonant frequency. You'll want to do that in a series of steps until the best SWR is in your favorite part of the band.

If you shorten your antenna too much, the best SWR will be at a higher frequency. You can add an extension, however, and just let it dangle.

Adding 15-Meter Coverage to the 40-Meter Dipole

Here's a bonus: Your 40-meter dipole will also resonate near the 15-meter band. Actually, the resonance will be above the band, but that's easily corrected with a form of capacitance loading. The concept, which is illustrated in **Fig 2-9**, consists of a pair of wires, which function as *capacitance hats*. These wires, or hats, lower the resonance on 15 meters, without substantially changing the 40-meter resonance.

To build the hats, measure two 2-foot-long pieces of stiff wire and connect the ends of each one together to form two loops. Twist the loops in the middle to form figure-8s, and strip the insulation (if any) from the wires where they cross.

Install these capacitance hats on the dipole about 11 feet either side of the center insulator, a quarter wavelength at 15 meters. If necessary, strip insulation from the dipole wire and attach the hats. Solder the hats to the wires to assure good electrical contact (see **Fig 2-10**).

Adjust the shape of the loops for best SWR on 15 meters. (Don't do the adjustments while you're transmitting.) Double-check your SWR on 40 meters.

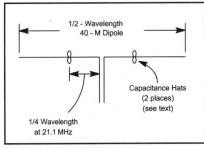

Fig 2-9—Figure-8-shaped capacitance hats, made and placed as described in the text, can make your 40-meter dipole resonate anywhere you like in the 15-meter band.

TO BALUN OR NOT TO BALUN—THAT IS THE QUESTION...

Hams get the strangest ideas sometimes. I once heard an old timer browbeating a young ham on 75 meters because the neophyte had been reckless (he might have meant *stupid*) enough to put up a dipole, horror of horrors, *without a balun*. I didn't have a working transmitter at that exact moment or I would have jumped to the poor youngster's defense. After all, how bad could things have been?—Wasn't he strong enough for both old crusty and myself to hear him, several states away?

So what's the big deal with some hams and baluns? In theory—and I want to emphasize that word *theory*—a dipole is a balanced antenna and it does require a balanced feed line to keep everything symmetric. Feeding a balanced dipole with an unbalanced feed line, such as a coaxial cable, upsets the inherent balance and therefore *bad things* must begin to happen. Right?

The real question here is what sort of "bad things?" Some hams have vivid imaginations,

because I've heard some very fanciful proclamations about what happens when a coax cable is used to directly feed a balanced antenna, without the benefit of a balun. In the regrettable situation above, the old timer swore that the inevitable result was going to be TVI and telephone interference and "the radiation pattern was going to be terribly distorted."

Before I start hyperventilating, let's back up a bit and consider two questions:
- What is a balun?
- What happens if you don't use a balun?

I guess you have already figured out that a balun must somehow be involved in making unbalanced coaxial feed line into the equivalent of a balanced feed line, suitable for feeding a balanced antenna. And, if so, you're quite right.

The word "balun" is a contraction of "**BAL**anced to **UN**balanced." (I suppose it could just as easily have been called UNBalanced to BALanced, but UNBBAL is too hard to pronounce and besides, it sounds too much

like some tower in ancient Babylon.)

I don't intend here to go into all the gory technical details about how a balun actually goes about its primary job of making the transition between balanced-to-unbalanced (and vice-versa, from unbalanced-to-balanced). *The ARRL Antenna Book* and *The ARRL Handbook* go into considerable detail about the theory of how baluns work, and these books contain a number of excellent, practical designs for baluns. So you'll have to trust me that a well-constructed balun can and will do its job properly.

What we want to examine here is what happens when you *don't* use a balun between your coax feed line and your balanced dipole antenna. **Fig A** shows the azimuth pattern for a typical flattop 75-meter dipole, properly fed with a balun, mounted 50 feet over flat, uniform ground. Overlaid on the same plot is that for a dipole without a balun, fed directly with coax without a balun.

Do you have a tough time discerning the differences between the two curves? I do. That's partly because at 50 feet in height, our 75-meter dipole is only 1/5 wavelength above ground. At that electrical height, the dipole doesn't show much directivity anyhow. The amount of imbalance created by the lack of a balun has very little practical effect on the radiation pattern. **Fig B** shows the pattern for a 20-meter flattop dipole at 50 feet in height, with and without a balun. The difference is almost imperceptible. So much for the myth that a balun is absolutely mandatory on a dipole!

Now, if you were to do the same comparison for a 10-meter Yagi mounted 50 feet above ground, with and without a balun, you'd see more distortion towards the rear of the azimuth pattern of the non-balun case. Here, the Yagi has been specifically

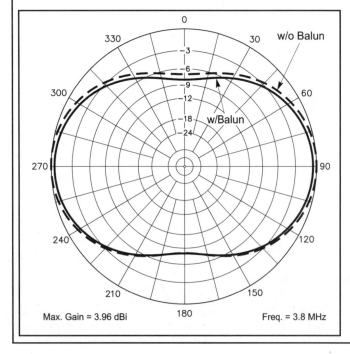

Fig A— Comparison of azimuth patterns for flattop 75-meter dipoles, 50 feet above flat ground, with and without a balun to transition from coax to the balanced dipole. Note that the distortion of the radiation pattern is very minor.

Max. Gain = 3.96 dBi

Freq. = 3.8 MHz

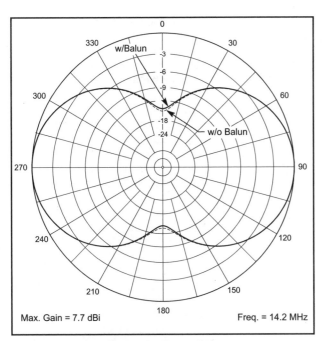

Max. Gain = 7.7 dBi Freq. = 14.2 MHz

Fig B—Comparison of flattop 20-meter dipoles, 50 feet above flat ground, with and without a balun. It's pretty hard to see any difference at all!

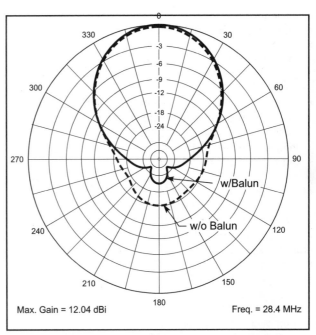

Max. Gain = 12.04 dBi Freq. = 28.4 MHz

Fig C—Comparison of two 5-element 10-meter Yagis, 50 feet above flat ground, with and without a balun. Now, the excellent rearward pattern of the Yagi with a balun is degraded considerably when the Yagi doesn't have a balun.

designed to discriminate highly against incoming signals off the rear, with signals almost 30 dB down from the peak level produced by the beam when a balun is properly employed. This comparison is shown in **Fig C**.

So, it *is* a good idea to include a balun for a highly directive antenna to ensure that the pattern isn't distorted by stray common-mode currents radiated back onto the feed line, but it hardly seems worthwhile to use a balun on an antenna that doesn't have much directivity, like a dipole. You'll find more information about the proper uses of baluns for Yagis in a later chapter.

And let me assure you that if you choose not to spend the extra bucks to buy a balun for your 20- or 75-meter dipole, you will not cause any *extra* TVI or telephone interference. If your neighbor is experiencing interference to his home electronic devices, the residual radiation from a coax used without a balun is *far* overshadowed by the radiation coming directly from your antenna—in other words, your antenna is doing exactly what it is supposed to do, radiate! In most cases of RFI, the fault lies with the device experiencing the interference because of inadequate shielding or filtering and manufacturers' cost cutting. But that's another story all in itself. —*Dean Straw, N6BV.*

Now Add 20 Meters

To complete this project, we'll add a 20-meter dipole. Leg dimensions are given in the table, and these (20-meter) legs will connect in parallel with the legs of the 40-meter dipole. However, you should install the two antennas at right angles to each other as shown in Fig 2-8. That will minimize interaction between the two.

Tune this dipole in the same fashion that you did the 40-meter dipole.

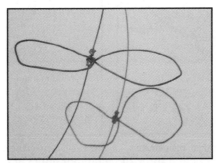

Fig 2-10—Photo of a capacitance hat. The shape is not critical.

That is, shorten the antenna to raise the resonant frequency. As before, if you shorten too much, just solder a little extra wire at the end and let it dangle.

Finished

When you've installed your assembled antenna, run the coax feed line to your operating position. Now, enjoy operating your three-band dipole. In a later chapter on dipoles we'll talk about some possible variations to this project.

HOW INVERTED-V ANTENNAS WORK

Life involves all sorts of choices, doesn't it? For example:

- Couldn't I snack (just a little) on that ice cream in the freezer? Do I really have to stay on my nasty old diet?
- Couldn't I just floor the accelerator pedal when the traffic light turns yellow before I get to the intersection? And why is that policeman flashing his lights at me?
- Can't I let my dipole droop, instead of hanging it level, straight and proud?

As my friend K8CH says, putting up an inverted-V dipole requires a single support for the antenna and its feed line. On the other hand, a flattop dipole requires at least two supports—one on each end. You might even need a support in the middle, if your dipole is very long and your feed line is heavy enough to make things sag badly.

Obviously, the inverted-V dipole is easier to install, since

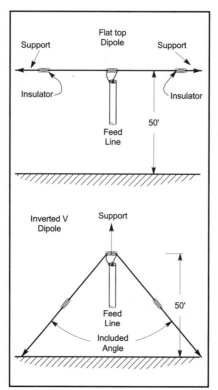

Fig D—Sketch showing a flattop and an inverted-V dipole.

one support is easier than two supports. But you don't get something for nothing. Most of the time, the degree of compromise is not that big a deal, providing you know what it is you are compromising.

Let's compare a 50-foot high flattop 20-meter dipole to two types of inverted-V dipoles. Each inverted V is installed with its apex at 50 feet. The first inverted V has both of its ends tilted down 30° below horizontal—in other words, the total angle included between the two wires is 120°. The second inverted V has an included angle of 90°, allowing it to take up less horizontal space. **Fig D** sketches the flattop and Inverted-V configurations. Note that I picked the top height of 50 feet just because this is a height that many hams actually use.

At 14.1 MHz, the fundamental half-wave frequency of the antenna, there is little to recommend between the three dipoles,

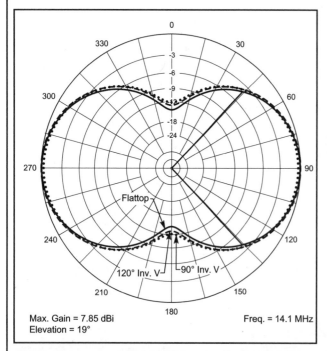

Max. Gain = 7.85 dBi
Elevation = 19°
Freq. = 14.1 MHz

Fig E—Comparison of 14.2-MHz azimuthal responses for three dipole configurations shown in Fig A for a 20-meter dipole at a height of 50 feet. There's precious little difference at the fundamental half-wave frequency.

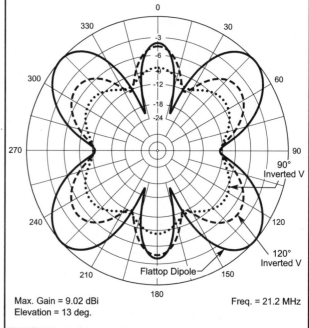

Max. Gain = 9.02 dBi
Elevation = 13 deg.
Freq. = 21.2 MHz

Fig F—Comparison of three 40-meter dipole configurations at a height of 50 feet, but at third harmonic operation on 15 meters. Now the flattop has it all over the inverted-V dipoles.

as shown in the azimuth patterns in **Fig E,** computed for an elevation angle of 19°. This is the angle of maximum gain for this height above flat ground. The flattop's azimuthal response is just a tiny bit better than either inverted V, but the difference is insignificant because few hams would be able to detect this small a difference in signals on the air.

In the comparisons above, done at the half-wave frequency of 14.1 MHz, I assume that each dipole is fed directly with coaxial cable and is used on that one band. A 10-meter dipole at a height of 25 feet would have the same performance as does the 20-meter dipole at 50 feet in Fig D, since it is at the same height in wavelengths. Now, what happens if you use a dipole at frequencies other than its fundamental, half-wave frequency?

As Chuck Hutchinson describes in this chapter, many hams use a coax-fed 40-meter dipole at its third harmonic, on 15 meters, where it's like getting a "free" band. Again, whether you mount the dipole as a flattop or inverted V doesn't matter much for 40-meter operation. However, the effect of mounting a 40-meter dipole as an inverted V has a much greater effect on its 15-meter performance.

Fig F compares the azimuthal patterns for a 50-foot high 40-meter flattop and two inverted Vs, one with a 120° and one with a 90° included angle, both with apexes at 50 feet and both operated at 21.2 MHz. The 15-meter elevation takeoff angle is 13°, the peak angle at 50 feet for a flattop dipole over flat ground. Now things get more interesting! On 15 meters, a flattop 40-meter dipole has six lobes, with the four major ones almost 3 dB stronger than the two at 0° and 180°. For example, at an azimuth of 54° (the lobe pointing toward the upper right-hand side), the flattop dipole has a peak gain 8 dB more than the 90° inverted V, and about 4 dB more than the 120° inverted V.

These are significant differences. At an azimuth of 0° or 180° (the lobes pointing directly to the right or left in Fib C), the difference is a little less dramatic, with the flattop dipole leading the acute 90°-angle inverted V by about 4.5 dB. Overall, the flattop dipole is superior to either inverted V at almost all azimuths, except those fairly narrow regions where there are deep nulls with the flattop. (And you should realize that in the real world, where the ground isn't always perfectly flat, these theoretical deep nulls are usually "filled in" significantly.)

The conclusion to this brief analysis is that whether you mount a dipole as a flattop or inverted V has little practical significance—if you only use that antenna on its fundamental, half-wave frequency. If you want to use it on higher frequencies then you should consider installing it as a flattop for best performance—if you have the luxury of being able to install it as such. If you're limited in space or in supporting structures, an inverted V will still get you on the air, even with compromises. Remember, everything works; some better than others.—*Dean Straw, N6BV.*

3 Facts About Transmission Lines

By Dean Straw, N6BV

In the first two chapters of this book, author K8CH made several brief references to *feed lines*, also commonly known as *transmission lines*. In this chapter we'll look at transmission lines in more detail, although I'll limit the main discussion to only a few commonly used types of *coaxial cable* feed lines, which are usually called "coax cables." Chapter 11 will deal with typical types of open-wire transmission lines.

By the way, the proper pronunciation of *coaxial* is "co-axial," where the prefix "co" (pronounced "coe") is short hand for "common." Thus coaxial means "common axis," since the axis for the center conductor is also the axis of the shield that concentrically surrounds the center conductor. See **Fig 3-1**, which labels the parts of a typical coax cable.

Coaxial cable is especially popular among hams because of its many advantages:
- You can use it indoors or outdoors.
- You can tape it to a tower leg or run it in a bundle of other coaxes and wires without any interaction.
- You can use it with a beam and rotator—in other words, you can flex it.
- The built-in shielding helps eliminate stray RF or EMI.

Flame Shields Up!

I'm writing this section up-front in this chapter because it's really pretty predictable. Whenever I write something even just a touch whimsical (maybe even *fun!*) about transmission lines, I can expect to receive a lot of finger wagging and scolding from highly technical people, telling me that I must give proper respect to this reverential subject. Phooey, I say! This book is meant to be *fun*. You don't necessarily need deep, highly mathematical treatises to have fun with antennas and feed lines. What this chapter is designed to give you is some down-to-earth advice about particular feed lines, ones you would actually use for practical applications.

If you really, really want to delve deeply into transmission lines, ARRL publishes other books that cover this subject, in sometimes mind-numbing detail. I suggest *The ARRL Antenna Book* as the flagship publication dealing with all aspects of antennas. *The ARRL Handbook* has an excellent chapter on transmission lines also.

You can also play with my *TLA* (Transmission Line, Advanced) DOS program. This software is available for free on the ARRLWeb site (**http://www.arrl.org/notes/1867/index.html-software**). The "big brother" of *TLA* is called *TLW* (Transmission Line for Windows) and this software is only available on the CD-ROM that comes with the 19th Edition of *The ARRL Antenna Book*. Both programs will give you a huge amount of information about feed lines and should keep you busy for hours and hours with technical details, if you are into that sort of thing. Now,

let's get into a few necessary details about transmission lines.

Why Do You Need a Transmission Line?

Let's start by considering exactly why you even need a transmission line. No doubt, you have been careful to place your radio somewhere where it is safe from wet or cold weather. Perhaps you are lucky enough to have a separate ham shack, or maybe a room dedicated mainly to ham radio pursuits. Outside, your antenna may be a dipole strung between two tall trees in your backyard, or you might be really fortunate because you have a tall tower with a rotatable beam antenna on top.

The express purpose of a transmission line is to carry the RF power generated by your radio up to your antenna —and it should do that job efficiently, wasting as little as possible of your precious RF power in the trip from radio to antenna (and for receiving, from antenna down to the radio). Another way of stating this is that the coax should be as low-loss as possible for a given application.

CHARACTERISTICS OF COMMON COAXIAL FEED LINES

If you go to your local radio store

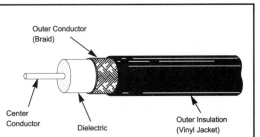

Fig 3-1—The parts of a coax cable: center conductor, insulating dielectric, outer shield and jacket.

Outer Conductor (Braid)

Center Conductor

Dielectric

Outer Insulation (Vinyl Jacket)

and ask for some coaxial cable, you'll probably be asked a question like this: "Do you want 50 or 75-ohm cable?" This refers to one of the most fundamental characteristics describing a transmission line, its *characteristic impedance*. Transmission lines are classified according to several factors, and we'll examine these one by one.

- Characteristic impedance
- "RG" number
- Loss characteristics—closely related to power-handling capability
- Velocity factor

Table 3-1 lists the most common types of coax cables used in the Amateur Radio service. I'm going to concentrate here on mainly three types of 50-Ω coaxial lines: RG-213 (also known as RG-8), RG-8X and RG-58. Probably 95% of amateur installations will use one of these three types. Hams use RG-213 for higher-power, RG-8X for medium-power and RG-58 for low-power applications.

In Table 3-1 I've also listed the LMR400 cable, an illustrative example of the "new breed" of high-tech cables available to amateurs. These cables have lower losses, but are more expensive than more garden-variety types. The last column in Table 3-1 shows the approximate relative cost for these coaxes, where LMR-400 is the reference, at 100%.

I've also listed RG-11 and RG-59 types of 75-Ω coax cables, since you might run into these in some antenna systems. Now, let's look at some more detail on what the main characteristics are for coax cables.

Characteristic Impedance

A line's *characteristic impedance* is a function of how it is built—mainly involving the diameter of the center conductor and the diameter of the shield conductor. To a smaller extent the characteristic impedance is also a function of the insulating dielectric material used to separate the center conductor and the shield. You'll often see characteristic impedance abbreviated as Z_0, as in "Z sub-zero."

Manufacturers design and build their transmission lines to operate into a load impedance equal to the line's characteristic impedance. This means that a 50-Ω coax cable is properly *matched* when it has a 50-Ω resistive load connected to the end of it. Simi-

Table 3-1
Common Types of Coaxial Cable

Type	Characteristic Impedance, Ω	Velocity Factor, %	Size Inches	Power Handling	Rel. Cost %
RG-58	50	66	0.195	Low	23
RG-59	75	66	0.242	Low	27
RG-8X	50	84	0.242	Med	23
RG-213 (RG-8)	50	66	0.405	High	60
LMR400	50	85	0.405	High	100
RG-11	75	66	0.405	High	77

larly, a coax with a Z_0 of 75 Ω works at its very best when feeding a 75-Ω resistive load. Actually, there are more than 50 and 75-Ω coaxes available. The range of characteristic impedance for practical coaxes varies from about 35 Ω to 200 Ω, but the most common varieties remain 50 and 75 Ω.

The earliest true coaxial cables were created back in the late 1920s for television, where the standard impedance for video work is 75 Ω. Theoretically, 75 Ω is the best value for minimum loss in a transmission line. Most amateur applications, however, use 50-Ω impedances, since this is the best compromise between loss and power-handling capability for a transmission line. I'd hazard a guess that about 90% of transmission lines used in Amateur Radio are 50-Ω lines.

And let me try to clear up something that newcomers may have wondered about. (I know that both Chuck Hutchinson and I wondered about this when we first started in ham radio about 40 years ago. We recently were laughing about our own long-lost naiveté on this subject.) While it is true that an infinitely thin, half-wave dipole in free space has a feed-point impedance of 73 Ω, this has nothing to do with 75-Ω coax.

"RG" Number

During World War II, when the military started using coax cables in large quantities, they needed a standard way to identify them, and they developed the so-called "Radio Guide Utility" numbering system. For example, "RG-8/U" was military nomenclature for a standard 50-Ω, solid-dielectric, roughly ½-inch diameter coaxial cable. Things became a bit more complicated

when improved versions of RG-8 were developed, leading to nomenclature with revision numbers tacked onto the end of the old RG numbers: "RG-8A/U" and such. Later, the "/U" portion was dropped and the cable became known simply as "RG-8."

Then scientists developed better dielectrics for use in coaxes, and then the generic name "RG-8" used by different manufacturers could refer to either old-fashioned coax or "new and improved" coax. Same name, different animal (or same name, improved animal). Then some manufacturers started to get cute by reducing the number of wires used in the outer shield or by using inferior insulating materials, giving them a cost advantage. By continuing to use the same "RG-8" name they could lure unsuspecting customers into paying the same amount of money for an inferior product. Same name, different species (or same name, inferior animal, if you like).

In reaction to the poor shielding being pawned off by less-than-upfront manufacturers, the percentage of shielding became something of a badge of honor among coax sellers. Genuine improvements over braided wire shields came about with combinations of aluminum foil and braid in newer types of coax. However, since many amateurs are still very familiar with the "RG" numbers, you'll see advertising that refers to "RG-8 like" or "RG-213 type" to describe new-and-improved cables.

In the midst of the resulting customer confusion, some manufacturers decided simply to get away from old-fashioned military nomenclature and they created their own part numbers. For example, Times Microwave Systems, a prominent high-quality manufacturer, labels their own "LMR" series of cables because the military "RG" lineup had no corresponding equivalents for these modern, high-tech types of coax. Andrew Corporation, manufacturer of the "Heliax" brand of cable had the same problem with the old military nomenclature and they use their own "LD" numbers. Belden, the volume leader in high-quality cable manufacturing, has its own series of four-digit part numbers for exact identification, supplementing the generic RG-numbering scheme.

In deference to the familiarity of RG numbers, ARRL publications like *The ARRL Antenna Book* and *The ARRL Handbook* use the RG numbers to roughly classify coaxes, while listing manufacturers' exact part numbers to differentiate the cable listings.

Loss Characteristics

As you might imagine, the *loss characteristics* of a coax cable are also related to the materials used to construct it. Smaller conductors and lossier dielectrics lead to more losses, while bigger conductors and less-lossy dielectrics lead to less losses. No big surprise there. The two main types of losses occurring in cables are:
• "Copper losses," related to resistance (or ohmic) losses in the center conductor and the shield wires
• Dielectric losses.

The dielectric losses show up generally at higher frequencies, usually at UHF and beyond, while copper losses dominate at lower frequencies. Losses rise with frequency. A cable that is fine on 80 meters may be a disaster at 450 MHz. **Table 3-2** shows the loss per 100 feet, as a function of frequency, for various coax cables. This is the so-called *matched-line loss*, meaning that at its end the coax has a resistive load equal to its characteristic impedance. You can see that at 1000 MHz the amount of loss for the small RG-58 cable is staggering.

Table 3-3 shows the same information as Table 3-2, but now in terms of how many watts of power (starting out with 1500 W at the input of the transmission line) actually make it to the end of a properly matched coax cable at each frequency. Somehow, this looks a lot starker than the rather innocuous dB numbers!

The *power-handling capability* of a coax cable is directly related to the loss mechanisms in a cable. The bigger the conductors used, the more power that cable can handle. Higher-temperature dielectrics allow cables to dissipate higher power losses safely, without melting.

Let me give you a concrete example. Years ago, I used to run about 120 feet of RG-58 coax to feed an 80-meter dipole on a 90-foot tower. The coax handled a full 1500 W of CW or SSB transmit power without any problems, since the coax loss was a maximum of about 2 dB, even at the top and bottom ends of the band. This meant that almost 1000 W of the RF from the amplifier actually got to the antenna, with 500 W dissipated in the coax. Over 120 feet of cable, this averages out to about 4 W per foot, and with the relatively low duty cycle involved in amateur CW or SSB transmissions the cable didn't melt.

Had I tried the same thing on 450 MHz, the worst-case loss would have been about 16 dB, meaning that for 1500 W at the input of the coax, only 40 W would have reached the antenna.

Guess where the other 1460 W went? It would have been very busy (for a brief time anyway) heating up the cable, which certainly would have melted. It should be clear that a larger, less-lossy cable would be far more appropriate for 450-MHz use.

Table 3-4 shows the approximate amount of power that can safely be used with each type of coax cable. You can see that I was pushing the capability of my RG-58 cable on 80 meters, but was saved by the intermittent duty cycle inherent in SSB or CW amateur communications.

Keep in mind another practical detail: The larger the coax, the more it weighs. Your dipole strung between two trees must support the weight of not only its wire, insulators and rope, but also the weight of a heavy coax feeding it. Or perhaps you are into backpacking in the mountains with your miniature HF transceiver. The weight of 50 feet of RG-213 (just over 5 pounds) may be more than you're willing to carry, considering that 50 feet of RG-58 would only weigh 1.2 pounds.

Table 3-2
Matched-Line Loss, dB/100 feet

Cable Type	1 MHz	10 MHz	100 MHz	1000 MHz
RG-58	0.4	1.5	5.4	22.8
RG-59	0.6	1.1	3.4	12.0
RG-8X	0.3	1.0	3.3	14.3
RG-213	0.2	0.6	2.1	8.2
RG-11	0.2	0.7	2.0	7.1
LMR400	0.1	0.4	1.3	4.1

Table 3-3
Power at End of 100-Foot Long Coax, Starting with 1500 W at Input.

Cable Type	1 MHz	10 MHz	100 MHz	1000 MHz
RG-58	1370	1060	430	8
RG-59	1310	1165	685	95
RG-8X	1400	1190	700	55
RG-213	1430	1310	925	225
RG-11	1430	1275	950	290
LMR400	1465	1370	1100	585

Table 3-4
Coax Cable Power-Handling Capability (1:1 SWR, 40° Ambient), Watts

Type	1.8 MHz	7	14	30	50	150	220	450	1 GHz
RG-58	1350	700	500	350	250	150	120	100	50
RG-59	2300	1100	800	550	400	250	200	130	90
RG-8X	1830	840	560	360	270	145	115	80	50
RG-213	5900	3000	2000	1500	1000	600	500	350	250
LMR400	11300	5700	4000	2750	2600	1200	1000	690	450

Velocity Factor

A feed line's *velocity factor* is a direct function of the characteristics of the dielectric used between the center conductor and the shield. The "velocity" referred to is the speed of light, which varies depending on the type of medium in which it is traveling. In a vacuum (closely approximated by dry air), the velocity factor is 100%, while in so-called "foamed dielectric" the velocity factor is typically about 84%, meaning that the speed of light is slower than it is in air. In a foamed dielectric, air bubbles are uniformly distributed throughout the plastic, bringing that dielectric closer to being like air. In a solid-polyethylene dielectric, the velocity factor is 66%.

So what's the big deal with velocity factor? The closer the velocity factor is to 100%, the lower the dielectric losses will be—after all, what's better than a vacuum as a dielectric? If a higher velocity factor is good, why don't all coaxes use air as an insulating dielectric? This would be great, at least in theory. Unfortunately, a center conductor suspended solely in air inside a shield conductor is going to short out when the cable is bent or flexed. So some sort of insulation is needed to prevent shorting between the center conductor and shield.

Foamed-dielectric coaxes generally have lower losses than solid-dielectric ones, but there are some attendant disadvantages too. Foamed dielectrics have lower voltage breakdown capabilities and they also can't dissipate as much power without melting, compared to solid dielectrics. Further, it's more difficult to solder the common PL-259 connectors on foamed dielectric cables without worrying about melting the center insulation. For HF use at powers up to the full amateur limit of 1500 W, I recommend that you use solid-dielectric RG-213 type coax, even though the losses are slightly higher. RG-213's solid dielectric is very forgiving when it comes to heat stresses during soldering.

Velocity factor also figures prominently in determining the physical length of a transmission line when you want to create a *quarter-wave transformer*, something I'll discuss in more detail a bit later.

Summary—Choosing a Coax

OK, you've been presented with a bunch of tables and lots of written information about coax cables. Let's go right to the bottom line. First and foremost: Buy from known manufacturers with high standards of quality, sterling reputations and the ethics to match.

For operation up from 1.8 to 29.7 MHz, use RG-213 if you can stand the size and weight. It's probably not worth the extra cost to go to a more expensive type of coax, such as LMR-400, for HF operation, but if you want to spend the extra bucks, that's your choice. Smaller-diameter RG-8X is also good up to 29.7 MHz, although it is a bit more lossy than RG-213.

Use RG-58 for short, low-power runs in the shack, say from your HF transceiver to a linear amplifier. On the lower HF bands, say on 3.5 MHz or even 7 MHz, you can use RG-58 to make the run to your antenna, although RG-213 is less lossy and is still preferred.

Stay away from RG-58 for VHF and UHF use. Use RG-213 for runs less than, say, 100 feet on 2 meters. Consider LMR-400 type of cable for VHF and UHF use because of its lower losses.

QUARTER-WAVE TRANSFORMERS

One of the more technical facets of transmission-line behavior comes up when the line is *not matched* with a resistive load equal to the line's characteristic impedance. The *mismatched* line now acts like a kind of impedance transformer. The exact nature of this transformation involves some fairly heavy-duty math, and if you really want to get into this please read the Transmission Line chapter in *The ARRL Antenna Book*.

However, one common real-world application involves so-called *quarter-wave transformers*, sometimes known as "Q Sections." See **Fig 3-2**. These transform certain resistances to other more-desired resistances—most prominently, 50 Ω. The length of transmission line needed is, as the name implies, a quarter-wavelength long at the frequency of interest. This is where the velocity factor of a line comes into play, because the physical length of a coax is different from its electrical length.

Let me give an example. Let's say you have a 14.2-MHz quad-loop antenna that exhibits a 100-Ω resistance at its feed point. You can use a quarter-wave transformer to create a 50-Ω point. See **Table 3-5**, which lists some common coax cables needed for various transformations to 50 Ω. You will need a quarter wavelength of 75-Ω coax, so let's choose RG-11, which according to Table 3-1 has a Velocity Factor of 66%.

A free-space wavelength at 14.2 MHz is 984/14.2 = 69.3 feet. However, a full wavelength of RG-11 is 66% of 69.3 feet, or 45.7 feet. Thus a quarter wavelength of this coax is 45.7/4 = 11.4 feet.

Another example: Your 21.2 MHz beam antenna has a feed-point impedance of 12.5 Ω. Here, according to Table 3-5, you need two paralleled 50-Ω coaxes (creating a net characteristic impedance of 25 Ω) to make your quarter-wave transformer yield a 50-Ω input impedance. Let's use two equal lengths of RG-8X coax, which has a velocity factor of 84%. So, a quarter wavelength is: ¼ × 984/21.2 × 0.84 = 9.7 feet each.

CONNECTORS

So now you know how to choose the coax cable appropriate to your application. Now, you need to know how to put on connectors so you can actually use that coax. For perhaps 90% of the projects in this book, you will be installing a form of the ubiquitous PL-259 "UHF" connector. See **Fig 3-3**.

Tom Schiller, N6BT, whose *QST* article "Everything Works" was featured in Chapter 2 of this book, once told me that some 95% of the customer problems he's seen over the years at his company (Force 12, Inc) are due to coax problems of some sort. And improper soldering of the shield braid in the PL-259 causes the majority of coax problems!

Tom emphasized that one of the

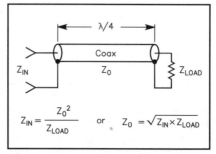

Fig 3-2—A quarter-wave transformer ("Q-Section").

$$Z_{IN} = \frac{Z_0^2}{Z_{LOAD}} \quad \text{or} \quad Z_0 = \sqrt{Z_{IN} \times Z_{LOAD}}$$

worst things people can do is not even solder the braid at all. Trying to rely on a mechanical connection of the braid against the body of the connector will eventually result in an intermittent poor connection. The SWR reading will become intermittent and the operator may hear static-like noises as the contact is made and broken when the wind shifts. Not good! See Sidebar *Putting on a PL-259—Properly!* for the procedure I use to install this common connector.

Every once in a while, a ham asks me about the so-called "crimp-on" PL-259 type connectors. My recommendation has been to steer clear of these unless you are willing to invest in an expensive crimping tool that properly handles both the shield and the center conductor. Proper soldering results in better long-term reliability in my experience.

SWR

What would you guess is the most common "measuring instrument" in a ham's shack? I would say that most hams own an *SWR bridge* or a variant thereof known as a *directional wattmeter*. They use it to measure SWR, or "standing wave ratio." SWR is one of the most misunderstood concepts among our amateur brethren, unfortunately,

Table 3-5
Quarter-Wave Transformer Cable Combinations For 50-Ω Input Impedance

Load Impedance Ω	¼-λ Cable Type(s) Ω
12.5	50/50 paralleled
25	75/75 paralleled
30	75/50 paralleled
100	75

Fig 3-3—The ubiquitous PL-259 connector.

with all sorts of myths and legends abounding about it. Once again, I'm not going to delve too deeply here into the theory of transmission lines and SWR but will give you enough information for practical applications of transmission lines. I'll also point out a few common myths concerning SWR. If you really do want to get into the nitty-gritty details, again I suggest you read *The ARRL Antenna Book*.

The Basics of SWR

First, the textbook definition of SWR is "the ratio of maximum to minimum voltage on a line, resulting from the interaction of incident and reflected voltages along the line." That's certainly a mouthful. What does it mean?

A fundamental property of an ideal transmission line is that if the load impedance is equal to the characteristic impedance Z_0 of the line, then the impedance seen anywhere along that line is also equal to Z_0. If the load resistance equals Z_0, then the maximum voltage will be the same as the minimum voltage anywhere along that line and thus the ratio of maximum to minimum will be a perfect 1:1 SWR.

However, whenever a transmission line has a load that is *not* matched to the line's characteristic impedance, there will be a wave reflection at the load end of the line. This bounces a *reflected wave* down the line back towards the transmitter at the same time that the *incident wave* is coming from the transmitter. These two distinct and separate waves react with each other as they travel and they set up points of maximum and minimum voltage (and current) along the line. These points of maximum and minimum occur at stationary (or *standing*) points along the line. Hence the term *standing wave ratio*. The standing points along a transmission line are related to the electrical distance in wavelengths from the load and the maxima and minima repeat at intervals of half wavelength, if the line is that long.

In the simplest situation, where the load is purely resistive, the SWR is the ratio (or inverse ratio) of the load to the characteristic impedance. SWR is always greater than or equal to one to one. Let's say we have a transmission line with $Z_0 = 50$ Ω and the load resistance is 150 Ω. The SWR is 150/50 = 3:1. If the load is 16.67 Ω, the SWR is the in-

verse, or 50/16.67 = 3:1, once again. When the load is not purely resistive, things get a bit more complicated and you've got to employ vector arithmetic, something we'll not get into here.

So, let's examine what that SWR bridge on your operating desk (or inside your desktop transceiver) is telling you. The term "SWR Bridge" is designed to bring up a mental image of a *Wheatstone bridge*, as shown in **Fig 3-4**. This is the most basic form of an SWR bridge. If R1 and R2 are equal (as they usually are), when resistance R3 is equal to the unknown resistance Z, the bridge is *balanced* and the detector shows no voltage. This means that the SWR is 1:1.

If R3 and Z are not equal, the voltmeter will now show a voltage, indicating that SWR is present on the line. In other words, the line is not terminated in its characteristic impedance. It's really quite that simple. An SWR bridge tells you that the impedance at the point where the bridge is inserted in the transmission line is not equal to the characteristic impedance of that line.

Additional Loss Due to SWR

If a line is mismatched to its Z_0, then as the incident and reflected waves bounce back and forth inside the line, additional losses will occur beyond those when the line is properly matched. **Table 3-6** shows the effect of three different levels of SWR on the overall loss in 100 feet of several typical kinds of transmission lines for three different frequencies.

A useful rule of thumb is to keep the SWR low enough so that the additional loss due to that SWR rises less than 1 dB. For 80-meter use of RG-213, this means keeping the SWR below about 6:1. For RG-58 on 80 meters, you'd want to keep the SWR below about 3:1 to keep additional loss reasonable.

However, for VHF use, you'd want to keep the SWR for RG-213 less than 3:1 to keep additional loss less than 1 dB due to SWR. And for RG-58, frankly, you'd better go to RG-213 anyway, regardless of the SWR! RG-58 is way too lossy at VHF and even worse at UHF.

Some Common Myths About SWR

• A high SWR does not result in radiation from a transmission line. *Imbalance* can result in radiation from a line but not high SWR.

PUTTING ON A PL-259—PROPERLY!

Putting on a PL-259 is not really difficult, but doing it right is critical for long-term, reliable connections. So, let's go through, in detail, how to install a PL-259 connector on the most common types of coax cable you'll encounter. We'll start out with the most common installation—RG-8-type (foam dielectric) or RG-213 (solid dielectric) cable.

PL-259 ON RG-8 OR RG-213 COAX

The steps are:

1. Slide the loose coupling ring onto the cable and move it back out of the way. Then measure 1 inch from the end of your coax. With a sharp knife, carefully score the outer vinyl jacket, taking care not to cut too deep and nick or cut through the shield wires. As you make the cut a little at a time, it helps to stop and flex the cable gently to reveal the depth of the cut. **Fig 3-A** shows the technique I use.

2. As you pull off the cut portion of jacket, rotate it clockwise slightly so that the shield braid is smoothed out and is not bunched up. If the jacket is really tight on the braid (as it should be for high-quality cable) you may have to make a longitudinal slice with your knife along the part of the jacket you are removing.

3. Place the coax in a small vise and with a hot soldering iron or soldering gun, tin the exposed braid, making one pass from the cut-end to the front and then rotating the coax in the vise to expose fresh braid to solder.

I prefer to use a UT-100Si "Ultratorch" butane-powered soldering torch, because it heats up quickly and provides a tremendous amount of heat at the tip. (Be careful, though, that you don't put it down on something that is flammable—like a kitchen table…) This portable torch is also great to do soldering up on the tower. **Fig 3-B** is a photo of the tools I use.

Don't be alarmed if some tiny beads of white insulation ooze out through the shield, particularly if your cable uses foamed insulation. If you look closely at the photograph in **Fig 3-C**, it shows a few

Fig 3-A—Using a sharp knife to cut the outer vinyl jacket.

Fig 3-B—Tools used to properly install a PL-259 connector: a small vise, a butane-powered soldering torch, a pair of side cutters, a sharp knife and a measuring ruler.

Fig 3-C—The first swipe at tinning the shield braid using the vise. Note that it isn't necessary to tin the shield all the way to the end because that part will be removed later. The coax is rotated in the vise for the next section of shield.

such beads of insulation. Let the coax cool off for several minutes before proceeding. If you've been careful tinning the braid there will be no bumps of lumps of solder that would interfere with putting the coax into the PL-259 connector body. Carefully file off any solder protrusions on the shield if there is a problem.

4. With either a sharp knife or a tubing cutter, cut off ¾ inch of tinned braid and center insulator, taking care not to nick the center conduc-

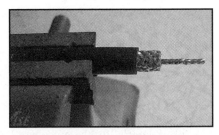

Fig 3-D—The tinned shield and insulation has been cut away with a sharp knife and the center conductor has been tinned also.

Fig 3-E—The result of scraping away the nickel coating around the soldering holes in the PL-259 body using a knife. All four soldering holes will subsequently be tinned after having been scraped in this fashion.

tor itself. (Your sharp knife will not remain sharp for long when you use it to cut tinned braid, but knives can be sharpened!) As you remove the cut-off cylindrical portion, rotate it clockwise slightly to twist the center conductor wires (assuming the center conductor is made up of braided wires) into a smooth shape.

5. Tin the center conductor. **Fig 3-D** shows coax ready for the final steps, with both the braid and center conductor tinned.

6. Check to make sure the outer coupling ring for the PL-259 is on the cable and pointed in the right direction! You don't want to have to redo everything because you forget to put the ring on first.

7. Make sure you tin the four holes in the PL-259 body used for soldering the coax shield so they will accept solder easily. Many connectors are nickel-plated brass and the nickel plating doesn't solder easily. Scrape the nickel plating away from

each hole using a knife and then tin each hole. Don't scrape the much more desirable, more expensive silver-plated connectors, but do tin the holes. See **Fig 3-E**, which shows a close-up of one of the holes on a plated-brass connector that has been scraped to all allow solder to flow easily. Make sure blobs of solder don't protrude down through the holes into the inside of the connector or else you'll find it difficult to insert the coax into the connector.

8. Twist the PL-259 body over the coax jacket until the tinned braid shows up through the four holes in the connector (and the center conductor is showing). You will be screwing the connector onto the coax's outside vinyl jacket. Depending on how strong your fingers are, you may have to resort to using a pair of channel-lock pliers. This idea of a tight fit here is to make a good mechanical strain relief for the connector.

9. Place the coax in the vise, grasping it a couple of inches before the connector, and solder each of the four holes in the body to the coax shield, one at a time, twisting the coax a quarter turn each time. It is absolutely vital that you use lots of heat to do this quickly, because you don't want to melt the coax insulation trying to use an under-powered soldering iron or gun! **Fig 3-F** shows the soldering process.

10. Once the connector has cooled off, solder the center conductor. Screw the coupling ring onto the PL-259 and use an ohmmeter to make sure you didn't cause a short somewhere. Once you get good at this procedure you can easily put on a PL-259 in less than five minutes. See **Fig 3-G**.

PL-259 + ADAPTOR FOR RG-58 OR RG-59 COAX

Working with smaller cables, such as RG-58 or RG-59, is a little easier than dealing with the bigger coax like RG-213. **Fig 3-H** shows the three parts involved in the process: the outer coupling ring, the adaptor (with coax installed) and the PL-259 body. The steps are:

1. Slide the coupling ring onto the cable and move it back out of the way.

2. Unless the adaptor (UG-175 for RG-58 and UG-176 for RG-59) is silver-plated, scrape off the nickel around the front edge with a knife to

Fig 3-F—Soldering a shield hole.

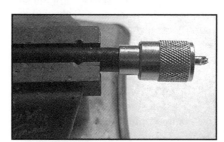

Fig 3-G—The finished product.

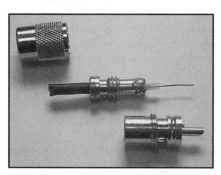

Fig 3-H—Coupling ring, UG-175 adaptor (for RG-58) and PL-259 connector body.

Fig 3-I—Splayed out shield wires. These will be trimmed and soldered to the tinned adaptor lip.

expose the brass. Lightly tin the adaptor's front edge and let if cool. Once it is cool, slip the adaptor onto the cable.

3. With a sharp knife, remove ¾ inch of vinyl jacket from the end of the cable. As always, be careful so that you don't nick or cut the shield wires.

4. Comb out the individual wires

Fig 3-J—UG-175 adaptor with solder shield and tinned center conductor.

Fig 3-K—The finished product.

in the braid. See **Fig 3-I**.

5. Now, fold back the braid over the adaptor. Then trim the shield wires so that they are about ¼-inch long. A sharp pair of scissors helps here. Catch the little shield wires so they won't go all over the place! Hold the cable in a bench vise and solder the braid to the adaptor, quickly so you don't melt the cable's insulation.

6. Cut off $^5/_8$" of the insulation surrounding the center conductor. Twist the center conductor wires and tin them. See **Fig 3-J**.

7. Inspect the shield carefully for stray wires. Trim off excess with sharp side cutters and make sure there are no lumps of excess solder that would prevent proper assembly. File off excess solder lumps, if necessary. Screw the adaptor into the body of the PL-259 connector.

8. Then solder at least one of the holes in the PL-259 to the adaptor. This prevents the adaptor from working its way loose over time, as it always seems to do if you don't "pin" it in the PL-259 by soldering it.

9. Solder the center conductor and screw the coupling ring onto the PL-259 body. Check with an ohmmeter to make sure everything is OK. **Fig 3-K** shows the finished product.- —*Dean Straw, N6BV.*

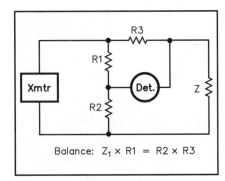

Balance: $Z_1 \times R1 = R2 \times R3$

Fig 3-4—The Wheatstone bridge, the basis of the SWR Bridge.

- A high SWR does not cause RFI or TVI or telephone interference. *Radiation* from the antenna can cause RFI/TVI or telephone interference.
- An SWR of more than 1.5:1 will not allow your signal to "get out." See section above on Additional Loss Due to SWR!

CHOKE BALUNS

As briefly described in Chapter 2, the word *balun* is a contraction standing for "*BAL*anced to *UN*balanced." There are a number of devices that can perform the basic function of transitioning from an unbalanced coax to a balanced antenna, but the ones you are going to see throughout this book are officially called "common-mode current choke baluns." That's a whole mouthful of words to describe a device that is in actuality pretty simple. You'll also see these devices commonly referred to as "choke baluns."

The basic idea behind a choke balun is literally to "choke off" the flow of extraneous (that is, "common-mode") currents that might otherwise flow on the outside shield of the coax. This choking action goes on without affecting what happens inside the coax. You accomplish this by using the outside shield of the coax as an inductive reactance—making it into a coil, in other words.

Fig 3-5 shows a simple but effective common-mode choke balun, where the RG-213 coax has been wound into a multiturn coil held together with electrical tape. This is wound like a coil of rope would be wound, with each loop carefully stacked directly on top of the one underneath it. As opposed to a "scramble-wound" method, this methodical technique minimizes the effects of stray, turn-to-turn capacitance. Stray capacitance across the common-mode inductance bypasses the effectiveness of the inductance at higher frequencies. The common-mode choke in Fig 3-5 is broadband and works well over a frequency range from 14 to 30 MHz.

You start winding the coil by taping the first loop together at the top and bottom. Then you coil each turn, one turn at a time, taping the assembly together at top and bottom at each turn. RG-213 is fairly stiff and you should make the diameter of the coil about 7 inches, using 6 turns in total. This requires about 8 feet of coax.

Fig 3-6 shows another form of choke balun, often called a "W2DU balun," in honor of Walt Maxwell, W2DU, who first described this method. Ferrite beads are slipped over the jacket of the coax cable to create a single-turn inductor.

W2DU originally used small-diameter Teflon-insulated RG-303 coax with 50 FB-73-2401 ferrite beads for his choke baluns, but you can also use RG-213 with larger beads. The choke balun in Fig 3-6 uses seven Chomerics CHO-SORB 9754 ferrite beads. The measured common-mode choking impedance is higher than $500\ \Omega$ at 30 MHz, and more than $2000\ \Omega$ at 3.5 MHz. Note that the final assembly of the choke in Fig 3-6 would have the ferrite beads taped to the coax using electrical tape and the end of the coax would be sealed to prevent water from entering the coax.

WEATHER-SEALING YOUR COAX

As mentioned at the beginning of this chapter, coax has lots of advantages. However, it also has one major disadvantage—coax deteriorates badly if water, any water, gets into it! While there are exotic (and expensive) types of coax that are less susceptible to water ingress because of the way they're made, most commonly used types of coax (RG-8, RG-213, RG-8X, RG-58) deteriorates permanently if water gets inside. Stripping back the outer vinyl jacket on a piece of coax where water has entered will reveal the sickly blue-green color of corrosion on the copper shield braid. Sometimes, the shield has become so corroded that it turns black. When this happens the losses in that fatally wounded coax will rise very dramatically, since the individual strands of wire woven together to make the shield will lose contact with each other.

Unless the outside jacket has been cut or abraded, the most common place

Table 3-6
Total Loss in 100 feet of Transmission Line

3.5 MHz

Coax Type	SWR	Additional Loss, dB	Total Loss, dB
RG-58	1:1	0	0.8
RG-58	3:1	0.4	1.2
RG-58	6:1	1.2	2.0
RG-213	1:1	0	0.4
RG-213	3:1	0.2	0.6
RG-213	6:1	1.0	1.0

30 MHz

Coax Type	SWR	Additional Loss, dB	Total Loss, dB
RG-58	1:1	0	2.9
RG-58	3:1	1.0	3.9
RG-58	6:1	2.5	5.4
RG-213	1:1	0	1.2
RG-213	3:1	0.5	1.7
RG-213	6:1	1.5	2.7

144 MHz

Coax Type	SWR	Additional Loss, dB	Total Loss, dB
RG-58	1:1	0	7.3
RG-58	3:1	1.2	8.5
RG-58	6:1	3.0	10.3
RG-213	1:1	0	2.8
RG-213	3:1	0.9	3.7
RG-213	6:1	2.5	5.3

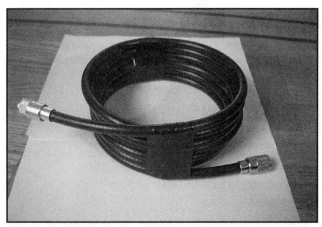

Fig 3-5—A common-mode choke balun made using RG-213 in a 6-turn, 7-inch diameter coil held together with electrical tape.

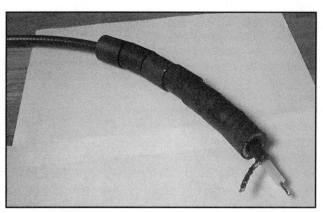

Fig 3-6—Another form of common-mode choke balun first described by Walt Maxwell, W2DU. This uses seven large ferrite beads slid over the jacket of a piece of RG-213. The final assembly would be taped in place and weather-sealed.

for water to get into a coax cable is through the connector. I'll admit that I'm just a little paranoid about water entry and I use lots of electrical tape to seal up all outdoor connections. Some folks swear that they will only use the highest quality electrical tape, usually preferring Scotch brand #33. While I love this tape too, I have settled for other "house brands" from local hardware stores on many occasions when I couldn't find Scotch 33. I just make sure I use plenty of whatever electrical tape I can find. Tape is cheap compared to intermittent, corroded connections that always seem to fail at the worst possible time, in the worst possible weather.

Here are some tips on weather-proofing coax connections. In this description, I'll assume that the female SO-239 UHF connector is pointing downwards from the antenna, as it normally does. Look back at Fig 2-6 in Chapter 2 for several examples.

1. Start out taping from the top of the connector, moving down with steady pressure applied to the tape as you wind it around the coax, overlapping by half the width of the tape.

2. Once you reach a point about three inches below the top of the PL-259 connector, reverse your direction and wind the tape back up in an upward direction. When you reach the top of the PL-259, cut off the end of the tape with a sharp knife or a pair of side cutters. [Resist the impulse to break off the tape by stretching it until it breaks. Doing this guarantees that the tape will come

loose later, like a flag in the wind.]

3. After making a clean cut with your knife or side cutters, fold back about $1/8$ inch of tape so that it sticks to itself. This makes a convenient tab to grab the end of the tape sometime in the future when you will want to remove the tape! Trying to find the end of the tape when it is stuck down without a convenient tab handle, especially when it is freezing cold outside, is not a lot of fun.

4. Now, do the same thing over again, following steps 1 to 3. Make sure that you end by bringing the tape back up the coax so that the tape tends to shed any water coming downwards—just like the shingles on a roof overlap to shed water.

Some people go to even more extreme measures in between steps 3 and 4. They spray or brush on a plastic sealer, such as PlastiDip "liquid electrical tape," let it dry and then apply the final layer of electrical tape. RadioShack sells the PlastiDip product from their on-line Web store (or call 1-800-THE-SHACK) and it comes in several different colors. The white variety can be ordered using the RadioShack part number 910-5166, while the red variety is 910-5164. There is a black color as well, but it's easier to see any voids or thin spots if the PlastiDip color is a contrasting color to black electrical tape. The container includes an applicator brush in the cap.

Fig 3-7 shows how Chuck Hutchinson treated the open ends of a piece of RG-8X coax using white PlastiDip and crimped connector lugs.

Note that Chuck also soldered, just to be sure, the crimped lugs. Not shown in Fig 3-7 is the final layer of black electrical tape Chuck later applied over the white PlastiDip coating, just to ensure that there was protection against UV (ultraviolet) from the sun.

GETTING THE COAX INTO YOUR HOUSE

The sidebar *Coax Entry Panel* shows a homemade entrance panel that Chuck Hutchinson installed at his house in Michigan. He made provision for four UHF bulkhead coax connectors (similar to the screw-on portion of an SO-239 on each end), plus two insulators for open-wire transmission line in this panel. A piece of #6 solid copper wire goes from the ground lug to a copper-clad steel ground rod driven into the ground below the entry panel.

This panel is more than a convenient grounding point and entrance to the house; it also provides some lightning protection for the coax lines. Lightning-induced currents flowing on the outside of the braid must flow across the panel and around the edges to get inside the shack. They are more likely to flow to ground. There is no similar protection for the ladder-line connections.

Once the coaxes are inside the shack they connect to a relay-operated antenna switch. When the power is turned off, the relays drop out, and all inputs plus the output are grounded. As an additional safety measure, Chuck has installed a Square D general-duty safety (knife) switch in the 240-VAC power lead to the shack. The switch is mounted in a steel box. When he "throws the big switch" he throws the *big* switch, and that removes all AC power, resulting in the antennas being grounded.

When storms are in the area, operation from the ham shack ceases and power to the station is shut off as K8CH and K8SYL switch to battery operation. They use their hand-held transceiver to commu-

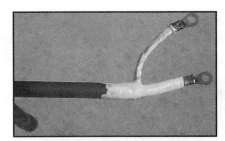

Fig 3-7—Sealing the coax center conductor and shield with PlastiDip "liquid electrical tape."

nicate through the Ionia County ARES repeater (N8ZMT). An indoor antenna assures reliable communications.

You too should develop a strategy to protect your equipment and your home. Lightning can strike anywhere, so be prepared. Remember that it's not only your antenna feed lines, but also the power line and telephone lines that can conduct those unwanted spikes into your home and ham shack.

COAX ENTRY PANEL

My wife Sylvia, K8SYL, and I had bought and moved into a house on a hill in the country. A perfect location for avid hams. In short order our ham shack began to take form in the basement. The next question was how to get the feed lines into the ham shack.

I had noticed a grill mounted on the end of the house (see **Fig 3-L**). A TV antenna coax and rotator control line had been run behind the grill and on into the house. The grill was covering the end of a duct that provided combustion air for a fireplace that would not be used. That duct ran right through the area of our ham shack. Because we would not be using the fireplace, I could (and did) use that opening in the house to bring feed lines into the house.

My favorite local hardware store doesn't carry sheet aluminum, so I bought a small sheet of Plexiglas and some aluminum flashing. I removed the grill and the duct, storing them away so that they can be replaced when the time comes to sell this house. Here are the steps that followed:

• Cut a rectangle of Plexiglas that's just a bit larger than the metallic grill. Be sure to leave the protective film in place.

• Mark the Plexiglas' protective covering for drilling mounting holes that align with the holes in the grill. Because Plexiglas is quite flexible, mark for additional mounting holes.

• Set the Plexiglas in place and mark the corners of the

opening. (You'll want to make sure that the parts you mount to and through the panel will be in an appropriate location.

• Layout positions for a grounding lug, for coaxial feed-through connectors and for your ladder line feed-through connections. See **Fig 3-M**.

• Cut a length of flashing aluminum. This will provide a grounding plane for the coaxial feed-throughs. Trim the flashing to size.

• Mount the aluminum flashing to the Plexiglas with a few pop rivets.

• Drill the holes. You'll need to be careful how you drill through the aluminum. The flashing is thin. For the ⁵/₈-inch holes needed for the coax entry, start by drilling a ¹/₈-inch pilot hole. Finish with a modified spade bit that drills the center first, then the outside edges and finally the part between.

• Mount the hardware. Don't forget to include two ground lugs. One for connecting to a ground rod. The other for continuing the ground connection into the shack. Use Penetrox or similar antioxidant on copper-to-aluminum connections.

• Mount the panel to the house with plated sheet metal screws. See **Fig 3-N**.

• Caulk around the edges of the panel. This is to keep out weather and insect intruders.

• Connect your feed lines to both sides of the panel and enjoy.
—*Chuck Hutchinson, K8CH*

Fig 3-L—The grill covers the end of a duct that provides combustion air to an unused fireplace.

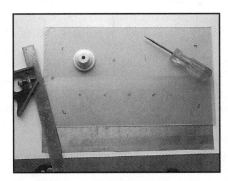

Fig 3-M—Lay out hole positions by marking the protective covering.

Fig 3-N—The panel in position. The extra flap of aluminum can be bent down to protect the ground connection lug if you like.

4 Antenna Masts and Supports

Sometimes the most difficult part of putting up an antenna is finding a hook to hang it from. This chapter provides you with some solutions that others have found useful to solve that problem.

First a word of caution: When installing any mast, be certain that it, and its associated antennas, cannot fall across or otherwise touch power lines. The results can be fatal!

Also, make sure that guy wires are secure and adequate to the task. Make sure of the mechanical integrity of all parts of your antenna installation. As one sage put it: "If something can go wrong—it will. If it can't—it will."

Make safety your top priority.

USING PVC TUBING FOR MAST

While preparing this chapter, I received an invitation to demonstrate Amateur Radio to a church group. To be sure of reliably getting into my favorite repeater, I decided to use my hand-held radio with a modified version of the simple W1VT ground-plane antenna that's described in the first chapter. What I needed in addition to the ground plane was an antenna support—it didn't seem right somehow to hang the antenna from, or lash the PVC mast to, the church furniture or fittings.

The answer came in the form of a 30-inch length of 2 × 6-inch lumber—nothing critical about the dimensions; I just happened to have this available. I used a hole saw to cut a $1^3/_8$-inch hole about 6 inches from one end (see **Fig 4-1**). The end of a length of 1-inch PVC tubing will sit loosely into this hole. I used a couple of 1-inch drywall screws to wedge the tubing securely in the hole (see **Fig 4-2**). This provides an adequate base for the mast and the coax will fit easily into the PVC, but how would you get the coax out at the bottom? I used a tee fitting as shown in **Fig 4-3**. Fortunately, this worked very well and the demonstration was a suc-

cess. Since then, I've had other opportunities to use this setup and it has performed satisfactorily.

As you've, no doubt, already surmised, the base I've just described will not keep the mast from tipping over in a wind. There are a couple of things that

Fig 4-3—A tee fitting in the PVC mast can be used to bring the coaxial feed line out of the middle of the mast. The tee also serves as a means of dividing the mast into two parts.

Fig 4-1—This length of 2 × 6-inch lumber has a $1^3/_8$-inch hole about 6 inches from one end. K8CH inserted a length of 1-inch PVC tubing into the hole and used the PVC to support a simple antenna.

Fig 4-2—A pair of 1-inch drywall screws can be used to securely mount the PVC mast to the wooden base.

you can do. You could place a weight on the 2 × 6 to give the assembly the stability you need. I drilled the hole off-center so that I'd be able to put a weight (even a vehicle tire) on one end of the base.

Alternatively, you could make an "X" shaped base as shown in **Fig 4-4**. Drill a hole through the centers of two pieces of lumber. Attach short lengths under the ends of the upper piece to keep

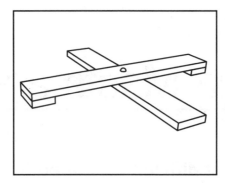

Fig 4-4—An "X" shaped base provides more stability for the PVC mast.

it from tipping. No need to fasten the two base pieces together—the PVC mast will hold them in place. Because they are not connected to each other, the separate pieces will be easier to transport and to store when they're not in use.

Build a Flagpole Antenna Booster

This project by Frank Ingle, KG4CQK, appeared in May 2000 *QST*. It can help you elevate your simple VHF ground-plane antenna, and it's a good idea for those of us who engage in public-service communications.

Some time ago, the Duval County, Florida, ARES team was conducting a drill with the local fire department. One of the operators who had been on duty at an outlying station had been unable to raise the repeater with his hand-held radio. During the exercise critique he commented, "Next time I'll bring a 'spider' antenna and hoist it up the flagpole!" That remark was the seed for an idea that blossomed into a solution for a common problem facing emergency-service operators: getting an antenna as high as possible above surrounding objects and doing it simply.

Post-Storm Operations

After a hurricane or other disaster, phone lines are probably knocked down and the need for emergency communications is immediate. In all probability, however, the same storm that took down the phone lines likely took down most "permanent" antenna installations as well, rendering many point-to-point radio links inoperable. If repeaters are also out of commission because of power failures and damage to fixed antennas, all that's left is simplex operation. For an ARES operator, the need to quickly erect a simple but tall antenna is one of our most pressing challenges.

In Duval County, many of our

served agencies have flagpoles. Red Cross shelters located in public schools, fire stations, neighborhood police headquarters and the weather bureau are a few such locations. Most of these flagpoles are taller than any surrounding buildings, so if there were an effective way to use a flagpole to support a temporary antenna, it would be an ideal solution to the antenna-height problem.

A Fly in the Ointment

The "spider antenna" referred to earlier is a nickname for the well-known ground-plane antenna that consists of a ¼-l vertical element and two or more counterpoise elements (also known as radials or the ground plane). My favorite example of this antenna is the homebrew antenna by Zack Lau, W1VT, which is shown in **Fig 4-5**. It's incredibly simple and costs little to make.

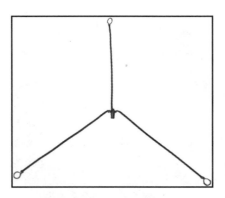

Fig 4-5—Zack (W1VT) Lau's inexpensive 2-meter ground-plane antenna.

At first glance, you might think that getting the antenna to the top of the flagpole is a simple matter of attaching the top of the antenna to the flagpole's halyard and hoisting the antenna up to the pulley. But this approach is deceiving. As you can see in **Fig 4-6**, when the antenna is raised to pulley level, the

Fig 4-6—In this position, your antenna becomes part of a capacitor, causing your transmitter to see high SWR.

halyard snap link keeps the top of the antenna lower than the top of the flagpole. That means that the vertical element is adjacent to the flagpole and parallel with it. Hence we have the antenna's vertical element (one conductor) situated parallel to the flagpole (another conductor, if it's metallic) and separated from it by air (a dielectric)— a capacitor. Therein lies the problem. At RF, this capacitor looks like a short circuit to the flagpole electrically connecting it to your antenna system. This will adversely affect the antenna's performance and likely cause your transmitter to see a high SWR.

What we need is a simple way to get the antenna above the top of the flagpole (see **Fig 4-7**). Then the antenna has a clear shot to the horizon. The flagpole is situated below the ground plane and is no longer seen by the antenna.

Build a Flagpole Antenna Booster in 10 Minutes

This simple gadget, easily used with virtually any flagpole, can be built for about $3. See the Bill of Materials.

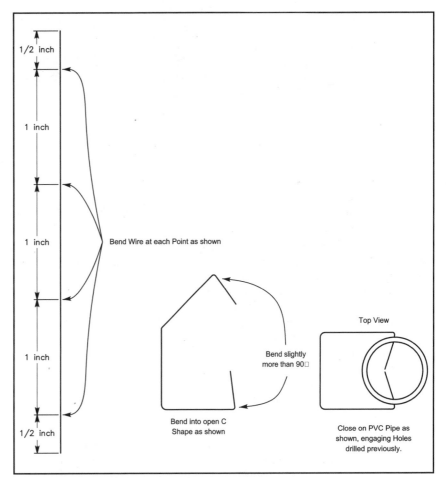

Fig 4-7—The flagpole antenna booster in action.

Assembly is straightforward: Cut the ½-inch PVC pipe to a length of six feet. Pick a point two feet from one end of the pipe and drill a ⁷/₆₄-inch hole through the pipe. (The end of the pipe nearest the hole is the top of the booster.) Liberate a coat hanger from your closet and cut off a four-inch piece of wire. Bend the wire into a C shape as shown in **Fig 4-8**. Insert the C-shaped wire into the hole you drilled. Use pliers to tighten the wire (by closing the C) so it won't pull out of the pipe. [It's likely that you can think of a number of alternate ways to ensure that the wire hanger doesn't slip out of the pipe. Consider making a complete wire loop with the ends joined. You could use #14 or #12 antenna wire in lieu of coat-hanger wire.—*Ed.*] Insert a #6 machine screw into one of the mounting holes

(enlarge if needed) in the antenna's SO-239 connector (see **Fig 4-9**). Secure the screw in place with the nut and your booster is finished.

When you're ready to hoist your antenna, attach the antenna to the feed line (RG-8 or RG-8X recommended for 2 meters). Insert the downward facing #6 screw into the open end at the top of the pipe. (It should fit tightly.) This places the feed line alongside the PVC pipe's outer surface. As shown in **Fig 4-10**, secure the feed line to the top and bottom of the PVC pipe with ³/₄-inch-wide electrical or masking tape. (Masking tape is easier to remove). Leave an inch or so of slack in the feed line between the two taped points. This ensures that the PVC pipe, not the PL-259 connector, carries the feed-line weight. The force helps keep the pipe

1/2 inch

1 inch

1 inch

1 inch

1 inch

1/2 inch

Bend Wire at each Point as shown

Top View

Bend slightly more than 90□

Bend into open C Shape as shown

Close on PVC Pipe as shown, engaging Holes drilled previously.

Fig 4-8—Hanger loop construction.

Bill of Materials
1—6 ft length of ¹/₂-inch PVC pipe
1—Two-inch-long # 6 machine screw, any thread pitch
1—Nut to mate with #6 screw
1—Four-inch piece of coat-hanger wire

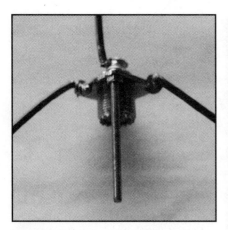

Fig 4-9—This two-inch screw slips inside the PVC pipe and helps secure the antenna to the flagpole antenna booster.

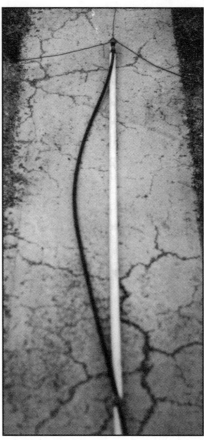

Fig 4-10—Antenna attached to the flagpole antenna booster, ready to be hoisted. Note the slack intentionally left between the top and bottom tape points.

vertical when raised on the flagpole.

Next, connect the coat-hanger wire to the top snap link on the flagpole's halyard. Raise the assembly to the top of the flagpole. Have an assistant pay out the feed line, ensuring that no kinks develop on the way up. (An antenna raising ceremony is optional...) The antenna should now extend above the top of the flagpole. It may lean slightly to one side of vertical, but that's okay. This slight tilt won't measurably affect the antenna's performance. Finally, secure the halyard to the flagpole's cleat. Allow the feed line to fall to the ground and run it loosely around the flagpole base several turns before routing to your H-T or portable rig. These turns at the base of the flagpole offer a small degree of extra lightning protection to your rig, but aren't a substitute for a real lightning arrester.

There you have it! Already-made antenna installation, right where you need it for a cost of about $3 (not counting the feed line, of course!) When not is use, your new flagpole antenna booster can find a home under the back seat of your car or in your trunk. That way it is sure to be handy in an emergency.

PVC Mast for HF

I entered the Home Depot store with every intention of proceeding to the plumbing department to buy some PVC pipe and fittings. I needed a mast to hold up one end of an Inverted-V dipole, and PVC pipe was what I had in mind. (Several decades ago, I would have gone to my local RadioShack and bought a push-up telescoping mast. But these convenient masts are not readily available nowadays and when you can find them the cost is not very attractive.)

My steps took me past the electrical department at Home Depot, and as I passed I saw just what I needed. It was 10-foot lengths of PVC conduit and right on them it said they were sunlight resistant. In other words, okay for outdoor use. One end of each section is straight, and the other end is flared so that it can accept the straight end of another piece. That means I wouldn't have to buy any fittings. Perhaps the best part was the price—less than $3 for 10 feet of 2-inch, schedule 40 PVC conduit.

I bought a few lengths of conduit and took them home. It was a very hot day, and so I just tossed the tubes on the ground. In the cool of the next morning, I went out to put together a couple of sections to make a mast and found that the conduit tubes had warped. Call that lesson number one: PVC is plastic. It is not stiff like metal. Or, if you prefer, it is apt to warp. Warped or not, it would—and did—work.

I started by pushing two sections together and lifting them into a vertical position. That experiment worked perfectly. Next, I tried to lift three sections into a vertical position. That did not work well at all. Lesson number two: PVC is plastic. One should bear in mind that this material was meant to protect wires. It is not meant to be used as a structural member. For that reason, you should use a PVC mast only for light-duty applications—such as supporting wire antennas.

Putting It to Work

After the initial experiments, I joined two of the 10-foot lengths of PVC conduit with sheet-metal screws. I used this as a mast (shown in **Fig 4-11**) to hold up one end of K8SYL's 75-meter dipole. The mast is wobbly, so it requires guys to stabilize it. I used $3/16$-inch Dacron rope to guy the mast. The reason for that choice is two fold: First, the Dacron is an insulator, and that means that it will not upset an antenna's

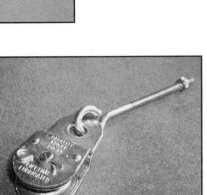

Fig 4-11—This light-duty mast is built from two 10-foot sections of 2-inch PVC conduit. The inset shows how the mast sections are held together by sheet-metal screws.

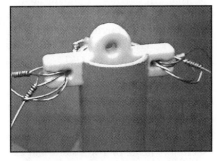

Fig 4-13—The light-duty PVC-conduit mast can be lashed to a short tree for an installation that has no guys.

Fig 4-12—A pulley can be fastened to the mast using an eyebolt and nut. See text.

Fig 4-14—The PVC-conduit mast can easily be cut to create a groove or notch that will hold a dipole center insulator. See text.

radiation pattern. Second, the $^3/_{16}$-inch size is large enough to be easy to handle, small enough to be inexpensive (about $0.10/foot) and strong enough (770-pound breaking strength) to easily handle the job.

Before erecting the mast, I installed a pulley near the top, using an eyebolt to secure the pulley to the mast. I opened the bolt's eye just enough for the pulley mount to pass through the opening. After the pulley and bolt were connected, I closed the eye. See **Fig 4-12**. Finally, I drilled a hole in the mast, passed the threaded end of the eyebolt through that hole and tightened the nut to hold the assembly in place.

A couple of times, I have used a PVC-conduit mast without guy wires. In these cases I have used short trees to support the bottom end of the mast, which I lashed to the tree with a couple of lengths of rope. One of those installations is shown in **Fig 4-13**. As you can see, the upper part of the mast bends quite a bit. Nevertheless, the mast worked well in that installation for

several months. It's not what you'd want to use for a permanent installation, but it worked well as a temporary support.

Support for the Center

Here's a way to support the center of a dipole with a PVC-conduit mast. This technique does not require a pulley or any other hardware to fasten the dipole's center insulator to the mast. How does it work? **Fig 4-14** tells the story.

Start by marking the top of the mast with a pencil to show the width of the insulator. Next, cut notches slightly smaller than the insulator. You can use a file to smooth any rough-cuts that you make. Remember the lessons from

earlier? That's right. PVC is plastic. That means that it cuts easily, and for that reason you'll want to cut with care.

For optimal mechanical stability, the notches should be narrow enough to hold the insulator very snugly. In Fig 4-14, I've shown the support hole on the high side of the mast. If you use a similar insulator, you will probably want to put that hole, actually its bump, down into the mast to help hold things in place.

Using TV Tower for Masts

My father-in-law took me to his barn and showed me a pile of TV tower. Another family member, having connected to the cable, no longer needed the tower. Dad thought I could use it and had saved it for me. I looked it over, and was very pleased to see that there was very little corrosion nor were there any other mechanical defects. Today, that tower supports a small VHF Yagi and a small 2-element HF Yagi plus K8SYL's 75-meter dipole. All I had to do was haul the tower home and install it there.

You may find a similar opportunity to obtain a used TV tower from friends or neighbors at little or no cost whatsoever. Your chances of a freebie are much greater if you're willing to take the tower down. However, you need to exercise great care if you remove someone else's tower.

I want you to know that a used tower can be cheap, but it can also be deadly. Hidden rust and corrosion can weaken a tower to the point that it will not safely support a climber. In addition, guys and anchors may not be adequate to their task. Don't take a chance—please—it's not worth it.

Used TV hardware (towers, masts and rotators) in good to excellent condition can be used to support VHF Yagis or HF wires. Take care not to overload these light-duty structures. For more information on this topic see the later chapter that deals with towers, masts and rotators.

A Lightweight Utility Mast

I almost put the words "old fashioned" in the title. No doubt, some of you will feel that I should have—especially when you realize that this project by Stephen E. McCallum, W2ZBY, (formerly K4URX) was published in July 1960 *QST*.

An outstanding feature of the 35-foot mast shown in **Fig 4-15** is that one man can put it up. This is largely due to the fact that most of the weight is in the base section. The long 20-foot center section is made of 1 × 2 stock and can easily be held in one hand. True, the mast requires guying. But light-duty guying presents only easy problems—nothing like those associated with the designing, building and raising of a self-supporting mast. And the guy wires make the task of raising or lowering the mast much easier.

This mast rendered good service at K4URX for several years. It's handy to put up when trying a new antenna, or a new location for an old antenna. For about a year it supported a 6-meter ground plane, the radials and radiator of which all were made of ⅝-inch thin-wall electrical conduit. In this service the mast was lashed to the side of the house with the top 10 feet and the antenna self-supporting. Here the mast withstood several gusty blows with winds up to 50 or 60 miles per hour. The structure is fairly flexible and gives with the wind. Fitted with wire, standoff insulators (either commercial or home-brewed of polystyrene strips), and perhaps a whip at the top, the mast can serve for a vertical antenna. In this use it would be self-supporting to a degree because there would he no lateral strain at the top from either the pull of a horizontal wire or the wind resistance of a beam.

Materials

Employing basic "A-frame" construction, the mast consists of a length of 2 × 4 for the base section, a latticed mid-section made of 1 × 2 wood, and a top section of 2 × 2 stock. Actual lengths shown in Fig 4-15 can be varied to some extent to suit the builder's requirements. It should be borne in mind, however, that a longer base section will add to the weight and a longer top section will weaken the overall structure. Two types of braces spaced 12 inches center-to-center are used on the mid section, all made of 1 × 2 stock. As illustrated at B, the outside cross braces are set at 45° and alternate in direction and from front to back. The short inside braces fit in between the sides and are graduated in length from slightly less than the width of the 2 × 4 base to slightly more than the width of the 2 × 2 top section. The exact lengths of the cross braces and internal braces can be determined as the mast is put together.

In the model illustrated, ordinary small finishing nails were used to fasten the braces to the 1 × 2 rails. However, aluminum nails would be preferable. Brass screws probably would be best, but they are expensive and require guide holes and a considerable amount of elbow grease. Cement-coated nails probably would provide stronger construction than noncoated nails, but still would subject the mast to rust damage over a period of time.

The mid section may be fastened to the 2 × 4 base with either nails, lag screws or bolts, the latter being preferable to anticipate future construction changes. The top-section 2 × 2 should be set into the 1 × 2 arms and secured with two 1/4-inch bolts. Nails here could split the wood all too easily.

Ideally, all of the wood pieces should be given a prime coat of outside white paint before assembly, and a second coat after construction is completed. However, the operator at K4URX (a lazy, shiftless type) used only one coat of white paint immediately after construction and the mast has suffered no appreciable damage in four years of exposure to the elements.

Assembly

If the lumber yard's 1 × 2 furring stock is composed principally of "knotty spruce," the chances of getting two clear 20-foot lengths are pretty slim and it would be best to have them cut from a 1 × 4 piece that is free of knots. Another point to watch in procuring these strips is their straightness. Crooked 1 × 2 rails will make a crooked mast. This also

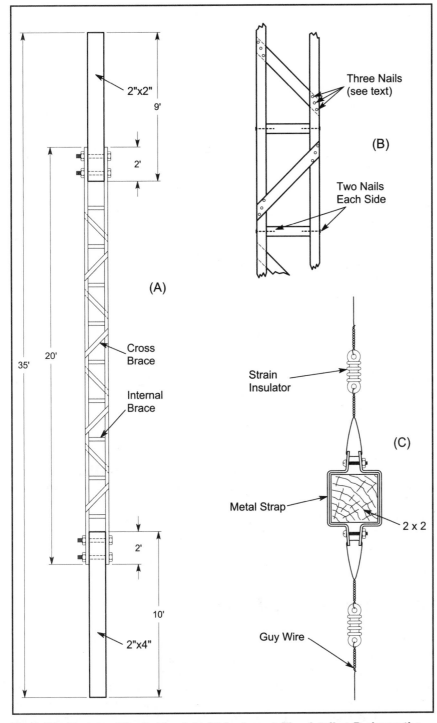

Fig 4-15—Sketch of the lightweight 35-foot mast. The detail at B shows the cross bracing. C illustrates a clamp for attaching guy wires at the top of the mast.

nails to hold the pieces in place. Then measure and cut the internal braces to the various lengths necessary to taper the 1 × 2 rails gradually from the width of the 2 × 4 base down to the width of the 2 × 2 top section. The taper is so gradual that it is not necessary to bevel the ends of these short inside braces. Nail them in place, taking care to keep the entire structure as straight as possible.

Nailing on the cross braces comes next. The trick that prevents the nails from splitting the ends of the cross braces is to use over-length braces—that is, to extend the ends a couple of inches beyond the outer edges of the long 1 × 2 side rails and then saw them off flush after they all are in place. If you think this is a waste of wood, just try nailing them on after precutting and see how many ends split. Also, anyone who can precut these angled braces to fit precisely this tapering structure is a minor mathematical genius who is wasting his time with structures like this! Alternate the placing of the cross braces on the rails between the front side and the backside. Use three nails at each end of each brace, aligning the nails diagonally across the side rails to reduce the danger of splitting the rails.

While the three sections are tacked together, drill the bolt holes in their proper places through all pieces at once. A clamp for top guys and antenna insulator or a pulley can easily be fashioned from two strips of scrap metal as shown in Fig 4-15C. Other means can be devised for fastening other types of antennas to the top of the mast although, as previously mentioned, this mast is for light duty. It is possible that a very lightweight rotator and small UHF antenna could be supported. However, no matter how light the rotator, the increased wind-loading surface adds danger; serious UHF work usually demands stacked arrays larger than can be handled by this mast.

Installation

Base anchoring is no problem. Two points should be observed: (1) prevent the base of the mast from moving sideways, and (2) keep the end of the 2 × 4 out of surface water in wet weather. Two methods are illustrated in **Fig 4-16**. The cinder-block mounting at

applies to the 2 × 2 top section and the 2 × 4 base.

Do not precut the braces. Instead, have a supply of 1 × 2 stock ready to use for bracing as you go along.

With all material on hand, lay the four principal pieces out to form the three sections on a surface as flat and hard as you can find. A level driveway serves excellently. Lacking this, the pieces may be laid on the ground, supported at strategic points by bricks or blocks of wood built up so that the entire mast is level and straight.

First, tack the two rails to the base and top sections with light finishing

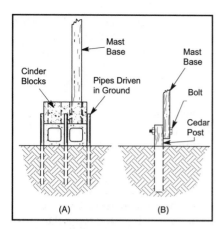

Fig 4-16—Methods of anchoring the base. At A, cinder blocks help to prevent deterioration of the base. At B the base of the mast is supported by a cedar post.

Fig 4-17—Sketch showing how the mast is easily raised by one man. With two guy wires attached to their anchorages, the erector "walks" the base of the mast in the direction of the third guy-wire anchoring point until the mast is nearly vertical.

A has been used successfully with the mast described here. Two cinder blocks are used with the bottom one on its side to raise the mast out of the mud, and the top block placed normally with the end of the 2 × 4 slipped into one of the holes in the cinder block. Four stakes driven into the ground around the cinder blocks prevent lateral movement of the blocks and the base of the mast. Loose construction permits good water drainage, and leaves the mast relatively free for easy removal, even in freezing weather, although you may have some trouble getting a cinder block out of frozen ground. It is feasible, too, to set a 4 × 4 cedar post in the ground and bolt the mast to it as shown in Fig 4-16B, although this imposes a degree of permanency on the location. At the time of this writing, the base section of the mast is clamped to the metal vertical member of a yardarm clothesline support, which itself is set in concrete in the earth.

Metal fence posts, sledged into the earth, make excellent guy anchors because they raise the lower ends of the guys off ground sufficiently to prevent the danger of tripping over them. Alternatively, trees, house corners, clothes poles or iron pipes can be used with confidence with a light-duty mast like this one.

Guys can be almost anything from heavy nylon cord to conventional TV mast wire. Naturally, the heavier the better. To reduce fraying of guy ropes, either standard thimbles or small egg insulators can be used.

Raising or lowering the mast becomes simple if at least two guys first are fastened in approximately their correct positions while the mast is still horizontal on the ground. One simply lifts the base section and pushes against the guys and—presto!—the top end of the mast soars upward as one walks toward the spot where the base will be set. See **Fig 4-17**. However, some caution must be exercised. Don't walk too far if you only have only two guys in place or the mast will soar *downward* in the opposite direction—and much faster, too! Set the base down on the ground before the mast reaches the perpendicular. It can be straightened and the guys tightened after the third guy or antenna wire is in place and ready to take some strain. With judicious juggling, neither a side wind nor a tail wind will interfere with this erection process, and it even takes a pretty stiff headwind to cause any trouble.

An A-Frame Mast

This project is of more recent vintage and illustrates how to use wooden building materials to fabricate an antenna support mast. It was described by Stan Kaplan, WB9RQR, in the Hints and Kinks column of May 1990 *QST*.

Here is an A-frame mast that has stood the Ozaukee Radio Club (ORC) in good stead for the past several years. It can be disassembled into short, lightweight pieces 10 feet or less in length, and is light enough for rooftop mounting. Including nylon guy ropes and hardware, it can be built for about $50—not bad for a 30 to 40-foot skyhook. This item first appeared in *The ORC Newsletter*.

Purchase 16 furring strips (8-foot 1 × 2s) from your favorite lumber store. Construction-grade lumber is fine, but make sure each piece is straight and has no major defects. A knot or two is okay, provided the knots are secure; no knotholes please!

Make the middle section (**Fig 4-18A**) as follows. Measure 2 feet from one end of two 8-foot furring strips and draw a line—perpendicular to the boards—across them. Run a bead of waterproof glue or construction adhesive (such as "Liquid Nails") along the 6-foot length of one of the marked boards, and overlap the 6-foot section of the second board as shown in Fig 4-18A. Two feet of each board should extend beyond the overlapped section. C-clamp the pieces together before proceeding.

Further fasten the two pieces together (while the glue is still wet) with countersunk no. 8 × 1¼-inch flat-head wood screws, (I prefer to drill a countersunk pilot hole in one board only, and then run in a screw. Splitting of the non-drilled board doesn't seem to be a problem, and this makes for a tight, permanent joint.) Put in a screw 1 inch from the end of the overlap, and every 6 inches thereafter. For maximum strength, alternate the sides that the screw enters; this is not critical to the integrity of the mast, however. Make sure the screw head is below the surface

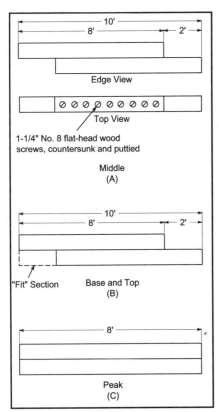

Fig 4-18—Stan Kaplan's A-frame mast consists of 1 × 2 furring strips, glue, wood screws and eyebolts. This drawing details the mast middle (A); base and top (B); and peak (C) sections.

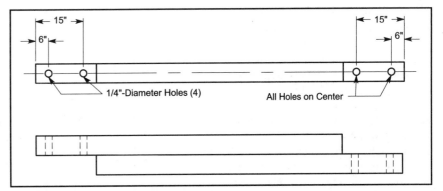

Fig 4-19—The mast-leg-section-fastener holes must be precisely located if the corresponding sections of both mast legs are to be interchangeable. Locate the fastener holes as shown here and described in the text.

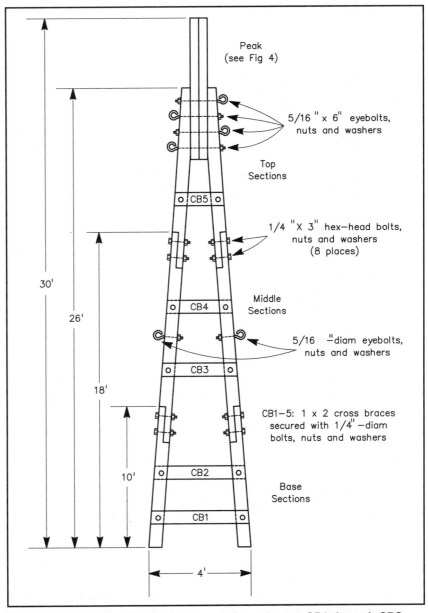

Fig 4-20—Plan view of the A-frame mast. Cross braces CB1 through CBS consist of 1 × 2 stock cut to the appropriate length; install CB5 first as described in the text. This mast must be guyed at the top and middle.

of the wood, and putty the hole. This will prevent rusting of the screw heads, which can ultimately lead to rotting of the adjacent wood.

To make the base and top sections (Fig 4-18B), follow a similar procedure, but "fill" one end of both of these assemblies with an additional 2-foot-long piece of 1 × 2, as shown. The base and top sections are identical; one end of each of these sections is a 2 × 2 square.

The peak section (Fig 4-18C) consists of two 8-foot lengths of 1 × 2 held together with glue and screws. Next, drill ¼-inch-diameter holes, as shown in **Fig 4-19**, in both ends of all middle sections and in the non-square ends of the top and bottom sections. Make sure these holes are placed exactly 6 and 15 inches from the section ends, *centered* in the board. If you locate and drill these holes carefully, corresponding mast-leg sections will be interchangeable. See **Fig 4-20**. Drill the top sections to pass, and then install, the four 6-inch-long, $^5/_{16}$-inch-diameter eyebolts used to anchor the mast's four top guy lines. Install another pair of eyebolts in the center of the mast's middle sections. These anchor the mast's four middle guy lines.

Fig 4-20 also shows how the sections go together. The cross braces (CB1-CB5) are simply 1 × 2s cut to an appropriate length. Cut the bottommost one to 4 feet and install it first. This provides ample separation of the legs at the mast base.

Fig 4-21 shows two eyebolts that have been pried open to allow a pulley to be slipped in, and then closed again. Mount these pulley/eyebolt combinations at 90° angles to each other as shown, at least 8 inches apart vertically. You can use both eyebolts to anchor antennas, or an antenna on one and a Field Day flag on the other. (We hoist our ARRL flag with the second pulley when the wind isn't too high.)

The procedure I've described yields a 30-foot mast. You can add one more pair of middle sections to form a 38-foot mast. Don't go higher than this, however: This furring-strip construction method is not substantial enough for heights above 40 feet.

A word about guy lines. For

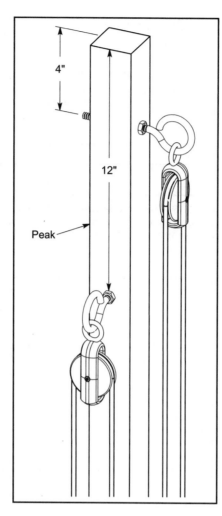

Fig 4-21—Pulley placement on the A-frame mast.

safety's sake, don't skimp on guying. You can purchase a 50-foot length of top-quality nylon "sash cord," which has a breaking strength of about 600 pounds, for about $5. Nylon is good because it doesn't rot, stretch or lose strength when wet. Moreover, in my experience, nylon cord can last for two to three years of constant outdoor exposure, which is more than can be said for hemp and other types of natural-fiber ropes. You'll need at least 50 feet for each of the top four guys, and it's probably a good idea to use that length for the four middle guys.

Don't forget a halyard for each pulley—to hoist whatever you need to hoist. (Remember, for a 30-foot mast, each halyard must be over 60 feet long: The halyard must go up to the pulley and return so you can tie stuff on!) To prevent tangles, snake one end of each halyard between the mast cross braces. The other end of each halyard—to which you tie your dipole, random wire or whatever—must swing free of the mast. Don't forget to tie on all guy lines and string the halyards before you erect the mast.

More on Building A-Frame Masts

The previous project brought a response from Harold A. Rogers, KE7MJ. This was published in the Hints and Kinks column of December 1992 *QST*.

I've used laminated construction techniques to build A frames by setting up a jig for the lower section (the A), and nailing together three 1 × 2s. Staggered butt joints, good waterproof glue (now, epoxy), and lots of clamps and long curing time make a very strong, permanently curved structure. Only one fabrication jig for half the A is required. The top section does not require a jig, but care is required to keep it straight.

If top guys are used, as described in many editions of *The ARRL Antenna Book*, only two 1 × 2s are needed. The A frame does not need side guys, since the base is wide enough to support the mast, with other guying (that is, a single

fore-and-aft guy) at the junction of the top and bottom sections, and a single guy at the top, offsetting the pull of the wire. Port and starboard top guys help in a high wind and are recommended.

All bolts used to join the sections of the A legs should have large-diameter flat washers on both sides, under the heads of the bolts, and under the lock washers and nuts. I strongly recommend stainless-steel hardware. Backing plates—possibly made from $^1/_8$-inch aluminum—would not be out of order.

Nylon line (landlubbers call it *rope*) and good blocks (pulleys) are available from mail-order marine suppliers. Recent advertising shows $^1/_4$-inch, three-strand nylon line at less than $10 per 100-foot spool. This line has a working load (W/L) of 925 pounds. If larger line (such as $^5/_{16}$-inch, W/L 1350

lbs) is used, splicing or seizing will be necessary to attach the line to the antenna, or the mast if the line is used for guying. If knots are used, use the right knot, and seize the "tail" coming from the knot, to the standing part of the guy or halyard.

Nylon line stretches, sometimes by as much as 20 percent, under full working load. That is why it is used to make dock lines and anchor lines. Dacron and polyester are almost as strong as nylon, with much less stretch. Laid or braid-on-braid Dacron line is very good, but somewhat difficult to splice. Be very careful if you use polypropylene line (frequently bright yellow), commonly sold in hardware stores. This stuff is very difficult to knot without slippage and deteriorates rapidly in sunlight.

Using (and Abusing) Trees as Antenna Supports

[It was 1989, I was *QST*'s Technical Editor, and we received an article for publication by Doug Brede, W3AS. It quickly became obvious to the technical staff that reviewed Brede's article that we held a classic in our hands. That article was published in the September 1989 issue of *QST* under the title "The Care and Feeding of an Amateur's Favorite Antenna Support—the Tree." I urge you to read this article carefully and follow its advice faithfully—K8CH.]

For most hams, trees are favorite antenna supports. Many radio amateurs begin their operating careers by hanging the far end of a wire up in the family's shade tree. On Field Day, resourceful hams find a hundred and one ways to get an aerial into the air; many (if not most) of these methods involve using trees as supports or aids.

During my 20 years as a radio amateur, I've used tree-supported wire antennas almost exclusively. Some of those antennas lasted several years; most didn't. Over the years, by trial and error—and because of my trade association with arborists and horticulturists—I've gained an understanding of what can (and can't) be expected of trees as antenna supports.

There are right and wrong ways to attach and maintain your tree-mounted skyhooks over the long haul. In this article, I'll share with you some pointers from two noted horticulturists who talk about attaching wires to trees. Safety is also discussed—your safety during antenna installation, and the safety of the tree.

Trees Are Alive

Few antenna supports can be classified as life forms. Trees are an exception. Tree experts usually cringe when someone brings up the idea of attaching a wire to a tree—especially when connecting a chunk of wire to its midriff (see **Figs 4-22** and **4-23**). The experts know that trees are made up of three basic layers: the bark, the living sapwood, and the nonliving heartwood. The bark protects the sapwood from

---

SOME QUESTIONS AND ANSWERS ABOUT TREE ANTENNAS

Q: A CBer in my neighborhood cut the top out of his pine tree and stuck a ground plane antenna up in it. Is this an acceptable way to mount an antenna?

A: Definitely not. Not only is this a hazardous way to mount an antenna, it essentially ends the useful life of the antenna. Topping of trees is strongly discouraged by professional arborists. Because topping removes the growing point of the tree, the tree recovers from the damage by sprouting numerous lateral buds around the top, which soon overrun the antenna.

Q: I've heard that if you fertilize a tree, your antenna will grow higher each year. True?

A: False. Although fertilizing is a desirable way to keep your tree healthy, it does not raise the height of your antenna one inch. Trees grow by extension of the apex. By the way, when you fertilize your tree, use regular garden fertilizer distributed around the drip line of the tree. The fancy tree spikes you see advertised are unnecessary because most tree feeder roots are near the surface.

Q: Is there any way to slow down the growth of a tree, so that it doesn't interfere with my antenna?

A: Some home-and-garden stores now stock growth regulators for trees. These products can be injected into the tree, dropped on the soil surrounding the tree, or sprayed on the leaves (follow label directions). Tree professionals can also perform this service. These growth regulators are used by some utility companies to reduce the need for tree trimming near power lines.

Q: Are certain types of trees better wire-antenna supports than others? What about hardwoods versus softwoods?

A: there's little difference between hard- and softwoods in their ability to hold up antennas. Conifers, because of their shape, are nearly ideal antenna supports. Avoid the use of red oaks and silver maples if possible, because they tend to rot easily if wounded. Avoid using poplars, too. In spite of their height and rapid growth, their branches are brittle and break easily.

Q: If I damage a tree during antenna installation, what should I do? Is tree replacement expensive?

A: If the damage is minor, your best bet is to do nothing. If it's a broken limb, saw the limb off cleanly, perpendicular to the axis of the branch. Never saw off a branch flush with the surface of the trunk, as this allows decay to set into the trunk. Using tree paint for repair is unnecessary (see text). In case of major tree damage, consult a trained arborist.

The answer to the second question is: Yes, tree replacement is expensive. The International Society of Arboriculture publishes a formula for calculating replacement cost of shade trees of various sizes. This pamphlet can be obtained from many tree services and libraries. Here's one point to ponder: A large, stately shade tree can add several thousand dollars in value to the property on which it sits.

---

injury. The sapwood contains the "skin and blood vessels" of the tree. If the sterile barrier between the bark and the sapwood is broken, infection can set in. Infection, if unchecked, can kill even a mighty oak within a year.

Trees have the same basic problems with infection as we humans do. If a tree gets a cut or gash, infection from bacteria and fungi is bound to set in. But there's one important difference between trees and humans: "Tree wounds don't heal," says noted tree expert Dr Alex L. Shigo. "People heal;

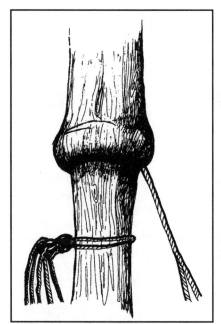

Fig 4-22—Attaching ropes or wires to trees can sometimes lead to major problems for the tree. Wrapping a rope around a limb or trunk and leaving it unattended will suffocate the tree and cause a distortion of growth or the death of the limb.

Fig 4-23—Over the years, this tree has grown around the cable of a roadside barrier. Dave Newkirk, W9VES, spotted this tree in Glastonbury, Connecticut. (photo *KC1MP*)

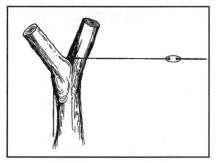

Fig 4-24—Most hams install tree-mounted antennas by throwing a line over a branch crotch. This should only be used as a temporary installation, because abrasion of the rope and tree results. Over time, girdling may occur, leading to the loss of one or more of the branches.

when you are wounded, you have forces that fight off the infection. Trees don't have these forces to fight off infection, and every wound will become infected."

Shigo, author of the book, *Tree Biology and Tree Care* notes that trees lack an immune system that fights off infection from wounds that occur from the actions of a careless climber or the attachment of an antenna support eyebolt. Trees treat their wounds by walling off the infected area and isolating it from the living part of the tree. "If you cut open a tree that's 2000 years old, you'll see every injury in that tree that occurred over its lifetime," says Shigo.

Whenever you wound a tree, you weaken the tree in that spot. The walled-off wood around the wound lacks the strength of healthy wood. When attaching an antenna to a tree, it's important to traumatize the tree as little as possible. This will ensure a strong, enduring connection.

Most people believe that tree paint or shellac is the best way to treat a tree wound. "Not so," says Shigo. "Wound dressing paints just protect the microorganisms." Scientific research

with tree-wound preparations has failed to show any benefit to the tree.

Making the Attachment

Although it's relatively easy to get a wire up into a tree, it's certainly more difficult to keep it there for the long term. Usually, annual (sometimes weekly) restringing is needed. It seems that trees "instinctively know" just when to drop a wire to the ground: during midwinter when the snow is high and the skip is long, or in the middle of a heated contest!

The bow-and-arrow method has become a standard of the wire-in-the-tree crew. But many other methods, slingshots, for example—even attaching a string to a golf ball and whacking it with a sand wedge—are common.

One of the easiest and most common ways to connect a wire to a tree is to throw a rope over a branch crotch (see Fig **4-24**) and tie off the loose end. This is the main method used in temporary (such as Field Day) installations. "Doing this probably won't hurt the tree if it's done as a temporary thing," says Washington State University horticulturist Ray Maleike. But with any of

these simple antenna-stringing methods, some problems for the tree (and the antenna) may develop later.

"First of all, you're not stabilizing the antenna very well with this type of setup. The other thing is that people have a tendency to forget the antenna's there. As the tree grows—as it increases in diameter—you can girdle the tree. If you've got this girdling rope or wire up there, you can actually kill that portion of the tree above the wire."

Another no-no when attaching an antenna to a tree is wrapping a wire around the trunk. This strangles the veins in the sapwood the same way a noose around your neck would strangle you. "It's important not to wrap anything around the trunk," says Maleike.

Many commercial nurserymen wrap stabilizing ropes around newly transplanted saplings to keep them from falling over. Recently, however, this practice has been questioned because of the restrictions these ropes place on the growth of the tree. People forget about these ropes; some remain on trees for years after transplanting.

Encasing the stabilizing (or antenna) wire in rubber or plastic hose is not the answer either. "Wire wrapped in hose is just as injurious to the tree as the bare wire itself," says Shigo. "If you remember your basic physics, you're applying the same number of pounds of force to the tree with or without the hose." Shigo recommends that if you must wrap something around the trunk of a tree, use a wide fabric strap to do the job.

PRACTICAL TREE BIOLOGY TIPS

Excerpted from *A New Tree Biology*,* by Alex Shigo, PhD

· Tree wood is not dead. There are more living cells than dead cells in sapwood.
· Tree wounds will become infected. Trees cannot restore, regenerate, or repair injured wood.
· Branches are attached to trunks by a series of collars; branch collars over trunk collars.
· Branch removal that injures or removes the collar will destroy a tree's defense system.
· Trees have five major growth periods during each growing season: (1) onset of growth, (2) leaf formation, (3) wood and inner bark formation, (4) storage, and (5) dormancy.
· Fertilize injured or stressed trees during growth periods (3) and (4).
· Trees get food (sugar) by trapping the energy of the sun.
· Trees get water and elements essential for growth from the soil.
· Substances for tree defense come mostly from stored energy reserves.
· Healthy trees have living cells with high amounts of energy reserves.
· When defense is low, opportunistic diseases attack.
· Because it grows big and fast does not always mean that a tree is healthy.
· If possible, cut tree limbs only when they're dormant or after leaf formation.
· There is no data to show that wound dressings stop rot.
· Tree topping is a crime against nature!
· Read and learn about trees.

*A. Shigo, *A New Tree Biology* (Shigo and Trees, Assoc, 1989), PO Box 769, Durham, NH 03824.

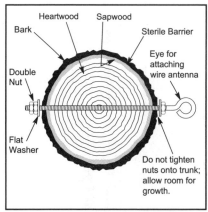

Fig 4-26—For heavy antenna loads, an eyebolt passed through the trunk or limb will support more weight than an eyescrew. Allow about 12 inches of play between the bolt and trunk or limb. Don't tighten the bolt completely; this allows for tree growth.

Two methods have emerged among leading horticulturists as the preferred way to attach a wire to a tree. For light antenna loads (eg, the end of a dipole), a threaded eyescrew (**Fig 4-25**) is the method of choice. Simply drill a hole into the tree about 1/16 inch smaller than the screw diameter, then twist in the eyescrew. Be sure to select a cadmium-plated eyescrew threaded for use in wood. A thread length of 2 or 3 inches should secure most antennas. Allow about 1/2 inch of space between the trunk and the eye; this allows for outward growth of the tree with time.

For stouter antennas, such as multielement wire beams, another method for securing wires to trees is recommended. This procedure involves using an eyebolt longer than the tree diameter, drilling clear through the tree and securing the eyebolt on either side of the tree with round washers and nuts (see **Fig 4-26**).

Drilling a hole through a tree causes much less trauma to the tree than wrapping something around it. Much of the core of a tree is dead tissue, used mainly for physical support. Although there will be some wounding of the tree at the site of the bolt or screw, such

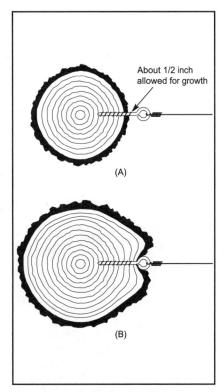

Fig 4-25—The best way to secure a wire to a tree is with an eyescrew mounted into the wood (A). As the tree grows and expands, however, the eyescrew will become embedded (6) and must be removed and replaced.

wounding will be far less than that which occurs from wrapping a wire around the trunk.

Over time, either type of eyescrew connection will have to be replaced. "If these fasteners are left on the tree for a long time, the fastener will eventually become embedded in the tree," says Maleike. "You're going to have to pull these fasteners out and replace them every now and then." Maleike recommends replacement of tree eyescrews every 5 to 8 years as the tree matures. Commercial arborists use drive fasteners for securing wires to trees; drive fasteners are similar to eyescrews. "These fasteners keep the wire away from the tree, allowing the tree to grow out to it," says Maleike. Drive fasteners are used for securing lightning rods and their accompanying wires to trees. The use of drive fasteners is common in the Midwest, where lightning strikes to trees are common. You may have to shop around to find drive fasteners—try calling tree-care services in your area.

It's easier to periodically service a tree-supported antenna if a pulley is used (see **Fig 4-27**). Raising and lowering the antenna for repairs can be done without the need to climb the tree each time. I use a flexible truck tie-down to provide tension to the antenna.

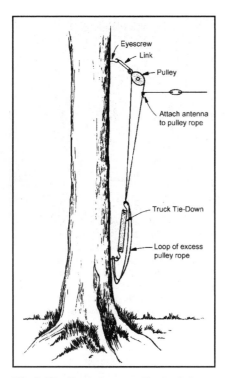

Fig 4-27—By using a pulley, raising and lowering the antenna for repairs can be done without the need to climb the tree. Flexible truck tie-downs can be used to apply tension to the antenna. (Early editions of *The ARRL Antenna Book* show a weight used to provide the required tension. A weight swinging from a tree can be hazardous.) Loop the excess pulley rope to a second eyescrew, in case the tie-down fails.

Fig 4-28—A professional arborist uses a safety belt and rope when climbing trees. Hams should take similar safety precautions. (*A. Douglas Brede, W3AS, photo*)

Your Safety in Trees

A fall from a 40-foot tree is just as dangerous as a fall from a 40-foot tower. Yet, many times you see hams scaling trees with no safety equipment! Wear a tower-climbing safety belt for all tree climbs (see **Fig 4-28**). Commercial arborists take the matter of safety one step further: They lob a rope over a tree crotch just above the height at which they'll be working. Then they tie the rope to their safety belt. The loose end of the rope can be held by a helper on the ground.

Be sure to use a good quality rope that is heavy enough to support your weight. Before use, inspect the rope for wear. Arborists prefer to use hemp rope rather than nylon, because hemp rope stretches less.

When you're climbing a tree to attach a wire, always have a buddy on the ground available to fetch tools or summon help in an emergency. Be sure your buddy wears a hard hat; tools or branches dropped from even a moderate height can be dangerous.

As an alternative to doing it yourself, consider procuring the assistance of a professional to install your tree antenna. A professional can clear away interfering branches and secure an eyescrew in short order. Professional tree trimmers generally work in pairs. They use a ladder or bucket truck to get up into the tree, and then they free-climb throughout the tree. A safety rope, saddle, and safety belt are worn. "A figure that I heard about how much this runs is about $50 an hour," says Maleike. Most antenna tasks can be done by professionals in about an hour.

Summary

Keeping your station in good operating condition is—or should be—a fundamental practice of every radio amateur. Part of that practice includes annual inspection of your antenna system. If trees are a part of your antenna system, take a good look at them. Are you keeping them healthy?

Guidance for Tree Climbers

This article by Herbert F. Slade, AA2BF, was published in February 2000 *QST* under the title "A Beginner's Guide to Scaling Natural Skyhooks." By learning how to safely climb your "antenna trees," you'll likely improve your antenna's performance and make life a little easier for your "natural skyhooks."

Remember the first wire antenna you planned? Some of us still exclusively use wires, and for good reason—they're cheap and relatively effective. (I confirmed more than 250 countries in nine years using only a variety of dipoles and other low-gain wires and 100 W.) Getting the wire "up there,"

A—The leg-wrap secure position. With one or both legs wrapped this way, both hands are free.

however, is the main challenge.

Some readers are blessed with convenient rooftop locations that leave everything easy to reach by window or ladder. But trees just seem to be ordained for use as wire antenna supports, so that's what I'll focus on here.

Conventional Wisdom

So, you have your 40-meter dipole assembled and ready to install between a couple of trees that are conveniently separated. What's next? Many short-term installations are launched with a slingshot or bow and arrow (and a fishing line leader for the wire to tie onto). That has one major disadvantage.

B—A handy climbing cleat. Drive 5-inch nails into the trunk through holes drilled in a 2 × 4.

Let's assume that you use the fishing line to pull up a rope that supports the antenna. If you were a good shot, the support rope will go over a desirable branch and return to the ground, where you can tie it off. The same effort will get a support rope into the tree on the other end. But because windstorms have a nasty effect on wires drawn tightly between trees, you're probably going to leave enough slack (and sag) in the antenna to minimize its chances of getting snapped by the next stiff breeze.

Because of this extra sag, the effective height of your dipole will be a few feet lower than you could achieve if you dared to pull it tight. Additionally, there's no way to protect your trees from the inevitable sawing action as the ropes move across the branches. In time, this will wear through the rope or bark and probably kill off the branch.

If you could physically get to the apex of each tree, you could add a pulley and a counterweight. You could put more tension on the wire, resulting in less sag. You could protect the tree with a piece of garden hose where the antenna support rope or pulley is tied off. From this vantage point you may be able to use trees that have obstructions between them—trees that would be impractical to work with from ground level. Being able to climb trees can be a distinct advantage!

Skyhook Scaling 101

Before climbing anything there are several things to keep in mind. The first

three are safety, safety and safety! A 40-foot fall is pretty unforgiving. But you can minimize its likelihood by taking practical steps to prepare.

The most obvious consideration is, "Do I have to?" Weigh an affirmative answer against, "Am I able to do this safely?" Not everyone can climb trees. I wouldn't be ashamed to answer "no" to both questions and look for a non-climbing solution to my antenna needs, if necessary.

You should certainly be in excellent physical condition. Being able to do at least several "chin-ups" is very desirable. Practice climbing a few times before trying to do any useful work aloft. You need to be limber for climbing, so get in the habit of doing stretching exercises regularly, especially just before going up.

Next comes planning. Naturally, you'll need to measure distances and estimate clearances, both for the finished antenna and the installation process. At this point, abandon any thought of running part of the antenna or its support ropes over or under any power line. In fact, do not climb into any trees that are in contact with, or adjacent to, power lines or any other commercial cables. The risk simply isn't worth it.

Assuming that the designated tree is free of power cables, inspect the branches. Which branches look dead (check during foliage season)? Where are branches far enough apart to make climbing difficult? Where is the logical point for tying off the antenna? Will you have to cut away any branches to make a clear path? Also, learn to recognize poison ivy and poison oak, including the hairy but leafless vines that sometimes grow on tree trunks. Most of this can be done from the ground, but a practice climb or two in your "target" trees is a good idea, too. Timing is also important. Don't start a tree project at sundown, with a storm approaching or when dinner is about to be served. I know it's obvious, but I've made all these dumb mistakes!

Think about what you can accomplish with each climb. For safety's sake, and to reduce wear and tear on the tree bark, it's probably better to finish the job with a minimal number of ascents. I recently planned a rather complicated project and found it helpful to write an

C—Moving between branches. Maintain a solid hold with one hand while reaching with the other. Always hold with both hands whenever you move your feet.

ordered list, with detailed tasks in one column and the tools and materials needed for each task in another.

If possible, work with a partner, even if he/she stays on the ground. You'll greatly appreciate having one the first time you're up a tree only to discover that you forgot a tool. (Let down a rope that you didn't forget and your helper can tie the tool on to be hauled up.) If your partner can also work in one tree while you're in another, so much the better.

What is high fashion for tree climbing? Well-fitting jeans, a work shirt with long sleeves and high-top sneakers are good for starters. Gloves are not, unless they fit very snugly and/or leave your fingertips exposed. Leave any necklaces or chains on the ground and eliminate protruding tool handles that could get snagged.

A utility pole-climbing belt is a good investment. There are ads for these in most ham magazines, including *QST*. Unfortunately, a climbing belt is hard to use while actually climbing most trees. Once you've arrived at your working position, however, secure yourself with the safety belt. I don't recommend belting in while climbing if you will have to detach and reattach your belt clip frequently while getting around branches. Manipulating the belt requires one or both hands that you need for gripping the tree. It's better to hold on and climb as described below and wear the belt clipped to itself until you reach your working height.

Beginning with your practice climbs, learn to look at each branch before committing your weight to it. Is it alive? Is it thick enough to support my full weight? Understand that certain trees are inherently weaker than others are. For example, oak, hickory and maple trees are strong, but watch out for wild cherry, sassafras and dogwood varieties. Dead branches are dangerous. Avoid hanging from or standing on these, especially if you are not able to also hold onto a trustworthy branch at the same time!

Where suitable branches are too far apart, it may be necessary to add cleats to the trunk. These can be two-foot pieces of common two-by-four lumber, predrilled to accommodate five-inch spikes for nailing into place against the tree trunk. There should be two holes, no less than three inches apart, drilled either side of center and not along the same grain line. The nails must set deeply into the tree trunk. When climbing, hold onto or stand on these as close to the trunk as possible to prevent loosening the nails. I have no experience with utility pole climbing irons, but I will point out that they take training to use properly and they cause more damage to the tree than a few semi-permanent nails.

Up, Up and Away

Are you ready to climb? Put up a good extension ladder and secure it by leveling the feet against the ground. If the ladder must stand on an uneven or potentially slippery surface, take the time to put non-skid blocks under the feet to make it safe. Remember that the top will probably rest against a single point on the tree (the curve of the trunk), making that end inherently less secure. Having a partner to hold the ladder while you climb up or down is a smart idea.

If this is a working climb, check your list for required tools and parts. Put small tools and parts in easy-to-reach pockets. (I like to button them inside my work shirt so they're right in front.) Tie a lightweight rope to any larger tools and leave them at a convenient place on the ground where you can pull them up. Tie the other end of

D—A tool as fundamental as this rock and cord can be surprisingly useful.

this rope loosely to your belt (behind you) and start up the tree. As you go, try to keep the rope ascending in a vertical direction toward your destination. This may require untying and retying it from your belt to pass it around branches. Do this only when you can belt yourself in or lock yourself in a secure position. When you get to your work location, belt yourself in and tie the lift rope to a branch where you can reach it when you need to pull up the tools.

If you don't think you'll need anything more than what you can carry in your pockets, carry a ball of lightweight cord and a small rock so that when (not if) you remember that "one more thing" you left on the ground, you can drop the cord down and your partner can tie it on for you. You'll also find this cord and rock handy when it's time to pull up the antenna (more about this later).

Back to the climb. Avoid poison ivy vines and leaves by climbing past them on your ladder or by moving around to the other side of the tree. Test each step, even when on the ladder. Move slowly and deliberately. Examine each branch and stump you come to, and consciously decide if it's trustworthy (and can bear your full weight). Place your feet and hands on branches as close to the trunk as possible, and always move only while holding on with at least one hand. Avoid stepping into tight crotches between branches and the trunk. They can trap you. Plan each move and avoid overreaching. It's better to prepare a cleat or two than to risk scrapes and injury. Stop and rest as necessary, belting in when you do. There is no rush. Enjoy the view.

With practice, your confidence will

increase. You will find ways to use your hands, feet, knees and back to help you climb and to lock yourself into place. But be sufficiently fearful, even then. You need to respect what you're doing at all times and not allow yourself to be distracted. Branches sometimes break. That's why you need to have a secure hold on one while you reach for the next.

What can you do, once you're belted in and standing on a strong branch? Depending on your situation, it may be necessary to clear away one or more branches so your antenna can be stretched out without interference. A hand saw—or even a chain saw—can be pulled up from the ground. Obviously, great care is needed, especially if a branch to be cut is of considerable size. Again, it's wise to ask yourself the two questions: "Do I have to?" and "Am I able to do this safely?" If your answers aren't "Yes," *don't!*

If you need to make the cut and are able to proceed safely, start by planning. Where will the branch fall? Will it be more manageable if you cut it off in sections or with one cut near the trunk? Should you tie the branch to a higher point on the tree while cutting? What will you need to do at the moment the branch begins to break? Should you get a professional to do this? Remember, with limb cutting as with climbing, haste is your enemy. Never give in to it.

Raising the Antenna

Once the passage is clear, the antenna can be pulled up, one end at a time. Your antenna should be stretched out on the ground—without kink-along its path between the support trees. From the tie point in either end tree, unroll enough cord from a ball of string (with a small rock tied to the end) to reach the ground. Next, carefully gather it in loops (to prevent tangling) in one hand and throw the rock out over the branches to the ground. Get your partner to tie the cord to the antenna tie rope (which is tied to the end insulator). From your vantage point in the tree, pull the cord, followed by the rope and the antenna, until the end insulator is where you want it to be. Then tie it off temporarily, while the other end is pulled up in the same manner. After final adjustments, the ends can be tied off permanently.

If there are obstructions between the endpoint trees (other trees, perhaps), you will need to go over or through them. If the obstruction is low enough it may be possible to throw your rock and cord over it to the other side. By the way, when you throw something from a treetop perch, both hands will be occupied. You must be belted in to do this safely. A slingshot or bow and arrow may work even better for this purpose.

The antenna may have to be strung through a space cleared for it in an intervening tree. This will require climbing that tree to cut away the obstructing branches. Then a rock and cord can be thrown out on either side of the opening in the third tree and tied onto the cord ends from the antenna end point trees. In this situation, the antenna must be rolled up on a large reel and carried to the top of one of the end trees, where it can be fed out without kinking as it's pulled across from the other end. When the cord has finally been stretched across or through all obstructions between the tie points, the end tie rope from the rolled up antenna can be tied onto one end of this cord. Then, rope and antenna are unrolled as they are pulled across from the other end tree. Could this be accomplished from the ground? I don't think so.

As I suggested earlier, tying off an antenna with a pulley and a counterweight provides a considerable advantage. In this configuration, the antenna is tied off to one of the end trees, while the counterweight is used to take up

E—The wire antenna and tie ropes can be kept under control with this simple homebrew device. The spool is a coffee can and the "drag" can be made from a piece of scrap wood and a bungee cord.

slack and maintain even tension from the opposite end. At the fixed end, after pulling up the antenna, run the end tie rope through a short piece of garden hose (length determined by the girth of the tree at the point of attachment). Cushion the tree from the rope by wrapping the hose around the trunk above a crotch and tie a bowline knot in the rope. (The bowline is chosen because it is not a slipknot. Leave enough space under

the rope loop for easy movement and tree growth.)

At the opposite end, attach a suitable pulley to a length of insulated wire rope (the kind sold for clotheslines) and run this through another piece of hose. Wrap this around the trunk as at the fixed end and tie a bowline knot as before. The wire rope to the pulley should extend no more than two to three feet from the tree. When stretched out in the direction of the antenna, the pulley must end up over a vertical space where a counterweight can hang down a few feet without banging into the tree or its branches.

For a counterweight I use a section of a four to six-inch log that's long enough to weigh about 30 pounds, which gets hauled up and tied off with the lifting rope. When the antenna has been pulled up, its end tie rope is threaded through the pulley and tied near one end of the counterweight. After loosening the lift rope and taking up the antenna slack, the counterweight hangs freely. Another piece of rope is then tied to the counterweight and to the tree above it, with a couple of feet of slack. This acts as a safety rope to prevent the counterweight from crashing to the ground if the antenna or a support rope breaks.

Conclusion

Certainly, climbing trees to erect antennas should be done with great care. The advantages are your personal safety, a much more permanent antenna installation, better elevation and minimal distress to your trees!

The EZY Launcher

This project built by Wade A. Calvert, WA9EZY, presents an easy way to get a line into a tree. It was published in the June 1991 issue of *QST*.

Would you like to raise your 75-meter flattop? Do you get a queasy feeling whenever you consider how you're going to get that nylon rope over that "perfect" limb at 50 feet? Try the EZY Launcher!

The EZY Launcher is made from a Zebco model 202 spin-casting reel (complete with fishing line), a Marksman slingshot, a piece of flat steel stock, a wood dowel, two small hose clamps and some no. 10 hardware. I obtained all the parts at a local hardware store for less than $15. If your hardware store isn't as well stocked, chances are you can get the fishing reel and slingshot from a sporting goods, discount or catalog-sales store. The accompanying photographs show how easy it is to build an EZY Launcher.

Construction

A view of the disassembled EZY Launcher is shown in **Fig 4-29**. **Table 4-1** contains the parts list. The U-shaped bracket is formed from a piece of $^3/_4$-inch-wide, $^1/_8$-inch-thick steel (or aluminum). Each leg is approximately $2^3/_4$ inches long, with a $1^3/_4$ inch gap between the legs. Adjust this gap to comfortably fit your hand and allow your thumb to operate the fishing reel's release button at the rear. To determine the gap width, grasp the slingshot in your shooting hand. Measure the distance from the side of the slingshot handle nearest you to the second knuckle of the middle finger of your shooting hand; to this dimension, add about $^1/_8$ to $^1/_4$ inch. Cut the metal stock long enough to allow for the leg lengths, the bracket's horizontal portion and the bends at each leg. Using a vise, bend the flat stock at the required gap distance to make the horizontal part of the bracket. Then, cut the legs to length.

Drill two $^3/_{16}$-inch-diameter holes at the top of one of the bracket legs on the centerline. Locate the first hole $^3/_8$ inch from the top of the leg. Make the second hole $^1/_2$ inch down from the first hole. Deburr the holes and countersink

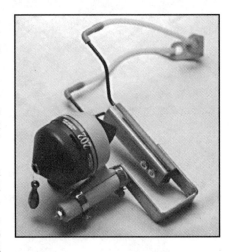

Table 4-1
Parts List
Qty Item
1 Zebco model 202 spin-casting reel (or equivalent}
1 Marksman Go model 3010 sling-shot (or equivalent}
1 1/8 × 3/4 × 12-inch piece of flat steel (or aluminum} stock
1 3/4 × 3-inch hardwood dowel
2 3/4-inch hose clamps
2 No. 10 × 1-inch flat-head machine screws
1 No. 10 × 3¹/₂-inch round-head machine screw
3 No. 10 nuts
1 No. 10 flat washer
1 No. 10 lock nut
1 ¹/₂-oz sinker

them on the outside of the bracket. Drill a single $^3/_{16}$-inch diameter hole $^3/_8$ inch down from the top of the other leg on its centerline. Deburr the hole and remove any sharp edges from the bracket.

Place the slingshot against the bracket and check for grip clearance. Drill two mounting holes in the slingshot handle. Position the first hole $^3/_8$ inch up from the bottom of the wooden part of the handle on its centerline. Locate the second hole $^1/_2$ inch from the first. These holes should line up exactly with the holes in the bracket. Attach the slingshot to the inside of the bracket using two no. 10 × 1-inch-long flat-head machine screws. To

keep the screw ends flush with the nuts, I used no washers beneath the nuts.

Drill a $^3/_{16}$-inch-diameter hole lengthwise through the center of a 3-inch-long dowel. A drill press comes in handy here, but a satisfactory job can be done with an electric hand drill and reasonable care. Use a $3^1/_2$-inch-long no. 10 machine screw to attach the dowel to the bracket leg opposite the slingshot. The bolt head should be inside the bracket. Secure the dowel using a no.10

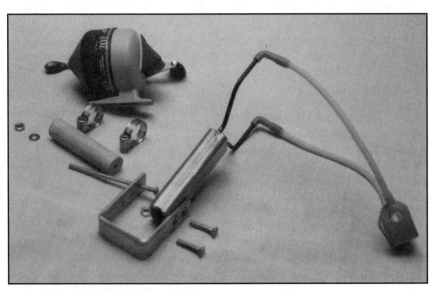

Fig 4-29—A view of the disassembled EZY Launcher.

flat washer and nut.

Attach the fishing reel to the dowel using two small hose clamps. Grip the slingshot and rotate the dowel until your thumb can rest comfortably on the release button. Slide the reel forward or backward if necessary.

Operation

Safety First!

Remember: A slingshot is not a toy! Wear eye protection and take any other precautions necessary to ensure the safety of people and property. Never shoot near power lines. Practice shooting in a flat, open area until you're confident in your ability to shoot predictably.

Remove the metal ring at the end of the fishing line. Make a 1-inch loop of line at the end. Carefully deburr the eye of a 1/2-oz sinker. Push the line loop through the sinker eye, pass the loop around the sinker body and pull it tight. This method of fastening the sinker to the line makes it easier to get the sinker off the line and provides a means of connecting light nylon line once the sinker has passed over the tree limb and returned to ground. (Please have regard for the trees. Doug [W3AS] Brede's article found earlier in this chapter is recommended reading.—*Ed.*)

When you're ready to shoot, wind the sinker tightly against the reel. Make sure that the reel crank is down and out of the way of the shot. If it isn't, press the release button while holding the sinker in place with your free hand, and wind the crank until the sinker is tight

Fig 4-30—K8CH's version of the Launcher. Note the plastic vial, used to hold a spare lead sinker.

against the reel and the crank is down. Position the sinker in the pouch with the sinker eye pointing down. Take short shots until you get the feel of the Launcher. Control the shot distance with the release button. The button not only releases the line for casting, it also acts as a brake when depressed further. You can set the degree of drag by adjusting the black adjustment wheel on top of the reel. When rewinding the line, apply a small amount of drag to it using your thumb and forefinger.

That's it! Have fun with the EZY Launcher. It's sure to make your antenna raising easy.

The K8CH Version of the Launcher

Slingshots come in a variety of models. Nearly a decade before the EZY Launcher appeared in print, I was using the unit shown in **Fig 4-30**. The extension allows for more power and the arm brace helps improve accuracy. The extension also allows a convenient place to mount the spinning reel. I've also mounted a plastic parts vial under the extension. I use it to store an extra 1-ounce sinker.

5 HF Verticals

In an ARRL Web Survey taken in March 2000, one in four respondents reported that their most used HF antenna is a multiband vertical. (Survey results may be found in the sidebar in Chapter 2 covering your first HF dipole.)

I can think of some good reasons for the vertical's popularity: First, a vertical is simple and relatively easy to install (no tower climbing involved). A vertical costs less than a small Yagi or rotary dipole. It has low visual impact—in other words, it's less conspicuous than a Yagi or even a dipole. A ground-mounted vertical does not require high supports.

Do you think you'd like to try one of these? Do you think it may be just what you need? Well, it might be exactly what you're looking for, but before you invest your hard-earned dollars, you should be aware of some limitations.

Caveats

A quarter-wave vertical—more correctly called a *vertical monopole*—requires radials. These may be elevated above the earth, laid on the ground or buried below the surface. The purpose of these radials is to provide the "missing half" or second side of the antenna (see the sidebar in Chapter 1, *How Ground-Plane Antennas Work*). Your ground radial system will determine your antenna's efficiency. You'll find a detailed discussion of this topic in the sidebar on *Optimum On-Ground Radial Systems for Vertical Antennas*.

A single vertical has an omni-directional azimuth pattern. At times that's an advantage—you don't need a rotator to point your vertical. At times

it's a disadvantage—you are unable to null out interference or noise while receiving. And on the last topic, verticals do tend to pick up more noise.

Do Verticals Really Work?

I've heard folks say, "A vertical antenna is one that radiates equally poorly in all directions." I don't believe that statement for a moment—it does not agree with my experience, and even more important it doesn't agree with the facts.

Vertical-antenna performance is highly dependent on ground conductiv-

ity, for reasons that are complicated. Verticals interact with the ground for an area that extends far beyond the limits of any ground-radial system. Unfortunately, there's not much you can do to improve the ground conductivity, unless you do so for thousands of feet around your vertical. [I remember diligently watering the ground under my vertical when I was an impressionable young ham in Hawaii about 40 years ago, hoping to improve my pipsqueak signal. It didn't help.—*N6BV.*]

Fig 5-1 compares the elevation patterns for a 40-meter ground plane

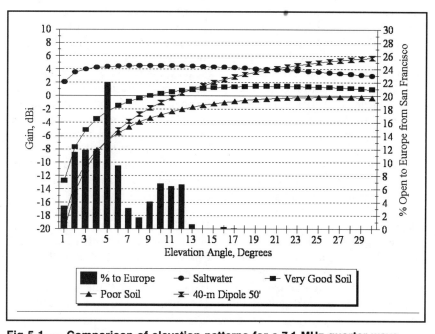

Fig 5-1——Comparison of elevation patterns for a 7.1-MHz quarter-wave vertical over three different types of ground: saltwater (representing virtually perfect ground because of the high conductivity), "poor ground" and "good ground." For comparison, the response for a 50-foot high horizontal dipole is also included, together with the elevation-angle statistics needed for the path from San Francisco to Europe on 40 meters.

Table 5-1
Conductivities and Dielectric Constants for Common Types of Earth

Surface Type	Dielectric Constant	Conductivity) (S/m)	Relative Quality
Salt water	81	5.0	
Fresh water	80	0.001	
Pastoral, low hills, rich soil, typ Dallas, TX, to Lincoln, NE areas	20	0.0303	Very good
Pastoral, low hills, rich soil, typ OH and IL	14	0.01	
Flat country, marshy, densely wooded, typ LA near Mississippi River	12	0.0075	
Pastoral, medium hills and forestation, typ MD, PA, NY (exclusive of mountains and coastline)	13	0.006	
Pastoral, medium hills and forestation, heavy clay soil, typ central VA	13	0.005	Average
Rocky soil, steep hills, typ mountainous	12 – 14	0.002	Poor
Sandy, dry, flat, coastal	10	0.002	
Cities, industrial areas	5	0.001	Very Poor
Cities, heavy industrial areas, high buildings	3	0.001	Extremely poor

antenna for three types of ground conductivity:

• Over saltwater (virtually a perfect ground).
• Over "poor" soil (typical of much of New England).
• Over "very good" soil (typical of the rich soil of the Texas gulf coast or river deltas in parts of California).

Also overlaid in Fig 5-1 for comparison are the elevation statistics from *The ARRL Antenna Book* for the path from San Francisco, CA, to Europe on 40 meters. Working Europe from California requires very low takeoff angles.

At low elevation angles the antenna mounted over saltwater is far more effective than one mounted over poor soil. For example, at an elevation angle of 5° (the peak elevation angle for San Francisco to Europe) the antenna over saltwater has 5.4 dB more gain than the antenna over very good soil, and a whopping 10.8 dB more than the antenna over poor ground.

And just because you are probably curious, there is a fourth curve overlaid in Fig 5-1. This shows the elevation pattern for a 50-foot high horizontal 40-meter dipole. The peak gain of this antenna is about 2 dB higher than even the saltwater vertical, but its peak occurs at an elevation angle higher than 30°, where no signal arrives—at least for the difficult 40-meter path from San Francisco to Europe. The elevation response of the 50-foot high dipole crosses that for the vertical over poor ground somewhere near 5°, meaning that even a vertical over poor ground will equal a moderately high 40-meter dipole much of the time into Europe from the West Coast.

Table 5-1 lists typical values of conductivity for various soil types. Over the poor, rocky soil of New England, a vertical will be a mediocre performer. By contrast, in the rich, very good soil of the Texas gulf coast, a vertical can be an excellent performer, even compared to high horizontal antennas.

And near or over saltwater, theory says that a vertical antenna will be hard to beat. Dean Straw, N6BV, described in *The ARRL Antenna Compendium, Vol 6* the experience of the 6Y2A expedition that did so well (over 19,000 QSOs) that they set a new multi-operator, multi-transmitter world record in the 1998 CQ World Wide CW Contest. They used vertical antennas at 6Y2A and proved that the theory about verticals and saltwater was exactly right!

Multiband verticals with traps will have additional losses caused by the traps. They will also have reduced SWR bandwidth (most notably on the lower-frequency bands). If you possible can, avoid traps and use full-size elements on each band.

I remember in the 1960s when Gus Browning, W4BPD, was travelling around the world. He had a 100-W transceiver and a 14AVQ, which is a 20, 15 and 10-meter trap vertical. Gus was never loud, but he was very workable. In other words, his multiband vertical worked well.

In the late 1970s I installed a ground-mounted 40-meter quarter-wave vertical with 16 radials. I managed to snag two new DXCC counters—counters that put me on the Honor Roll and all thanks to that vertical. I've described that tree-supported vertical antenna later in this chapter.

So, the answer is "Yes, verticals can do very well," particularly on the lower bands, where putting a horizontal antenna up high in terms of electrical wavelength is really challenging.

Build a 30-Meter Vertical

I built this project because I wanted to have an effective antenna for the 30-meter band. It is a full-size, self-supporting, ground-mounted, ¼-λ vertical. Further, I wanted the antenna to survive 60-mph winds. (It has already handled gusts of 55 mph with ease and, according to calculations, should handle 70-mph winds.) See **Fig 5-2**, which is a photograph of my 30-meter vertical.

To begin the design, I decided to build the vertical from telescoping lengths of aluminum tubing. The tubing would slide over a length of fiberglass rod, which would serve as the base insulator. The bottom end of this insulator would slide into a length of water pipe that would be set in a hole, which would then be filled with concrete to create a strong and stable base.

The next step involved choosing the size of the base insulator. For that, I selected a 24-inch length of 1.25-inch diameter fiberglass rod. This rod has the strength to support the vertical, and it conveniently slips into the end of a piece of 1.25-inch water pipe.

The vertical radiator is constructed from 6-foot lengths of 6063-T832 drawn aluminum tubing with 0.058-inch wall thickness. This tubing is available in telescoping sizes, with diameters from 0.375 to 2.125 inches, from Texas Towers in both 6 and 12-foot lengths. The limit for shipping by United Parcel Service (UPS) is 9 feet, so only the 6-foot lengths will ship by this popular carrier. That's why I chose the shorter tubes.

Starting from the bottom, a length of 1.375-inch tube (1.259-inch ID) slips over the base insulator. The bottom of this tube is reinforced with a 51-inch length of 1.5-inch tube. Next, 24 inches of a 1.25-inch tube fit into the 1.375-inch base. The construction scheme is shown in **Fig 5-3**. Except for the bottom two tubes, I used three ⅛-inch pop rivets to secure one tubing section to the next (see **Fig 5-4**). The 1.5-inch tube is secured to the 1.375-inch tube by a single pop rivet in the center of the larger tube and by the #8 machine screw that fastens the vertical to the base insulator and provides a connection point for the feed line.

Another exception is found at the joint between the top two sections. A stainless-steel, worm-gear hose clamp secures these sections. In the top of the 1-inch tube, I used a hacksaw to make a pair of inch-and-a-quarter-long cuts opposite each other (see **Fig 5-5**). These

Fig 5-2—K8CH's finished 30-meter vertical is mounted in a clear area of the lawn.

Fig 5-4—Three ⅛-inch pop rivets are used to secure tubing sections at the joints.

Fig 5-3—Drawing of the 30-meter vertical. Tubing diameters are: a, 1.5-inch; b, 1.375; c, 1.25; d, 1.125; e, 1; and f, 0.875-inch. See text.

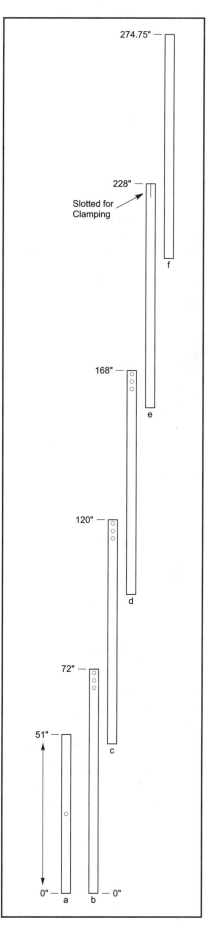

cuts allow the tubing to close when the hose clamp is tightened. This makes an adjustable joint, which allows the builder to tune the antenna to resonance at the desired frequency.

For the base, I used a 40-inch length of 1.25-inch water pipe. This is placed in a 34-inch-deep hole. I used

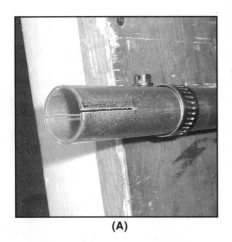

(A)

(B)

Fig 5-5—At the adjustable joint, the larger size tubing is slotted with a hack saw, as shown at A. At B a stainless-steel worm-screw hose clamp secures the two tubes.

post-hole diggers to dig that hole, but rocks and clay made the going difficult. No problem. A pry bar came in handy for breaking up clay and loosening rocks (See **Fig 5-6**).

Assembly and Installation

I started the assembly and installation phase by putting together the bottom 10 feet (three tubing sections) of the vertical. I took this portion of the vertical, along with the insulator rod and the 40-inch length of 1.25-inch water pipe to my garage workshop, where I used a drill press to drill $^{11}/_{64}$-inch holes through the vertical and insulator rod and the water-pipe base and insulator. These holes will just pass the #8 machine screws that I used to fasten the pieces to each other. Having secured the vertical and base to the insulator, I took the entire assembly to the hole that Sylvia, K8SYL, and I had dug. I also took with me three 50-lb bags of quickset cement mix and a large bucket of water.

I set the base into the hole and fastened a post level onto the vertical at eye level. A post level is made for setting posts in a perfectly vertical position. This is done by setting two bubbles in the center of their respective tubes. In **Fig 5-7**,you can see how this works. The post level is a convenience for this job—it is not a necessity.

Time for a workout. I poured a small amount of the cement mix from the first bag into the hole, poured in

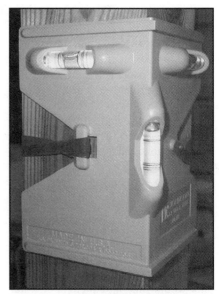

Fig 5-7—A post level is a handy device for setting a post, support, tower or antenna in a perfectly vertical. See text.

water and mixed the two with a length of PVC pipe. The mixing process involves a cutting and stirring motion with the pipe. The photo in **Fig 5-8** can't capture the action, but you should be able to get the idea. Once I had thoroughly mixed cement and water, I added more cement and water and repeated the process. Don't try to mix the whole bag at once. This technique is not suitable for doing large quantity batches. After shooting the photo, Sylvia held the assembly vertical while I mixed cement

Fig 5-6—K8SYL takes a turn at loosening soil and rocks in the hole for the base of the 30-meter vertical.

Fig 5-8—K8CH mixes quickset concrete in the base hole.

Fig 5-9—K8SYL held the vertical in position while her OM mixed the concrete.

(Fig 5-9). If you have a suitable container, you'll probably find it less work to mix the cement and water before you put it into the hole. However, you'll have more to clean up afterward than I did.

Once all three of the bags of cement were mixed, the bottom part was already beginning to set. That meant that we could leave it without support while the cement finished setting—in this case 24 hours was enough.

I had only assembled the bottom 10 feet of the vertical so that there would be enough to set the base vertical, but not enough for the wind to blow it out

of vertical while the cement in the base was setting. While the base was setting, I prepared the radial system and feed line.

Radials

My friend John Stanley, K4ERO, wrote one of the better articles I've read on designing radial systems for vertical antennas. John's article, "Optimum Ground Systems for Vertical Antennas," appeared in the December 1976 issue of *QST* starting on page 13. You'll find some of John's wisdom in the sidebar *Optimum Ground Systems for Vertical Antennas.*

Before going on, I'd like to emphasize the fact that low SWR, and particularly low SWR over a broad bandwidth, is frequently an indication of ground losses. Take my first 40-meter vertical as an example. It was a shunt-fed tower with a single 6-foot ground rod for the ground system. After adjusting the gamma match, I had a 1.1:1 SWR from band edge to band edge. I was elated until I started using it and discovered that a dummy load would have worked as well as that antenna! The dummy load would have about the same SWR.

For this vertical, I opted for a 15-radial system. Each radial is made from 20 feet of insulated #12 copper wire and is connected to a copper ring that goes around the base of the vertical. Twice that number of radials would have been better, but that's what I could do with the wire I had at hand. Based on feed-point impedance readings, I estimate ground losses of approximately 8 Ω.

This in turn translates into nearly 1-dB loss, and that's a figure that I (and my budget) can live with.

You should read the sidebar on optimum ground systems, examine your budget and then make a decision about the size and extent of your radial system. You may find it strange that the radial lengths described in the various configurations presented in the sidebar are, in many cases, shorter than a quarter wavelength. These wouldn't work for an elevated radial system, such as is found in a ground-plane antenna. The length of the radials of a ground plane determines the resonant frequency, as does the vertical radiator. However, when the radials are placed on or beneath the surface of the earth, their lengths are not a critical factor in determining the resonant frequency.

I had two 40-foot lengths of insulated #12 wire plus some more on the original spool. I estimated that I had a total of about 300 feet of wire. I cut the two 40-foot lengths in half and then began cutting 20-foot lengths off the spooled wire. The fifteenth wire was 22-feet long. Close enough? It was for me, so I left it a little bit longer than the rest.

Next, I took a 30-inch piece of bare #12 copper wire and clamped the ends to wooden blocks that I had placed on a desk. See **Fig 5-10**. I stripped about an inch and a quarter of insulation from one end of each radial and wrapped the stripped end around the ring wire. I placed the radials about an inch and a half apart. Once the radials were all neatly placed along the ring wire, I soldered them to the ring.

In the past, I've soldered radial systems outdoors. That's okay on a warm summer day when there is little breeze. On a very cool autumn day with a stiff breeze, you may want to do as I did and do the soldering inside. Another advantage of soldering inside was that I was able to do the job on a cold, rainy night.

I formed the ring wire into a circle, and twisted each wire end around the opposite wire. You can visualize this if you grasp your left wrist with your right hand and vice versa. I left a double-width gap at this splice, as this would be the place that the feed line would leave the antenna on its way to the house. In other words, this ring looked

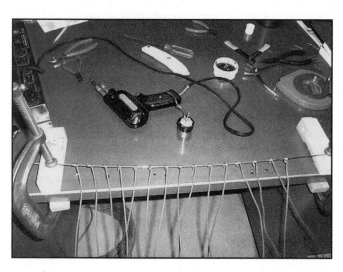

Fig 5-10—The radials were attached and soldered to a length of bare #12 copper wire that was later formed into a ring. See text.

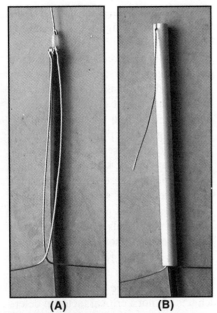

Fig 5-11—Extensions of #12 copper wire are soldered to the antenna end of the coax feed line (A). A length of PVC pipe is used to protect the feed line connections from the weather and from the lawn mower (B).

like a 16-spoke wheel with one of the spokes missing.

Attaching the Feed Line

My top priority for the feed-line connection was for it to be protected from the weather and from the lawn mower. I considered several different schemes, and opted in the end for simplicity.

To make the coax termination, I stripped the outer insulation from the end of a length of RG-213. I used about three feet of solid #12 copper wire and wrapped the middle of that wire around the base of the exposed braid. I then soldered the braid to the #12 wire and bent the wire back along the coax.

Next, I stripped the dielectric (center insulator) from the end of the coax center conductor. I then added a 12-inch extension to that center conductor by soldering a length of #12 solid copper wire. You can see how this works in **Fig 5-11A**. My plan was to slide a 10-inch section of PVC pipe over the coax to provide protection from the weather and from the lawn mower (see Fig 5-11B). In the top end of the PVC, I had cut a $^1/_8$-inch slot about a half-inch long. I used a small triangular file to make a

OPTIMUM GROUND SYSTEMS FOR VERTICAL ANTENNAS

A frequent question brought up by old-timers and newcomers alike is: "So, how many ground radials do I *really* need for my vertical antenna?" Most hams have heard the old standby tales about radials, such as "if a few are good, more must be better" or "lots of short radials are better than a few long ones."

John Stanley, K4ERO, eloquently summarized a study he did of the professional literature on this subject in his article "Optimum Ground Systems for Vertical Antennas" in December 1976 *QST*. His approach was to present the data in a sort of "cost-benefit" style in Table 1, reproduced here. John somewhat wryly created a new figure of merit—the total amount of wire needed for various radial configurations. This is expressed in terms of wavelengths of total radial wire.

Table 1
Optimum Ground-System Configurations

Configuration Designation	A	B	C	D	E	F
Number of radials	16	24	36	60	90	120
Length of each radial in wavelengths	0.1	0.125	0.15	0.2	0.25	0.4
Spacing of radials in degrees	22.5	15	10	6	4	3
Total length of radial wire installed, in wavelengths	1.6	3	5.4	12	22.5	48
Power loss in dB at low angles with a quarter-wave radiating element	3	2	1.5	1	0.5	0*
Feed-point impedance in ohms with a quarter-wave radiating element	52	46	43	40	37	35

Note: Configuration designations are indicated only for text reference.

*Reference. The loss of this configuration is negligible compared to a perfectly conducting ground.

The results almost jumping out of this table are:
- If you can only install 16 radials (Case A), they needn't be very long—0.1 λ is sufficient. You'll use 1.6 λ of radial wire in total, which is about 450 feet at 3.5 MHz.
- If you have the luxury of laying down 120 radials (Case F), they should be 0.4 λ long, and you'll gain about 3 dB over the 16-radial case. You'll also use 48 λ of total wire—For 80 meters, that would be about 13,500 feet!
- If you can't put out 120 radials, but can install 36 radials that are 0.2 λ long (Case C), you'll lose only 1.5 dB compared to the optimal Case F. You'll also use 5.4 λ of total wire, or 1,500 feet at 3.5 MHz.
- A 50-Ω SWR of 1:1 isn't necessarily a good thing—the worst-case ground system in Case A has the lowest SWR.

Table 1 represents the case for "Average" quality soil, and it is valid for radial wires either laid on the ground or buried several inches in the ground. Note that such ground-mounted radials are detuned because of their proximity to that ground and hence don't have to be a classical quarter-wave length that they need to be were they in "free space."

In his article John also made the point that ground-radial losses would only be significant on transmit, since the atmospheric noise on the amateur bands below 30 MHz is attenuated by ground losses, just like actual signals would be. This limits the ultimate signal-to-noise ratio in receiving.

So, there you have the tradeoffs—the loss in transmitted signal compared to the cost (and effort) needed to install more radial wires. You take your pick.—*Dean Straw, N6BV*.

Fig 5-12—The wire extension from the coax center conductor exits the top of the PVC protective pipe via a slot with a V-shaped groove filed in the bottom. See text.

Fig 5-13—An end cap on the PVC pipe protects the coax and extensions from the weather.

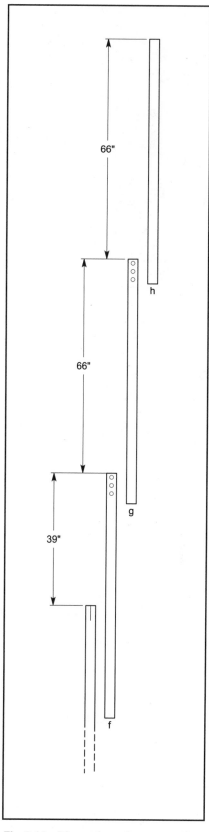

Fig 5-14—Dimensions for converting the 30-meter vertical to 40 meters. Three 6-foot sections are required the diameter of the sections is: f, 0.875-inch, g, 0.750 and h, 0.625-inch diameter. See text.

vee-shaped slot at the very bottom. The wire extension from the coax center conductor would come up the tube and bend over the slot and pass down through the vee. I made the vee deep enough so that I could slide a PVC end cap over the end of the pipe and over the wire where it emerged from the slot. See **Fig 5-12**.

I connected the wire extensions from the coax braid to opposite sides of the ring, leaving the coax (with its PVC shield) a couple of inches off center. I then soldered these wires to the ring.

Installing the Radials and Feed Line

The next day was sunny and mild—just like the forecasters promised. With help from Sylvia I hauled the radial assembly and feed line to the base of the vertical. We laid out the 15 radials like evenly spaced spokes from a wheel, with the coax taking the position of a 16th radial. I pushed the ends of the radial wires into the ground to hold them in place.

I had not filled the top of the hole that had been dug for the base, and the concrete lacked several inches from coming up to the level of the surrounding ground. That was perfect for placing in

their respective positions the ring and the bottom of the PVC pipe that protects the antenna end of the coax feed line.

Sylvia and I spent the day slitting the earth and burying the radials plus 120 feet of coax. I've used all kinds of hand tools for this job. A lawn edger works well and has been my favorite tool. You can use whatever you have at hand. Your goal is to slit the earth and insert the wires. Finish the job by stepping on the ground over the wire, thus closing the slit. You don't need to go very deep—just below the surface is fine and will protect your radials from foot traffic and machinery.

I used a pair of hose clamps to hold the protective PVC pipe in place against the vertical's water-pipe base. The photo in **Fig 5-13** was taken before I trimmed the connection to the vertical and installed a lug on the end.

Tune Up and Operation

The vertical proved to be a bit too long, being resonant around 9.9 MHz. I shortened it a bit and the resonance moved to 10.12. Perfect! The dimensions given here are my final dimensions. You may have to adjust the length of the vertical for best SWR in the 30-meter band.

On-the-air results are most grati-

Fig 5-15—A hose clamp is used to secure guys at the bottom of sections g (see Fig 5-13).

fying. I worked many stations in Europe, Africa and the Americas in the first couple of evenings. I suspect that a dipole at 90 feet might work better, but that's not a possibility for me.

Other Bands

It didn't take long for me to start thinking about adapting the 30-meter vertical for operation on 40 meters. I decided to go ahead and try it. As before, I used *EZNEC* to modify the 30-meter design by adding two additional telescoping sections at the top. The design looked good electrically.

To check the physical factors, I plugged the design into the equations in Dave Leeson's book, *Physical Design*

Fig 5-16—The 40-meter vertical ready for action.

of Yagi Antennas. Whereas the 30-meter version is good for 70-mph winds, my 40-meter design was good for up to 50 mph. In other words, it should be guyed.

After considering the electrical and physical factors, I decided that I

wanted my vertical to be useable on either 30 or 40 meters. To change bands, I would have to lower the vertical and replace the top of the antenna.

I removed the top (0.875-inch) section from the vertical and replaced it with a three-tube replacement. Only one joint needs to be adjustable, and for that reason I used a new 6-foot length of 0.875 tube with 0.750 and 0.625-inch tubes telescoped as shown in the dimensions given in **Fig 5-14**. In a repeat of my experience with 30 meters, this antenna was resonant just below the band. The dimensions shown in the figure are my final dimensions; yours may vary.

Based on impedance readings, I estimate ground losses of about 9 Ω, which still means less than 1 dB loss in efficiency. SWR is very good.

Finally, for peace of mind and to assure survivability, I added $^3/_{16}$-inch Dacron guys just above the adjustment clamp (see **Fig 5-15**). I used a file to remove the sharp edge at the top of the section below the guys. I also did not over-tighten the clamp. Guys become useless if they are cut by the clamp or by a sharp edge. Before the guys were added, the antenna flexed quite a bit in even a gentle breeze. Now it doesn't. See **Fig 5-16**.

On-the-air results are very good. More radials could improve the performance, but you'll have to decide what you'd like to do.

WA5ABR's Homebrew Seven-Band Vertical

Paul I. Protas, WA5ABR, built this antenna to replace an aging four-band trap vertical that had been in service for about 12 years. Paul's article appeared in *ARRL Antenna Compendium Vol 5*. Here's what Paul had to say:

I had looked around at various manufactured verticals but decided to build one myself. This antenna should out-perform any trap vertical and should be at least comparable to any of the "half-wave" or "elevated-feed" products on the market today. My vertical cost around $130—considerably less than most commercially available units. If you have any scrap aluminum tubing from other projects, your cost could be even less.

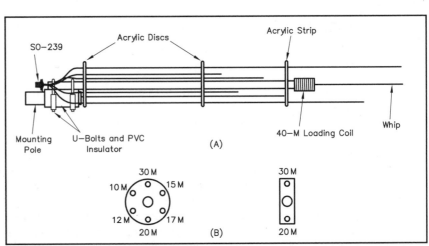

Fig 5-17—At A, layout of WA5ABR seven-band vertical. The acrylic discs at top and bottom support the aluminum-tubing elements. The acrylic strip at the top keeps the longer elements stable. At B, detail for the acrylic discs and strip.

Fig 5-18—Photo of assembled antenna at WA5ABR.

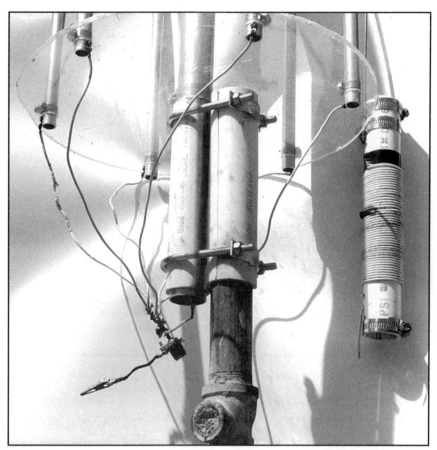

Fig 5-19—Photo detail of the bottom acrylic disc, with insulating "clam-shell" clamps of PVC pipe around 40-meter element and mounting pipe using U-bolts. The seven elements are connected in parallel to the SO-239 connector. In this photo an alligator clip was used to connect to the ground radials during experimentation.

My design philosophy is that if a full-size λ/2 dipole is an efficient radiator, then a full-size λ/4 radiator would also be efficient, given a good ground system, of course. On 30 through 10 meters, the vertical uses six full-sized λ/4 elements. On 40 meters a loading coil is used at the 16-foot level, with a 4-foot whip above the coil. You could elect to use a full-sized 40-meter element, but this will definitely mandate the use of guy ropes.

There are no traps or matching circuits. One feed line is used, connected to all seven elements in parallel at the base. See the drawing in **Fig 5-17** and the photo of the assembled antenna in **Fig 5-18**. All elements are made using 0.058-inch-thick aluminum tubing so that they may be telescoped easily.

If you want to build a really low-cost version, you might consider making your antenna like the wire prototype I made before changing to aluminum tubing in the final design. In the prototype I used #14 wire supported by a 23-foot tall 2 × 2 wood support, with wooden discs at the top and bottom to separate the individual wires. I used heavy fishing line to support the shorter elements from the top disc. While it certainly was not as durable as the final aluminum version, the prototype worked fine and only cost about $20.

Construction

See **Table 5-2** for the Parts List to build this antenna. To start construction of the aluminum-tubing version, cut two 15-inch diameter discs out of acrylic sheet. In one disc, drill six $^5/_8$-inch holes at points $6^3/_4$ inches out from the center of the circle (center to center) at $60°$ intervals. Drill a $1^1/_2$-inch hole in the center. This will be the bottom support. In the second disc, drill six holes as above, but make two opposing holes $^5/_8$ inch and the other four $^1/_2$-inch OD. The center hole in this disc should be $1^1/_2$ inch. This will be the top support. See the photo in **Fig 5-19**, showing details of the bottom support disc.

From the remainder of the acrylic sheet, cut a rectangular piece $2^1/_2$ by 15 inches. Drill a $1^3/_8$-inch hole in the exact center of this piece and two $^1/_2$-inch holes, $^1/_2$ inch in from each end. This

Table 5-2
Parts List

Qty	Description
3	12 foot sections, $\frac{1}{2}$-inch OD
4	12 foot sections, $\frac{5}{8}$-inch OD
1	6 foot section, $\frac{1}{2}$-inch OD
1	6 foot section, $1\frac{3}{8}$-inch OD
1	12 foot section, $1\frac{1}{2}$-inch OD
1	48 inch aluminum-wire whip
1	2 foot section, $1\frac{1}{4}$-inch Schedule-40 PVC
7	solder lugs, $\frac{1}{8}$-inch holes
1	S0-239 connector
1	34 foot length of insulated #14 solid copper wire
1	36´18-inch sheet of $\frac{1}{4}$-inch thick acrylic (Plexiglas)
2	2-inch U-bolt clamps
20	$\frac{3}{4}$-inch hose clamps, non-rusting
9	$1\frac{1}{2}$-inch hose clamps, non-rusting
7	6-32 × $\frac{3}{8}$-inch screws, lockwashers, and nuts

Note: all aluminum tubing is T-6061 material, with 0.058-inch-thick walls

Table 5-3
Preliminary Dimensions for Telescoping T-6061 Aluminum Tubing; 0.058" Wall

Band	Overall Length	$1\frac{1}{2}$" OD	$1\frac{3}{8}$" OD	$\frac{5}{8}$" OD	$\frac{1}{2}$" OD
10 meters	7' 6"			6'	4'
12 meters	8' 6"			6'	6'
15 meters	10' 3"			6'	6'
17 meters	12' 3"			6'	8'
20 meters	15' 9"			12'	6'
30 meters	22' 10"			12'	12'
40 meters	16', plus whip	12'	6'		

will support the top two longest elements.

Next, separate the aluminum tubing into three batches according to size. The $1\frac{1}{2}$ and $1\frac{3}{8}$-inch sections can be telescoped and set aside as one batch. The other two batches will be the $\frac{1}{2}$-inch and the $\frac{5}{8}$-inch OD pieces. Cut two 12-foot pieces of $\frac{5}{8}$-inch tubing in half (each 6 feet long). Cut one piece of $\frac{1}{2}$-inch tubing into a 4-foot and an 8-foot section. Cut another piece of $\frac{1}{2}$-inch tubing into two 6-foot sections. The remaining two 12-foot sections of $\frac{5}{8}$-inch tubing and the one remaining 12-foot section of $\frac{1}{2}$-inch tubing will not be cut.

You should now have six sections of each smaller-size tubing. Drill a $\frac{1}{8}$-inch hole, $\frac{1}{4}$ inch from the end of each of these sections. Saw two opposing slots $\frac{1}{2}$-inch deep into the other end of each section of $\frac{5}{8}$-inch tubing. This will

be the place where the $\frac{3}{4}$-inch hose clamps tighten around the next telescoping section. These hose clamps can now be attached loosely. Telescope the different sections of tubing using **Table 5-3** as a preliminary guide. You will adjust the final length for SWR at installation. The starting lengths may seem to be short, but the length of wire attached to the SO-239 coaxial connector makes each element electrically longer.

Drill a hole, similar to the ones drilled in the $\frac{5}{8}$-inch sections, in the end of the 12-foot section of $1\frac{1}{2}$-inch tubing. Also, cut two opposing slots $\frac{1}{2}$-inch deep in the other end of this section. Similar slots need to be cut in the end of the 1-3/8-inch section. Cut six lengths of the #14 insulated copper wire about 11 inches long. Remove $\frac{1}{4}$ inch of insulation from each end. Install solder lugs

onto one end of each wire.

I made a small loop on the other end of the six wires and slid each onto a short wire soldered to the center pin of the SO-239 connector. (I crimped another solder lug on the end of this wire so the other wires didn't fall off while soldering the individual wires to the feed bus.) Also attach (either with small screws and nuts or solder) a five-inch loop of #14 wire to the ground hole on the SO-239. This makes a bus where ground radials are attached. Use at least 8 to 12 radials, 16 feet or longer and a 4-foot or larger ground rod for lightning protection.

Now, place the bottom disc (the one with six $\frac{5}{8}$-inch holes) about eight inches from the bottom end of the $1\frac{1}{2}$-inch tubing. Secure this to the tubing on either side with $1\frac{3}{4}$-inch hose clamps. Slide another hose clamp, the top disc, and another hose clamp after that, over the other end of the $1\frac{1}{2}$-inch tubing, where the $1\frac{3}{8}$-inch tubing is sticking out. Secure this disc about $7\frac{1}{2}$ feet up from the first disc by tightening the hose clamps.

Attach a seven-inch piece of Schedule-20 or 40 PVC pipe to the bottom end of the $1\frac{1}{2}$ inch tubing. I used a piece of $1\frac{1}{4}$-inch ID Schedule-40 pipe, cut in two lengthwise as the clamp-on insulator. Place the two U-bolts over the PVC at each end (so that the U-bolts don't touch the $1\frac{1}{2}$-inch tubing) and temporarily tighten them. Now, attach the solder lug on the SO-239 bus wire to the hole in the end of the $1\frac{1}{2}$-inch tubing with a 6-32 × $\frac{3}{8}$-inch screw, lock washer and nut.

Next, put the two longest sections of tubing, for 20 meters and 30 meters, through the larger holes in the uppermost disc. They should be opposite each other (at 0° and 180°). Slide a $\frac{3}{4}$-inch hose clamp over the bottom end and insert the element into the bottom disc. Attach one of the feed wires to the element with a screw, lock washer and nut. Keep the disc perpendicular to the larger center element, and press the tubing against the disc and tighten the hose clamp. Also, slide another hose clamp over the smaller telescoped end of the elements and tighten at the point where the element comes out of the upper disc. Do the same with the remaining elements so that they are positioned as shown in Fig 5-17. Once all the elements are in place, make sure that the feed wires don't cross each other.

Next, slide a 1¹/₂-inch hose clamp, the 15-inch piece of acrylic, and another hose clamp over the top section of 1³/₈-inch tubing and over the 20-meter and 30-meter elements, stopping just below the top of the 20-meter element. This keeps these two elements from moving in the wind and affecting resonance. Place ³/₄-inch hose clamps on these two elements above the acrylic, keeping it level, and then tighten the large hose clamps also.

If you are going to use a full-size element on 40 meters, telescope the center three sections (the top section is 1¹/₄-inch OD) to an overall length of 33 feet and tighten the hose clamps. If you are using a loaded 40-meter element, as I did, you will only be using the 12-foot long 1¹/₂-inch section and a 6-foot long 1³/₈-inch section. This telescopes to a total of 16 feet long.

For the 40-meter loading coil form, cut a piece of the 1¹/₄-inch ID Schedule-40 PVC pipe 12 inches long. Cut two lengthwise slots about one inch long at right angles to each other on one end. Draw a line running the length of the pipe on one side. Drill two ¹/₄-inch holes on this line. One should be one inch from the end with the slots and the other 1¹/₂ inches from the end. Drill two similar holes on the line 2¹/₂ and 3 inches from the other end.

Starting at the end with the holes near the slots, insert five inches of #14 coil wire through the inside hole and back out the outer hole. This end will attach to the 1³/₈-inch tubing with a sheet metal screw. Wind 48 turns of the #14 wire tightly around the PVC and put the end of the wire through the inner hole in the far end and back out the outer hole. Leave about two inches and snip off the extra. Strip one inch of insulation off this end and make about three loops with an inside diameter the same as the whip you will be attaching to the top. Press this loop close to the PVC pipe, insert the whip into the loops, and attach the whip to the PVC pipe with two 1¹/₂-inch hose clamps. Squeeze the wire loops tightly around the whip with vise grips or similar pliers.

Slip a 1¹/₂-inch hose clamp over the slotted end of the PVC and install onto the 1³/₈-inch aluminum. Drill a hole in the aluminum just below where the PVC pipe is mounted and attach a small, uninsulated loop of the lower coil wire with a solder lug and sheet metal screw.

Finally, mount the antenna on its support pipe placed in the ground and attach the ground wire loop connected to the SO-239 to the ground radial system. Using low power, check the SWR on all bands. If necessary, adjust the length of each element by loosening the clamps at the joints and above the acrylic discs and retighten to check the SWR again. If the 40-meter SWR is too high, you may have to remove a few turns of the coil (if changing the length of the element is not sufficient). The SWR on all bands except 40 meters will typically be 1.1:1 over most of the band and less than 2:1 at the band edges. The 40-meter bandwidth will be similar if you use a full-size element. The loaded 40-meter element I used had a 2:1 SWR bandwidth of about 90 kHz.

I have been using this antenna for about one year and have worked over 60 countries during low solar-flux conditions (including ZD7, 3B8, VR6, 5NØ, V6, CY9, A3, YB, and EA9, to name a few). A vertical like this is a viable option for hams with small lots, tower deed restrictions, or limited finances. It should provide years of operating enjoyment due to its simple construction.

A Three-Band, No-Tune Inverted-L

This project by Mitchell Lee, KB6FPW, appeared in the April 1997 *QST* Hints and Kinks column. Lee started with an 80-meter inverted L, and in the process of improving the antenna's efficiency he also added 40 and 30-meter coverage. This design will be sensitive to surrounding objects and may be a bit tricky to adjust. It also has some power limitations. Nevertheless, if you're willing to accept those factors, you may find this antenna a useful addition to your antenna farm. Here's Mitchell Lee's story.

As a low-band enthusiast, I find my postage-stamp, 5000-square-foot lot to be quite a handicap. At $10 to $11 per square foot, however, I'm not likely to add to my land holdings any time soon.

Since I have room for only one antenna of any size, I must make it count on several bands. The best antenna I have developed thus far is a λ/4, 80-meter inverted L. I'm constrained to about 30 feet vertically (a 20-foot, roof-mounted TV mast, plus another 6 to 8 feet of feed line), top-loaded by a 30-foot horizontal wire.

At λ/4 resonance, such an inverted L exhibits an impedance of 18 Ω, a less than ideal figure. My 80-meter inverted-L, together with a ground loss of about 18 Ω, exhibits 30-40 Ω at resonance on 80 meters. This isn't a bad mismatch in a 50-Ω system, but the ground losses make this arrangement inefficient.

Over the years I've laid out about all of the "ground" I can deploy, so I

can do little else to reduce the magnitude of these losses. There is another way to reduce the effect of ground loss: Increase the feed-point impedance of the antenna by increasing its electrical length. Because I am unable to extend the antenna length to 3/8 λ, I instead introduce inductive loading at the apex of the antenna. An apex coil of 7 to 10 µH improves the system efficiency by increasing the feed-point impedance to 50 to 60 Ω at midband and allows me to resonate the antenna with a simple series combi-nation of a 500-pF variable capacitor and 5-µH inductor. Above 3.8 MHz, the feed-point impedance climbs rapidly, reaching 80 Ω at 4.0 MHz.

Inductive loading at the apex has a nice side benefit; it moves the antenna's center of radiation from the ground part way up the vertical radiator. This improves the radiation angle for long skip.

You can operate an inverted-L on several bands. With the 80-meter loading coil shorted, the antenna becomes $\lambda/2$ on 40 meters. The vertical and horizontal sections each exhibit $\lambda/4$ properties. The horizontal section is useful for daytime, short-skip operation, and the vertical section lays down low-angle radiation for nighttime contacts.

If the horizontal wire is disconnected, the vertical section loads as $3/8 \lambda$ on 30 meters, a particularly effective dimension for a vertical. As a bonus, it's easy to resonate a $3/8$-λ element by means of a series reactance at the base.

For several years, I used relay-switched loading networks at the apex to implement each configuration, as I operated the antenna on 80, 40 and 30 meters.

Relays have many disadvantages that make them undesirable for installation atop an antenna. Among these are weight, the possibility of RF rectification in the contacts (a prolific source of TVI and BCI), mechanical wear and the need for wiring to control the relay(s).

Although a stepping relay eliminates the need for continuous control power, it is a problem to isolate the control wire and still allow easy operation. These factors led me to search for a multielement trap/loading network that could replace my relay system.

Fig 5-20 shows my results. This network seems magical in that it exhibits the correct impedance on each band (80, 40 and 30 meters) with *no* moving parts. **Fig 5-21** illustrates the operation of the network by showing the equivalent reactances at each band center.

In Fig 5-21A, L1 and C1 resonate at approximately 6200 kHz. On 80 meters, they exhibit about 2.2 µH. Together with L2, the total inductive component is approximately 6.7 µH (159 Ω) at mid-band. C2 exhibits approximately –633 Ω, which combines with L1, C1 and L2 to total 8.9 µH— just the amount required to center load the inverted-L 80 meters.

On 40 meters (Fig 5-21B), the L1-C1 network exhibits a net capacitive reactance of –202 Ω, which combines

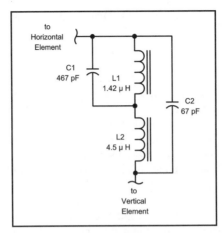

Fig 5-20—A schematic of the inverted L and its multiband loading network. L1 is 11 turns of #18 AWG enameled wire on a T-106-6 core. L2 is 20 turns of #18 AWG enameled wire on a T-130-2 core. C1 and C2 are formed by the PC board (see text).

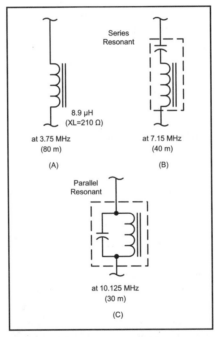

Fig 5-21—The network in Fig 5-20 appears as different loads on different bands. A shows the 80-meter equivalent circuit, B shows 40-meter, C shows 30-meter.

with L2 (199 Ω) to form a series-resonant circuit. The vertical and horizontal antenna sections are effectively shorted together, creating a $\lambda/2$ antenna. The reactance of C2, shunted by the series-resonant network of L1, C1 and L2, is of little conse-

quence on 40 meters.

On 30 meters (Fig 5-21C), C2 forms a parallel-resonant trap with the C1-L1-L2 combination. This isolates the horizontal section of the antenna, leaving a very effective $3/8$-λ vertical.

To prove out the concept, I first built the network using a combination of fixed and variable capacitors. I aligned the network (using a grid-dip meter) as follows: first I removed L2 and C2 so that I could trim L1-C1 to resonate at 6200 kHz. Next, I added L2 and C2, shorted C2 and dipped L2 (adjusting C1 slightly) at 7.05 MHz. It didn't require much adjustment. Lastly, I opened the short across C2 and adjusted C2 to dip the whole network at 10.125 MHz.

To test the network on 40 meters, I simply connected it in series with my dummy load. I found that my grid-dipping procedure was accurate; the SWR was essentially 1:1, indicating that the network was series resonant. I applied 100 W, sending 1.4 A (RMS) through the network. L2 warmed slightly to the touch (checked with transmitter off, of course) after several minutes of operation.

On 80 meters, a series capacitor (500 pF, air variable) was necessary to cancel the 8.9 µH net reactance. With the capacitor in place and adjusted, several minutes of operation warmed L1 only slightly. I saw no capacitor arcing on 80 or 40 meters.

I didn't have a convenient way to test the network on 30 meters, so I made those tests after installation. C2 apparently arced at 100 W (SWR fluctuated wildly), but it did handle 20 W without problem. The final version, where the PC board forms C1 and C2, handles 100 W with no problem.

After several weeks of operation, I was quite satisfied with the performance of the preliminary network. Measurements at the antenna feed point and behavior at full power indicated everything was working as predicted.

For permanent installation, I decided to build the network using toroidal inductors and double-sided PC board for the capacitors (see Fig 5-20). Since the capacitors share a common connection, one plate can be common to both.

I measured the capacitance of some

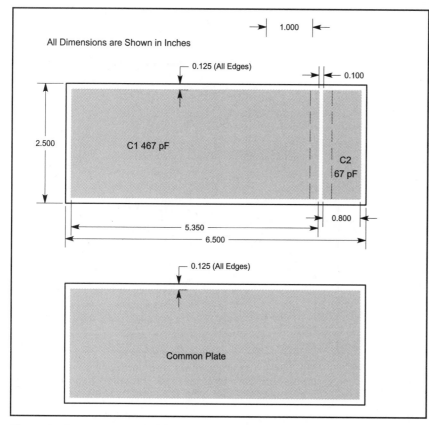

Fig 5-22—Etching pattern for the PC board (approximately one-half size).

0.031-inch, 1-ounce, double-sided PC board at 39.4 pF per square inch. The punch-through voltage for this material is between 350 and 500 V dc per mil, so it's reasonable to expect 31 mils to withstand 500 V of RF. As a point of reference, the equivalent dielectric constant (ε) was computed to be approximately 5.

I wanted to house the network in a 2-inch, type-C electrical enclosure, which contains a clear 6.5 × 2.5-inch space for the PC board. **Fig 5-22** shows a pattern for my circuit board. I didn't cut the back foil at all; that serves as the plate common to C1 and C2. Notice that I removed 0.125 inch of foil at the PC-board edges on both sides of the circuit board; this prevents flashover. I left a little extra copper in the gap between the two plates to provide for later capacitance adjustment.

You can adjust C1 and C2 by very gradually removing foil from the gap between them. If you remove too much, solder a flap of 5 to10-mil brass or copper foil to the board at the gap. Bend this flap to precisely adjust the capacitance.

It's a good idea to seal the circuit against humidity and surface contamination. Mask the board connections for the vertical and horizontal antenna elements then coat the board with a few coats of Krylon, or an equivalent coating. (Krylon paint is available from most hardware, paint and discount department stores.)

The fiberglass core of a circuit board has significant dielectric loss. Nevertheless, I tested both capacitors under the expected voltage stress and detected only very slight heating after several minutes of operation. I believe that poor test connections caused some of the heating.

Although B & W's Airdux coils are less lossy, I chose to use powdered-iron toroids. If you use solenoidal coils, orient the axes of L1 and L2 90° from each other to minimize coupling. For toroids, I calculated the total worst-case losses in the network to be less than 5 W, or about 0.22 dB for my 100-W station.

The 0.031-inch PC board I used is relatively thin. Common surplus material measures 0.062 inch ($^1/_{16}$), and its capacitance is about 20 pF per square inch. The higher punch-through voltage rating would be better for high-power operation, but the lower capacitance per unit area would require about 27 square inches of active plate area.

Building a 10-Meter L Antenna

This easy-to-build antenna was described by L. B. Cebik, W4RNL, in December 1999 *QST*. You will find it useful for local and DX work!

The L antenna has been around for quite a while. The basic idea seems to have originated with VK3AM in the early 1950s as described by L. A. Moxon, G6XN, in his book, *HF Antennas for All Locations*.

I stumbled across the idea accidentally, trying to answer some questions from a new ham who lived in an area where locals used both vertical and horizontal antennas on 10 meters. How could he communicate effectively with both groups using only one compact antenna? And could he cover the entire band and all its modes with this antenna?

One simple answer to these questions is the L antenna (or just "L"), as shown in **Fig 5-23**. We'll look at more precise dimensions further on, but for 10 meters, each leg is between 8.25 and 8.5-feet long, depending on the material we choose. Let's review the basic properties of the antenna and where it might be useful.

First, the L is simply an inverted V rotated to place one leg straight up and

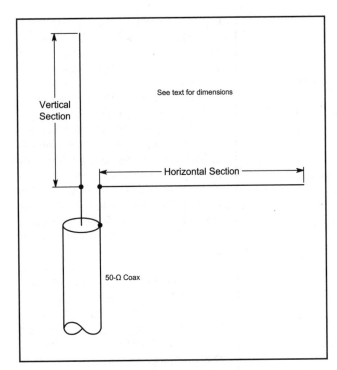

Fig 5-23—The basic outline of an L antenna.

Vertical Section

See text for dimensions

Horizontal Section

50-Ω Coax

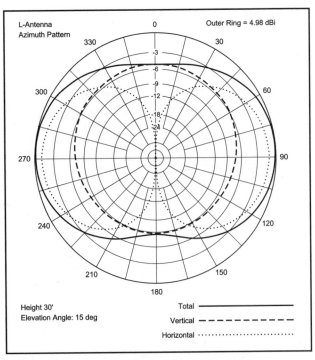

L-Antenna Azimuth Pattern

Outer Ring = 4.98 dBi

Height 30'
Elevation Angle: 15 deg

Total ———————
Vertical – – – – – – – – –
Horizontal ·····················

Fig 5-24— The horizontally and vertically polarized far fields—plus the total far field—radiation patterns of an L antenna for 28.85 MHz at 30 feet over average ground.

the other straight out. One result of this move is to reduce the footprint of the antenna. It is now only a little over 8 feet from side to side. You can support this antenna easily, making the L attractive for hams with very limited space.

Second, the L has a feed-point impedance at resonance of about 45 Ω. This makes it suitable for direct use with 50-Ω coaxial cables. However, since the nonsymmetrical physical structure seems ripe for common mode currents on the line, the use of a choke or bead 1:1 balun at the antenna terminals is strongly recommended. With elements at least ³/₈-inch in diameter, and with the antenna resonated at about 28.85 MHz, the system should show less than a 2:1 SWR from 28.0 to 29.7 MHz. Moreover, if you use reasonable care in setting the length of the vertical section, you can do almost all pruning to the more accessible horizontal section.

Third, the L has both vertically and horizontally polarized radiation. The horizontally polarized radiation is concentrated broadside to the horizontal leg. Positioning this leg to catch the most desired directions is important. The vertically polarized radiation forms a nearly circular pattern from the verti-

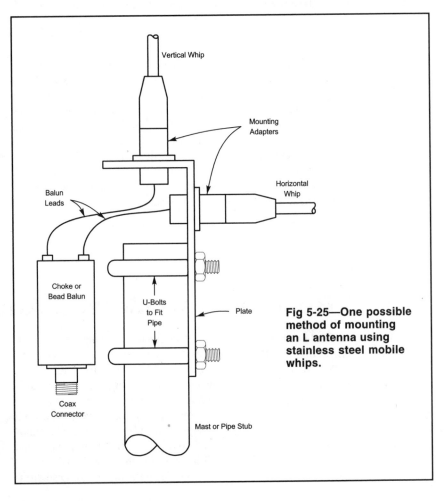

Vertical Whip

Mounting Adapters

Horizontal Whip

Balun Leads

Choke or Bead Balun

U-Bolts to Fit Pipe

Plate

Coax Connector

Mast or Pipe Stub

Fig 5-25—One possible method of mounting an L antenna using stainless steel mobile whips.

cal leg. **Fig 5-24** shows how the overall radiation pattern of the L develops from combining both the vertically and horizontally polarized fields.

For DX communication, polarization is not usually very significant, since refraction through the ionospheric layers tends to skew the initial polarization. For local point-to-point communication on 10 meters, however, cross polarization can severely reduce signal strength. Fortunately, the L can permit communication with both horizontal dipole and Yagi users on the one hand and with vertical users or repeaters on the other.

Whips

Ready-made elements already exist in the form of the ubiquitous stainless steel mobile whip. These elements are both sturdy and handy, since they come with a threaded base that promises bolt-together construction. They stand up to the weather very well and are more impervious to corrosive atmospheric effects than most materials. They seem to be good candidates for use in the L.

The use of ready-made elements sometimes involves more work than we initially anticipate. **Fig 5-25** shows perhaps the simplest way to mount two whips, one horizontal, and the other vertical. Because whips are fairly heavy, the plate to which they mount must also be heavy: steel at least $1/8$-inch thick. The plate requires one major bend to form a

lip about 2 inches long. The vertical portion should be about 12 to 18 inches long and about 3 inches wide. Dimensions are not critical. The values suggested here are designed to ensure maximum strength for the mounting plate.

The weight of the plate plus the whips requires a sturdy mast or stub (for rooftop mounting), and secure attachment. The sketch shows U-bolts, but $5/16$-inch stainless steel nuts and bolts through the plate and mast would work, if properly aligned. Stainless steel hardware, which is now readily available at hardware depots, is advisable for corrosion resistance.

The plate itself requires treatment to prevent rust. A good coat of metal primer and a top coat of rust-retarding

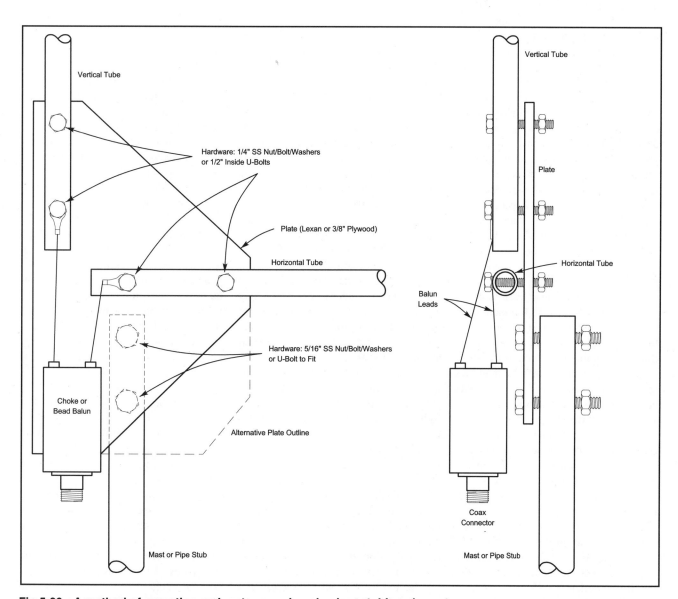

Fig 5-26—A method of mounting an L antenna using aluminum tubing elements.

paint is the minimal treatment. However, normal scarring of the surface will permit rust to form. An alternative is a professional chroming job.

Whips come with threaded studs that must be insulated from the mounting plate. Mounting adapters are available, and most are between 1 and 2 inches long. The adapters require a half-inch hole in the plate and normally use an insulated shoulder washer. The horizontal element is more likely to create wear on the shoulder washer than will the vertical element. Careful tight connections with locking washer are necessary for a durable installation.

The sketch in Fig 5-25 also shows a 1: 1 choke or bead balun. Since these devices come in many shapes and sizes, I have not shown a specific mounting method. I placed the balun in the sketch just as a reminder that its use is advisable.

The whips themselves will be something over 100 inches long. You'll find whip antennas at Radio Shack that are 102.5 inches long. When you add the length of the adapters, each element becomes up to 105 inches long. The most desirable length for each is about 101 inches, which requires some trimming. Be careful of sharp ends after cutting. Every inch of length change will move the resonant point about 100 kHz. Because whips are well under $^3/_8$ inches diameter, full band coverage may not be feasible with an SWR of less than 2:1.

Aluminum Tubing

Aluminum tubing at least $^3/_8$ inches in diameter will provide full band coverage. I recommend 6061-T6 or similar tubing of good strength for antennas. Since this tubing often comes in 6-foot lengths, the elements may be made up from 4.5-foot sections of $^1/_2$-inch diameter stock, with extensions using $^3/_8$-inch stock. Expect the stepped-diameter elements to be longer than uniform $^3/_8$-inch elements, despite the use of a larger size tube for the inner portion. Computer models suggest that an 8-foot 3-inch vertical element and an 8-foot 7-inch horizontal element provide resonance at 28.85 MHz. With the two-step elements, the vertical should be about 8-feet 6-inches long. If you use larger diameter tubing, expect slight decreases in the required lengths.

Fig 5-26 shows one possible way

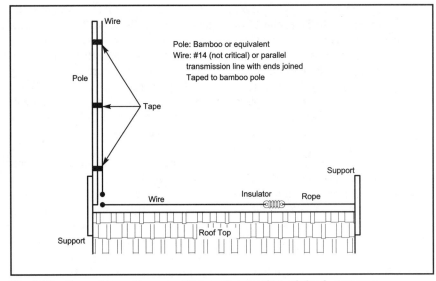

Fig 5-27—Some ideas for mounting a wire version of the L antenna.

to mount the elements. Basically, both elements mount to a plate that in turn mounts to a mast or stub. The plate in the sketch shows alternative lower shapes. If the stub is metal, use the larger size to space the mounting hardware for greater security. If the stub is (weather-protected) wood, it can extend into the upper area of the plate, and the more sharply triangular shape will secure all of the parts.

The plate makes up a right triangle, with the corners trimmed. It should be about 2 feet long vertically and at least 1 foot long horizontally. The material may be a plastic rated for strength and UV resistance, such as Lexan. You may also use $^3/_8$-inch thick plywood rated for outdoor duty, so long as you provide good weather protection. Pay special attention to sealing the edges.

Fig 5-26 also shows the recommended balun, mounted according to its size and shape. The aluminum L is lighter—and probably cheaper—than the whip version. It also provides full 10-meter coverage with ease.

Wire

Both the whip and the tubing versions of the L allow you to orient the horizontal leg broadside to the greatest number of local stations using horizontal polarization. If the desired broadside directions happen to allow the horizontal element to align with the crest of a roof (see **Fig 5-27**), then you can make

an even cheaper and lighter version of the antenna from wire.

The key to a wire version of the antenna is something to hold up the vertical section. After a long absence, bamboo is again becoming available at garden centers. A time-honored ham tradition is to use vinyl electrical tape to secure the wire to bamboo to make antenna elements. The technique still works effectively.

The horizontal element may be constructed in the same way, which would give you the option of orienting it away from the roof crest. However, you can also simply stretch the horizontal wires across the rooftop, using convenient supports. The higher the wire is from the roof, the better.

If the wire used is #14 AWG copper or similar, each element should be about 8-feet 5-inches long. The 2:1 SWR operating bandwidth will not extend to the band edges, though. The maximum 2:1 SWR operating bandwidth is about 1.5 MHz. For full band coverage, we need a "fatter" wire.

To solve this problem, we can turn to another ham tradition. Instead of using single wires, we can use a pair of wires; each taped on opposite sides of the bamboo. Alternatively, we can use parallel transmission line as our antenna wire. Solder together the two wires at the center and at the far ends of each section to form a single "fat" wire. Be sure to choose a sturdier bamboo (or similar) support to handle the extra weight. Expect to prune the antenna to resonance, since the required lengths of the double wires will be a bit shorter than the single-wire version.

These construction ideas only sample the possibilities. I hope that they inspire you to create even better ways of making not only the L antenna, but as well many antennas for other uses

and other bands. As a start for full band, all-mode, and all-polarization coverage of 10 meters, the L antenna is a simple and flexible design for both the newcomer and the old-timer.

Inverted L for 80 Meters

The inverted L is a variation of the basic quarter-wavelength vertical antenna. The difference is that this vertical has a 90° bend in it. As you can see in **Fig 5-28**, the inverted L has a vertical portion (V) and a horizontal portion (H).

I consider the inverted L a good utility antenna. By that I mean that it is good for both DX and local contacts. Because the whole antenna radiates, the inverted L has both vertically and horizontally polarized energy in its radiation pattern. The vertical tends to predominate because that's the high-current portion of the antenna.

The azimuthal radiation pattern is mostly circular. The horizontally polarized component will cause the pattern to be about a dB or two stronger off the sides of the horizontal portion of the antenna. While that's a measurable amount, you probably won't notice it in

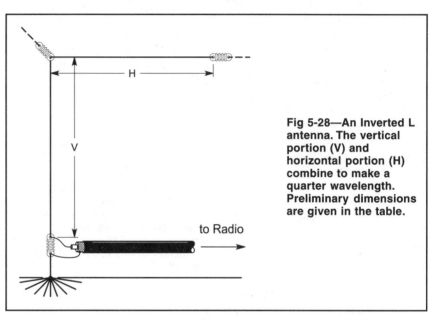

Fig 5-28—An Inverted L antenna. The vertical portion (V) and horizontal portion (H) combine to make a quarter wavelength. Preliminary dimensions are given in the table.

to Radio →

actual use. The horizontal section also fills in the vertical pattern so that you will have good local coverage.

Inverted L Construction

In its simplest form, the inverted L is a quarter wavelength of wire with a bend in it. A tree, tower sidearm or mast can be used to support the antenna. You could also use a non-metallic building, but I wouldn't install a vertical (or inverted L) close to a house or other building where people are apt to be. The main reason for that is that radiation in the near field will probably exceed permitted limits for human exposure. If you need another reason, and you shouldn't,

the near-field RF levels are apt to cause interference to consumer devices such as telephones, stereo equipment and VCRs located in the building.

No trees or towers? You can add a horizontal wire to a vertical tube or mast. As with the quarter-wavelength vertical, you'll need to have a ground-radial system if you want acceptable performance from your inverted L.

You'll find preliminary dimensions for V + H (as shown in Fig 5-28) in **Table 5-4**. For best performance, make the vertical leg (V) as long as you can practicably can. Adjust the overall length for best SWR at your favorite frequency or band portion.

Table 5-4
Preliminary Dimensions for Inverted L Overall Length

kHz	Feet	Inches
3550	65.92	791.0
3750	62.40	748.8
3950	59.24	710.9
7025	33.31	399.7
7125	32.84	394.1
7225	32.39	388.7
10125	23.11	277.3

A 10-meter Ground Plane

I enjoy operating on the 10-meters band, where atmospheric noise is low. And when the band opens, the propagation characteristics are great. You never know whom you might encounter as you tune this band. Sporadic-E openings bring excitement to the band during the summer doldrums and again in December. During years of high solar activity, worldwide contacts are not only possible—they are routine.

A beam would be nice, but I wanted something simpler: An omni-directional antenna that would be easy-to-build and that would allow me to make QSOs with DX stations. It didn't take long to decide on a ground plane. You might want to try one, too.

Design and Construction

In years past, I've built and used wire ground-plane antennas with good results. However, for this project I wanted something sturdier. I was looking for the kind of antenna that doesn't require a tree or a mast to support the upper end of the vertical portion. For that reason, I used aluminum tubing for the vertical portion, but to keep it simple and to save money, I used #12 copper wire for the three radials. You can see the final result in the photos. See **Fig 5-29**.

The design of this antenna starts with the base insulator, which is a 16-inch length of ¾-inch-diameter solid fiberglass rod. The bottom portion of the vertical is a 6-foot length of 0.875-inch tubing, and the top portion is 0.75-inch tubing. The three radials are made from insulated #12 stranded copper wire. Three telescoping sections of aluminum tubing comprise the support mast. Dimensions are given in Fig 5-29.

Although I used aluminum tubing for the support mast, you can use something else to support your ground plane. For example, 2 × 2 treated lumber would work well. You want to have the radials far enough above head level to avoid inadvertent contact while the antenna is used for transmitting. Be aware that the radial ends are high-voltage points. With the dimensions I used, the radial wires are over my head, but I can reach up and touch them, and that's not good. For that reason, I plan to add another

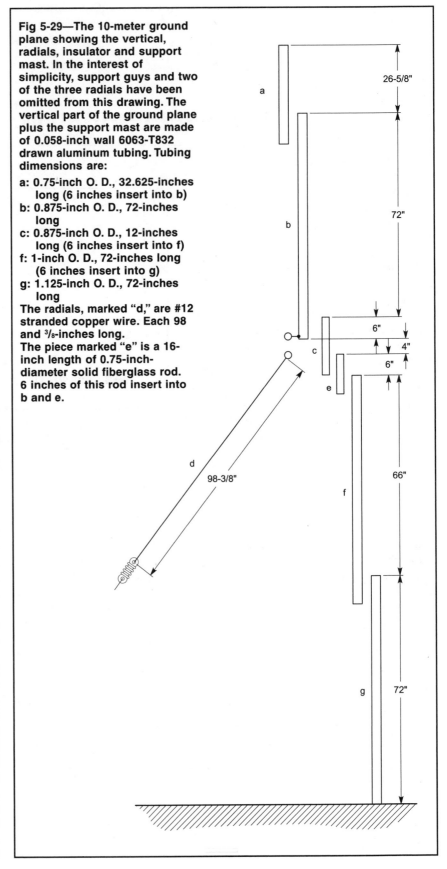

Fig 5-29—The 10-meter ground plane showing the vertical, radials, insulator and support mast. In the interest of simplicity, support guys and two of the three radials have been omitted from this drawing. The vertical part of the ground plane plus the support mast are made of 0.058-inch wall 6063-T832 drawn aluminum tubing. Tubing dimensions are:

a: 0.75-inch O. D., 32.625-inches long (6 inches insert into b)
b: 0.875-inch O. D., 72-inches long
c: 0.875-inch O. D., 12-inches long (6 inches insert into f)
f: 1-inch O. D., 72-inches long (6 inches insert into g)
g: 1.125-inch O. D., 72-inches long

The radials, marked "d," are #12 stranded copper wire. Each 98 and ³/₈-inches long.

The piece marked "e" is a 16-inch length of 0.75-inch-diameter solid fiberglass rod. 6 inches of this rod insert into b and e.

6-foot tubing section at the bottom of my support mast before I consider the installation as permanent.

If you mount your ground plane on a roof, here's a word of caution about radial wires. As I said before, the radial ends are high-voltage points, and you should insulate those ends. The importance of this was illustrated to me by a friend who had mounted his multi-band trap vertical on his roof. He laid four radials for each band on the cedar shake roof, and pruned their length for best SWR in his favorite part of the bands. The antenna worked for him, and he had even better results when he turned on his legal-limit amplifier. A couple of days later, one of his friends visited him and was operating the radio when my friend decided to go for a short walk. As he stepped out of the house, he heard a strange *frying* sound. Even stranger, that frying sound seemed to be sending Morse code. Next he noticed a charred wood odor. You've guessed it. High-voltage at the ends of the radials was arcing into the damp cedar shakes of the roof. Fortunately, it did not start a fire—but it could have. The next day, my friend installed insulated wire for radials and added insulators at the ends to keep them above the roof and to prevent arcing.

I used pop rivets to fasten together the lengths of tubing in the vertical portion of the ground plane and in the support mast. This is a good method of fastening tubing because it's fast, easy and economical. This method can be permanent if you want it to be, but you can remove the rivets with a 1/8-inch drill if you ever have the need.

If you wanted to use this ground plane as a portable antenna, say on Field Day, you might want to use machine screws and nuts to join the aluminum pieces. This would allow you to easily assemble and disassemble your antenna.

Installation

I used 3/8-inch Dacron line to guy my support mast and ground plane. As shown In **Fig 5-30**, I used a stainless-steel hose clamp to connect the guy lines to the center of the insulator.

The center conductor of the RG-213 feed line connects to the vertical portion of the ground plane. The feed-line shield connects to the radials, but

Fig 5-30—Support guys of 3/8-inch Dacron line are fastened to the insulator center using a stainless-steel worm-screw hose clamp. Radials connect to the coax shield. A choke balun is used at the feed point and is made from 8 feet of RG-213 wound into 8 turns. An optional second choke can be used at 8 feet, 4 inches below the first choke. This second choke does not show in this photo. See text.

not to the support mast. (This was done in an effort to avoid stray common-mode currents.)

The radials could be used as part of the guy assembly. I chose to have separate guys mostly because I wanted to be able to adjust the radial lengths without having to be concerned with the antenna falling. I did have to adjust the radial lengths, and it was nice to have the antenna firmly guyed during adjustments. See **Fig 5-31** for a view of my burgeoning vertical antenna farm.

Tune-Up and Results

Tune this antenna for best SWR by working on the radials. Adjust their length to set the resonant frequency. I tuned my radials for the lowest SWR at 28.4 MHz—my favorite part of the band. I found that this adjustment is not *critical*, because the SWR bandwidth is excellent. I found better than 1.5:1

Fig 5-31—The 10-meter ground-plane antenna is installed near the house. In the background you can see a 40-meter vertical.

over a range of greater than 1 MHz. My experience confirms the *EZNEC* analysis, which shows less than 2:1 SWR across the entire band with best SWR at 28.4 MHz.

You can adjust the *angle of the dangle* (droop angle). I used a 45° droop angle, and found a nearly perfect 50-ohm match at resonance. For that reason, I did not change the angle of my radials.

Initial on-air testing has been most gratifying. I hear well and am easily able to make lots of DX QSOs. Pity I don't have more time to use and enjoy my 10-meter ground plane.

Building a Ground Plane for Other Bands

Would you like to try a ground plane like this on a band other than 10 meters? **Table 5-5** contains dimensions for the radials and vertical portion of the ground plane. Dimensions in the table are for lengths in inches. Tubing lengths are for the exposed portion and do not include where the tubing pieces overlap internally. An overlap of 6 inches will provide a very sturdy joint, and that is reflected in the table. For example, the vertical portion of the 20-meter version comprises three 72-inch lengths of tubing with 6-inches overlap at the joints.

On 20 meters, you may not be able

Table 5-5

Ground-Plane Dimensions

Band	Radials	Section 1	Section 2	Section 3
20	200.5	72	66	66
17	154.5	72	66	20
15	132.375	72	60.5	
12	113	72	40.625	
10	98.375	72	26.625	

All dimensions are linear lengths given in inches.
Section 1 is 0.875" O. D. (identified as "b" in Fig 5-28)
Section 2 is 0.75" O. D. (identified as "a" in Fig 5-28)
Section 3 is 0.625" O. D. All tubing is 0.58-inch wall thickness 6063-T832 drawn aluminum.

to get the base of the vertical high enough for the radial ends to be safely overhead if you're using a 45° droop angle. In that case, you should elevate the radial ends and use less droop angle. You should still have an acceptable match—in fact, you should be able to achieve less than 2:1 SWR across the entire band.

A Portable Ground Plane for Mobile Antennas

This interesting project by Mike Aiello, N2HTT, was published in October 1997 *QST* under the subtitle "Use your mobile antenna anywhere!"

Spring couldn't arrive fast enough in 1996. I had spent a brutally cold and snowy winter building a low-power (QRP) CW transceiver kit. I also spent some time brushing up my Morse skills and chasing down a gel-cell battery. As the thermometer climbed and snow melted, I was raring to go.

I decided that the easiest way to get started in QRP was to set up a mobile station. Aside from being inexpensive, a mobile installation would allow me to operate during my lunch hours from the parking lot at work. This would provide some brief relaxation during the stressful business day.

I equipped my little station with a QRP antenna tuner and two monoband mobile antennas, one for 20 meters and another for 40 meters. The antennas, which share a $10 magnetic mount, had cost about $20 each. A straight key, borrowed from my shack, completed my "stationary mobile" QRP station.

As it turned out, I didn't get to operate much (rarely do I actually get to take a lunch hour), but the QRP station worked very well. The antennas were easy to match and "played" well enough for me to make quite a few contacts.

The big QRP event of my summer was our annual week at the Jersey shore. I had been planning my antenna strategy for months and settled on a 40-meter folded dipole of my own design. I made the antenna small enough to squeeze into the backyard of our rented house. I also designed it for a certain level of stealth; if you squinted your eyes the thing looked like a New-Age clothesline.

The antenna was not a stellar performer, but I managed to avoid damaging the house, my equipment or myself. The experience left me pondering ways to improve the situation next year.

Fig 5-32—A close-up of the tripod ground plane with one of my magnetically mounted mobile antennas attached. Notice how the radial system is attached to the center tube of the tripod. (*Photo courtesy of Mike Aiello, N2HTT.*)

That's when I saw visions of tripods dancing in my head.

The Tripod

My plan was to attach wire radials to a photo tripod to create a ground plane for a monobander mobile antenna. A key factor, of course, is the ownership of a camera or video tripod. Luckily, I already had one in my inventory, having been an avid amateur photographer for many years. If you are "sans tripod," don't worry. They're readily available for about $30 at discount stores, RadioShack and many other sources. No permanent alteration of the tripod is required, so it can serve both photographic and ham needs interchangeably. See **Fig 5-32**.

I already possessed a mobile magnet mount, so attachment to the tripod would have to be accomplished by some kind of steel platform big enough to accommodate the magnet. Because the platform and radials form the complete ground plane for the antenna, the radials must have dc continuity with the platform. Think of the steel platform as being the body of your car. Electrically speaking, the radials "emulate" the rest of the imaginary vehicle.

The design challenges were: (a) find attachment points for the radials that had a dc path to the antenna mount, (b) figure out an attachment method for the wires, (c) come up with a steel *something* (preferably cheap) that would become my platform, and (d) find a way to attach that *something* to the tripod head.

The first task was to examine the tripod. I unscrewed the pan/tilt head to reveal a flat platform with a short, threaded stud protruding. A few minutes with a volt-ohm meter showed that my original idea of attaching wires to the tripod legs wouldn't work (fiber sleeves insulated the leg sections from each other and the head). However, the center post of the tripod showed continuity to the stud. This meant that my radials could be connected to the center post, which reduced the number of attachment points to one. Sparing no expense, I purchased the best 2-inch diameter stainless-steel hose clamp that $1 could buy. The ends of the radials were tucked between the hose clamp and the center post, and the clamp tightened just securely enough to hold the wires. I was particularly careful not to over tighten the clamp and crush the tripod's center tube.

The steel platform took a little longer to find. I spent a pleasant evening wandering the aisles of our local home supply store, looking for anything that could serve as an inexpensive steel support. I had already committed to the idea that it might be necessary to drill a hole in whatever I bought. After several unsatisfying passes through the housewares department, I was about to give up. I turned down the electrical aisle, and in an instant I knew my quest was ended. It was homely, but it was the right size and definitely the right price.

Fig 5-33—A view of the electrical junction box with the cover removed. The box is secured to the tripod stud with a single wing nut. (*Photo courtesy of Mike Aiello, N2HTT.*)

I purchased a square electrical junction box and cover for $1.69. It even came with the hole already drilled. The purchase of a $1/4$-20 wing nut (20 cents) completed the materials for the magmount platform. See **Fig 5-33**.

In my prototype, I used one of the predrilled holes in the junction box, placing it over the tripod stud and securing it with the wing nut. I then attached the flat cover with the two supplied screws. This approach places the box slightly off-center on the tripod (an aesthetic but not practical problem), and requires a screwdriver to convert the tripod back to photographic use.

A word of caution about junction boxes. Since these things are meant to be buried under sheet rock and forgotten, they don't have finished edges. The edges of both the box and the cover plate may be sharp or have nasty burrs on them. A few minutes spent with a file removing rough/sharp edges could save a cut later on.

Radials

I made my radials out of 24-gauge solid speaker wire that I happened to have on hand. I cut two lengths of 16.5 feet (roughly a quarter-wavelength on 20 meters) and split the two strands apart to give me four radials. I attached these to the center post with the hose clamp. I extended the four radials on the ground in a roughly perpendicular arrangement, using a small stone at the end of each to keep the wire stretched out. I plopped my monobander and magmount on the junction box support and hooked up the rig. The band came alive!

A quick check with an antenna

noise bridge showed that I had a better than 2:1 SWR over the whole 150 kHz band segment covered by my rig. By switching in my antenna tuner, I was able to provide a 1:1 SWR for the transceiver.

Version Two

Shortly after my first experiments with the portable ground plane, a knowledgeable ham to whom I had described the setup pointed out a few flaws in my scheme:

1. The very broad SWR bandwidth was due to the low radiation efficiency of the antenna (think of the SWR bandwidth of a dummy load!). This was most likely because . . .

2. I really should have used a minimum of 16 radials, not just four!

The good news, however, was that the radials did not have to be full quarter-wavelengths long. They only needed to be long enough to equal the height of the antenna above ground. He predicted that the radiation efficiency, and the performance of the antenna system, would improve markedly with additional radials. (He also predicted that my 2:1 SWR bandwidth would decrease sharply.) I was willing to give it a try, but 16 radials would pose new logistical challenges in the field of wire management!

The first thing that occurred to me when thinking about 16 little bundles of tangled wire is that I would rather think about eight. Falling back on my vast experience with speaker wire, I decided to cut 10-foot radials (I keep the tripod to its minimum height, and the antenna whip is only seven feet high) out of 20-gauge

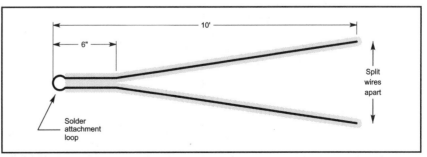

Fig 5-34—It's easy to fabricate two radials from a single 10-foot piece of two-conductor insulated speaker wire. Just split the insulation down the middle, leaving about six inches together at one end. At the unsplit end, solder the two conductors together to form a small loop for attachment to the tripod.

stranded speaker wire. I split each wire, leaving about six inches together at one end. At the unsplit end, I soldered the two conductors together to form a small loop for attachment to the tripod. This process produced eight 10-foot double radials as shown in **Fig 5-34**.

The total length of speaker wire necessary for the eight double radials is 80 feet. A 100-foot spool of 20-gauge stranded speaker wire costs about $7 at RadioShack and provides one set of radials for all bands.

Rather than leaving eight little bundles of wire permanently dangling from the center tube of my tripod, I decided to add a fixture to make attaching and removing the radials quick and easy in the field. I call the fixture a "grass skirt," because it consists of eight short pigtails of wire, each with an alligator clip at the end, dangling from a short length of ground braid. The braid (you can use the shield stripped from a bit of coax) is cut to a length equal to three times the diameter of the tripod tube. Solder the pigtails to the braid, equally spaced along its length. I attached the fixture to the tripod by wrapping the braid around the tube and securing it with the hose clamp. The grass skirt added about $3 to the total construction cost. Construction of the grass skirt is shown in **Fig 5-35**.

Setting up of the radials in the field is remarkably easy. I made my pigtails two different lengths and alternated them. This makes it easier to find opposing pigtails. I laid out the double radials in opposing pairs, spreading the ends about three feet apart. The entire radial set takes about 10 minutes to deploy.

It doesn't seem to matter whether the radials are laid out straight or bent to fit the area you have available. Of course, you *do* need something to tack the radial wires to the ground so they stay extended to their full length. After trying several different hold-downs, I hit upon the perfect tool for the job: those little plastic corn-on-the-cob holders. Their short, sharp tines fit easily around the radial wires and their bright yellow handles are easy to spot when it's time to clean up. During the summer picnic season they can also serve to hold corn, but you have to wash them carefully first! Mine cost about $1 for a set of

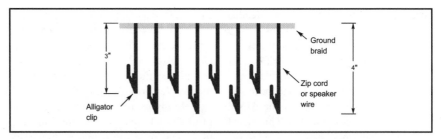

Fig 5-35—This is the "grass skirt" fixture I used to attach my radial network to the center tube of the tripod. The skirt consists of eight short pigtails of wire, each with an alligator clip at the end, dangling from a short length of ground braid. The braid is cut to a length equal to three times the diameter of the tripod tube. Solder the pigtails to the braid, equally spaced along its length.

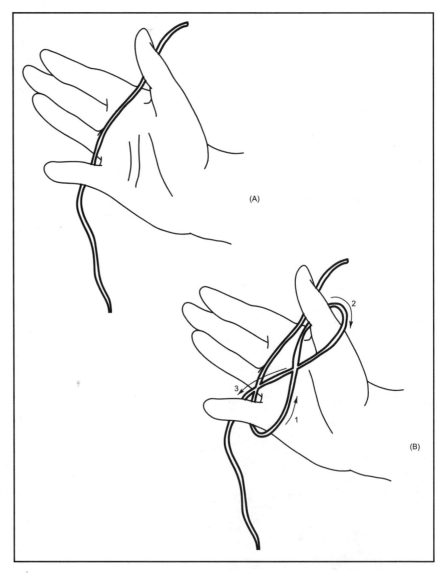

Fig 5-36—A little "hand jive" is all it takes to bundle up lengths of wire so that they never tangle. This technique is known as the "butterfly." Start with an end of the wire placed across your palm, behind your thumb and little finger (A). Loop first in front of your little finger and behind your thumb, then in front of your thumb and behind your little finger (B). On my hand it takes about 10 loops to wrap up a 10-foot length of wire.

six; three sets were enough for tacking down 16 radials with two spares left over. Although this added another $2.98 to the project budget, I haven't lost any holders yet.

Wire Management

Wrestling eight tangled bundles of split speaker wire could really put a damper on an afternoon of working QRP, but there is an easy way to bundle up lengths of wire so that they never tangle. With a nifty technique known as the "butterfly," you can bundle the wire in figure-eight loops around your thumb and little finger. Take a look a **Fig 5-36**; this maneuver is much easier to perform than to describe.

Start with an end of the wire placed across your palm, behind your thumb and little finger. Loop first in front of your thumb and behind your little finger, then in front of your little finger and behind your thumb. On my hand it takes about 10 loops to wrap up a 10-foot length of wire. Secure the resulting figure-eight bundle with a twist-tie around the middle. You'll be ready to instantly deploy an untangled radial system the next time you set up.

But Does It Work?

The first tune-up with 16 radials showed a much narrower SWR bandwidth as predicted, but a 1:1 match posed no problem for my antenna tuner on either 20 or 40 meters. Increasing the number of radials to 16 appears to have greatly improved the system's performance. My first attempt on 20 meters resulted in working a station in central Texas from my home in southeastern New York—on 2 W! This was at night, about 9 PM local time, on a very active band.

On 40 meters the arrangement seems a little less effective. This is not surprising, because a center-loaded seven-foot whip is significantly less efficient on 40 meters than on 20. Additional radials can be added for very little outlay, and might improve the 40-meter performance. This is an approach I intend to try. On the whole, for a total outlay of about $17 plus the equipment I already had on hand, I am very pleased with the outcome.

Final Notes

The ground plane I have described here should be adaptable to any band and any tripod with a little ingenuity. Of course, the situation you encounter with your tripod might be a little different than what I experienced. If you buy a tripod for this project, purchasing one without a pan/tilt head will save considerable money but, of course, will limit the tripod's photographic usefulness. Don't overlook the possibility of picking up an inexpensive used tripod at a photo fair: it doesn't have to be pretty, or even fully functional, for this purpose. If the center tube of the tripod doesn't offer dc continuity to the pan/tilt head, you can simply use a short piece of wire to make the connection between the steel platform and the radial system. And if you don't want to use a magnetic antenna mount, the steel platform can just as easily accommodate a standard body mount.

And, don't forget that a portable tripod mount like this one places your antenna in proximity to your operating position and any passers-by. You should restrict your power output to low levels (I recommend 10 W or less) and make sure that no one comes in contact with your antenna while transmitting.

Have fun operating QRP from that picnic table, beach, backyard, campsite . . . wherever! Maybe I'll work you next summer from the shore.

Packable Antenna for 80 Through 2 Meters

This article by Dennis Kennedy, N8GGI, appeared in November 1997 *QST* under the subtitle "N8GGI converts a Hustler mobile antenna into a versatile airline-shippable antenna for mobile, marine or portable operation." See **Fig 5-37**.

The growing popularity of pint-sized HF and HF/VHF transceivers convinced me that I need one. I use it as a mobile rig, on business trips, vacations and to activate some US Islands. While the radio and power supply now travel easily, the antenna was the limiting factor for travel.

I bought a Hustler mobile antenna mast and 20 meter resonator and began using them with good success on the car. The fold-over 54-inch mast doesn't suit all the possible operating situations my wife might allow because it only folds to 90°. I wanted a versatile, compact antenna system that could pack compactly enough to ship as airline baggage. It would have a segmented mast and a variety of antenna bases for use on rental cars, sailboat stern rails, condominium balcony railings or anyplace else I might possibly want to use the radio.

Splicing the Mast

First, I had difficulty locating $^3/_8$-24 (UNF) hardware to fit most HF mobile antenna bases and the Hustler resonators. Common bolts in hardware stores are $^3/_8$-16 (UNC). I needed a way to fit $^3/_8$-24 threaded studs onto aluminum tubing and join the sections. My solution is to use a piece of $^1/_2$-inch aluminum tubing with a 0.065 inch wall thickness. This leaves an inside diameter of 0.370 inch, five thousandths under $^3/_8$ inch. I bought some $^3/_8$-24 stainless steel bolts, cut off the heads and then ran a $^3/_8$ inch drill a few inches into each end of each tube. The drilling is fairly easy because it only removes a few thousandths of an inch.

The unthreaded ends of the headless bolts slide snugly into the tubes, with about $^3/_8$ inch of threads protruding as a stud. To secure each assembly, I mounted it in a vise and cross drilled (a drill press is helpful, but not necessary) the tube and bolt for #8-32 hardware (see **Fig 5-38**) that locks each shaft

in place. Some antioxidant paste in the joints prevents corrosion and ensures conductivity. Combine the mast sections by screwing one end of each into a $^3/_8$-24 stainless steel coupling nut.

The aluminum tubing comes in 72-inch lengths, and I discovered that I had

Fig 5-37—Here are 40, 20, 6 and 2-meter antennas, two radials for 20 meters, mounts and case.

exactly enough to make two mast sections for the HF antenna and a piece 19$^1/_8$ inches long for 2 meters. To suit my ICOM 706 that covers HF, 6 and 2 meters, I have an antenna for any HF band (with suitable resonators), a 6-meter antenna (the 54-inch mast alone) and a λ/4 antenna for 2 meters (the 19-inch tube). Next, I needed antenna bases and mounting options.

A Mixture of Mounts

A Hustler MBM magnet mount works fine on the trunk lid of a rental car. (I wouldn't try driving at freeway velocities with the HF antenna on this mount, but it's okay for the 2-meter radiator or at low speeds.) I also bought a RadioShack 21-937 mount, which works well on small horizontal pipe rails such as those found on boats. A small C-clamp or a couple of wood

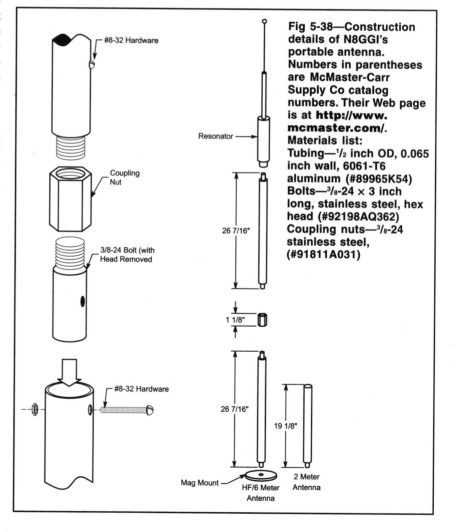

Fig 5-38—Construction details of N8GGI's portable antenna. Numbers in parentheses are McMaster-Carr Supply Co catalog numbers. Their Web page is at http://www. mcmaster.com/. Materials list: Tubing—$^1/_2$ inch OD, 0.065 inch wall, 6061-T6 aluminum (#89965K54) Bolts—$^3/_8$-24 × 3 inch long, stainless steel, hex head (#92198AQ362) Coupling nuts—$^3/_8$-24 stainless steel, (#91811A031)

#8-32 Hardware

Resonator

Coupling Nut

3/8-24 Bolt (with Head Removed)

#8-32 Hardware

26 7/16"

1 1/8"

26 7/16"

19 1/8"

Mag Mount

HF/6 Meter Antenna

2 Meter Antenna

screws can easily attach the RS mount to a wooden deck railing. Attach λ/4 wire radials to the clamping bolts.

To make a free-standing antenna for a deck, dock or lawn, I cut a circle of thin steel plate about eight inches in diameter and put three bolts through it to attach radials. The ground connection couples capacitively to the steel plate through the mag mount, and the plate must be large enough to accomplish this. For my first test of this arrangement, I used one of my wife's steel cookie sheets with the radials secured to a bolt through the hole in the handle. (Thankfully, the neighbors didn't see me sitting on the deck working Houston on a cookie sheet!) Use monofilament fishing line as guys in windy situations.

By replacing the untuned car body with λ/4 wire radials, the bandwidths of the resonators seem to be greater than twice what Hustler claims for mobile operation. [More likely, this is evidence of greater losses. More radials should improve performance and narrow the SWR bandwidth—*Ed.*] Using only two radials, I get about 125 kHz on 40 meters and 250 kHz on 20 meters at an SWR of less than 2:1. Antenna resonance changes with environment and the particular mount used. You can regain resonance by adjusting the resonator tip rod according to the manufacturer's recommendations.

A Suitable Case

My final design task was to create a carrying case that prevents airline baggage "gorillas" from killing the antenna. I use a piece of 4-inch Schedule-40 PVC pipe and two end caps to make a shipping tube. Use glue or screws to secure one end cap. Nylon straps (with plastic catches like those used on fanny packs and life jackets) hold the removable cap. Pop rivet the nylon straps to the pipe and cap. Rivet on a strap handle for convenience. The only items that don't fit into the shipping tube are the magnetic mount and the steel radial plate. A tube large enough to accommodate these pieces would be too heavy and unwieldy.

All the parts for this project come from local fastener distributors and metal dealers. You can also buy them from a commercial supplier, such as McMaster-Carr Supply Company in Chicago.

This antenna obviously won't compete with a full-size antenna, but I've had plenty of good signal reports from the US and Europe while running 100 W. Variations of this theme should allow some pretty stealthy antennas for those in apartments, condos or under antenna restrictions. Run the wire radials through a flowerbed or along a deck railing to hide them. You can disassemble the antenna in seconds when the "antenna police" are patrolling.

A 40-Meter Tree-Supported Vertical

A quarter-wavelength vertical on 40 meters is about 33 feet long. That means that, in most cases, one has to use guys to support one of these antennas. Here's an alternative to guys for supporting a vertical

In the late 70s, my family and I were living in a small Michigan town. I wanted to install a 40-meter vertical that I had used in another location. Because the vertical would have to go in the yard beside the house, I did not want to guy the antenna as I had in the previous location. To further complicate the situation, a walnut tree filled most of the prime antenna area.

While I was surveying possible sites for my vertical, I noticed that the branches of that walnut tree grew in a regular pattern—a pattern that I could exploit to support my 40-meter vertical.

The Vertical

My 40-meter vertical was built from 4 sections of aluminum TV mast. Because the mast sections were only 7.5 feet long, I used a short whip to resonate the vertical. The whip had been a ⁵/₈-wavelength VHF mobile antenna. I attached the whip to the top of the vertical with a pair of hose clamps.

I've tried to buy more aluminum mast in the last few years, but have not been able to locate it anywhere. Most TV mast these days is made from steel, which is stronger. Steel is not a good choice for antennas, however, because of its ohmic resistance. Galvanizing is a much better conductor, and I've had good results using galvanized steel wire for temporary antennas. After a couple of years in the weather, those antennas had lost the galvanizing, and I had to discard them. K8JP/V31JP used sections of galvanized downspout to build a 40-meter vertical. That antenna worked well for Joe for a few years.

These days, I prefer to use telescoping 0.058-inch 6063-T832 aluminum tubing. You can find construction details elsewhere in this chapter.

The Base

I used a 2-foot length of pressure-treated 4 × 4 lumber for a base insulator. I buried a foot and half of this lumber to hold the piece in place. This left about 6 inches above ground.

I drove a 20-penny common nail into the center top of the base. (This nail is about 4-inches long.) This nail prevented the vertical, which sat over the nail, from sliding off the base.

I drove a couple of nails on each vertical face about two inches from the top, and these served to hold a wire ring in place. This wire ring became the attachment point for the radials. I ran the 32 radials from the ring to and down the 4 × 4 to the ground. I then buried the radials about an inch below the surface of the earth.

Installing and Supporting the Vertical

I identified three branches on the backside (away from the street in front of the house) of the tree. These were located at about 12 to 24 feet above ground, and while not perfectly aligned, they formed a V shape. I had installed the base directly beneath the branches and about three feet from the tree.

My son, Bryant, (then a teenager) was my helper. He had wanted to climb that tree since we had moved in. He finally had his chance. Up the tree he went; and when he was in place, I pushed the vertical up to him and sat it in place on the base.

Bryant started at the center branch and at that height on the vertical he made a double wrap with an approximately 6-foot length of nylon line. Next, he tied a series of four square knots in the line. Finally, he made a double wrap around the branch with the line ends and tied them to together to secure them.

He followed the same procedure at the other two branches and then climbed back down. The vertical was kind of wobbly, but that meant that it was free to move as the tree moved in the wind. (See **Fig 5-39**.)

Results

It was not beautiful. In fact, it looked ugly. It did, however, work very well. That part of the lawn was always a bit wetter than anywhere else, and that might have contributed to the excellent results that I enjoyed.

Shortly after installing this vertical, I was able to work a couple of Pacific DXpeditions, which gave me

two new DXCC counters. My only contacts with these operations were made with this antenna on 40 meters.

Finally, Clay Whiffen, KF4IX and Ben Zieg, K4OQK, wrote a short article that was published in November 1991 *QST* Technical Correspondence column. They recounted their experience with tree-mounted verticals. They noted unusually high feed-point resistance, which they discovered was caused by dielectric losses from the supporting trees. They were able to reduce this effect on 80 meters by moving the top of their vertical so that it was 6 feet from the tree trunk. Smaller branches (up to 2 or 3-inches diameter) did not seem to cause significant loss. You may want to take this into account if you try a tree supported vertical.

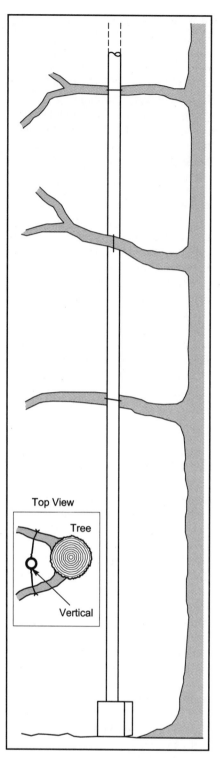

Fig 5-39—The 40-meter tree-supported vertical. Knotted ropes tied to the antenna and the support tree hold the vertical in place.

Top View

Tree

Vertical

The K8CH Tree-Mounted 30-Meter Wire Ground Plane

A tree-mounted vertically polarized antenna? Why not! Perhaps textbooks don't recommend it, but I've had good luck with a 30-meter tree-mounted ground plane. The antenna did not cost much, is inconspicuous and works quite well for DX QSOs. See **Fig 5-40**.

The evolution of this idea began when my friend Al Francisco, K7NHV, was a doctoral candidate at Michigan State University. Al was living on campus and wanted to get on the air from there. University rules did not permit outside antennas. How would he solve this dilemma?

Al's solution was simple, and it worked! He ran a piece of RG-58/U cable from a bedroom window to the ground. From there, he slit a shallow trench to a nearby tree and buried the cable. At the base of the tree a couple of radials were soldered to the coax-line braid, then buried. Another piece of wire formed the main radiator of his 20-meter vertical. You had to walk right up to the tree to see it! Even more amazing to Al and his friends was that it worked about as well as you would expect for any 20-meter vertical with only a couple of radials. It was a good idea, the kind one doesn't forget!

Several years later I moved to a new location in Connecticut. In short order, a modest tower with a triband beam sprouted from the back yard. Dipoles for the 40 and 80-meter bands were hung in the trees. It was possible to work DX on 40 meters, but while the low dipole worked too well on short skip, a vertical antenna would be a much better alternative. I knew from experience that a vertical with 16 or more radials would be a good performer. It was, and I've described the tree-supported vertical elsewhere in this chapter.

An Antenna for 30-Meter DXing

On the day the 30-meter amateur band was opened by the FCC, I used a Transmatch and 40-meter dipole to make a few contacts. Later, I tried an 80-meter dipole. Both were okay, but each worked too well on short skip. Stations within a couple of hundred miles were very loud—not the best situation for DXing!

Fig 5-40—Photo of K8CH tree-mounted 30-meter ground plane.

A vertical antenna would cure that. There was a serious problem, however. Limited space and rocky soil meant that a good radial system would be almost impossible to realize. Rats! But wait, why not build a ground-plane antenna? I could make it all from wire, and two radials should be sufficient. I reached for my calculator and came up with the proper length using the formula:

$$\text{Length (feet)} = \frac{234}{f_{MHz}}$$

The vertical portion and each radial of the ground plane should be about 23 feet 1½ inches long for resonance at 10.12 MHz. The wire and insulators were on hand. It did not take long to assemble the antenna as shown in **Fig 5-41**.

This time, the perfect tree was found at the back of the lot. Beneath it grows a lot of brush—it makes it hard to work around, but great for camouflage. Only one obstacle stood in the way of speedy installation. How to get a line through the crotch 40 feet above the ground?

Getting a Line into a Tree

Many methods are used to get an antenna support line into the "right" crotch of a tree. You could use a bow and arrow or a slingshot. A strong person can throw a no. 18 nylon line, with a proper weight on the end, to about 40 feet. That's good enough for this project.

There are a few tricks you should avoid learning "the hard way." First, make sure there is nothing breakable within throwing range. Unless you are extremely fortunate, at least one throw will go astray. Second, secure the free end of the line so it does not end up out of reach in the air. This is particularly frustrating when you have just managed to "hit the target."

I like to use an 8-inch adjustable wrench for a throwing weight. It has just about the right heft, and it is nice and smooth. If you don't like to gamble, use something else. For this project, I found a floor flange that weighed a bit less than a pound. It worked quite well.

When you miss your target, as I frequently do, don't try to pull the

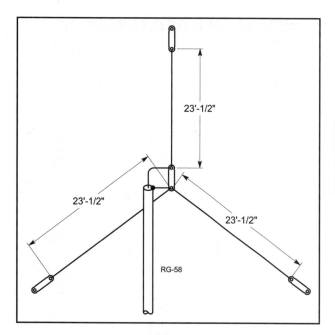

Fig 5-41—Dimensions and construction of the 30-meter ground-plane antenna.

23'-1/2"

23'-1/2"

23'-1/2"

RG-58

weight fly in the direction of the "right" crotch. Success may require several attempts, but keep trying.

Working on a recently mowed lawn is much easier. Lay the line out in front of you in large S shapes. Make sure there are no twigs or stones for the line to catch on. You want the line to feed smoothly from the ground as the weight goes flying on its way.

Final Steps

It took a few tries to get the line through that crotch at 40 feet. After that, things went easily. I tied the top insulator to the end of the line and hauled it up to just below the crotch. A doubled-up section of the downhaul line was wrapped around the tree at head level, and tied. Excess line was secured as shown in **Fig 5-43**. Shorter lengths of line were tied to the radial ends and were secured to convenient trees above head level.

After several weeks of operation, I found myself well satisfied with the tree-mounted ground-plane antenna. It worked at least as well for DX as does a dipole at 60 feet. For stations less than a couple of hundred miles away there was pretty good rejection. (The dipole worked better for them.) There was no "dent" in my pocketbook, but perhaps best of all; the antenna was almost invisible.

throwing weight back over a branch. Take it from one who knows the indignity of viewing a beautiful, shiny adjustable wrench swinging in the breeze from a stinkin' old tree branch. It takes only a few seconds to let the weight fall to the ground and then pull the line on through the tree. That way you get another try with the same weight. Trees look ugly when they are decorated with dangling wrenches, transformers, pipe fittings and rocks!

Make sure your throwing line does not tangle, or you will have a mess. Ben Hassell, W8VPC, uses a method that is particularly effective in brush or tall grass. Ben lays the throwing weight on the ground. He then scramble-winds the line into a ball around his fingers (**Fig 5-42**). The end of the line tied to the weight comes out of the middle. For a right hander, lightly grasp the ball in the left hand. ("South paws" would reverse hands.) With the right hand, lift the weight by the line and swing it 'round and 'round. Let the

---

ADAPTING THE TREE-MOUNTED GROUND PLANE FOR OTHER BANDS

You say you like the idea in the article, but you want to use it on another band? No problem!

In the years since this article first appeared in print, many hams have used this idea for an easy-to-install antenna. For the most part, the antennas have been used for temporary or portable operations-such as Field Day. That is as it should be. You probably understand that a line run through a tree crotch works well as a temporary support, but should not be used in a permanent installation.

To use this antenna on other bands, start with the lengths given in the table. You can make the radials a bit longer and adjust their lengths for best match at your favorite operating frequency. Yes, you can tune the ground plane by adjusting only the radials. It works as well as adjusting the vertical radiator, and it's much easier to do.—K8CH.

Leg Lengths for Dipole and Ground-Plane Antennas

Operating Freq (MHz)	feet	Length inches
3.50	66	10
3.75	62	5
4.00	58	6
7.00	33	5
7.20	32	6
14.00	16	9
14.25	16	5
18.11	12	11
21.00	11	2
21.30	10	12
24.93	9	5
28.00	8	4
28.40	8	3

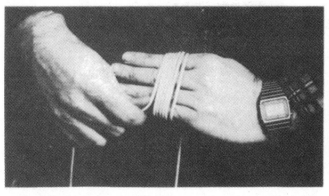

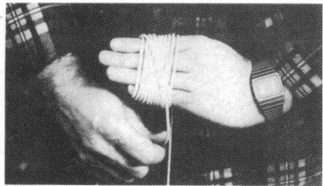

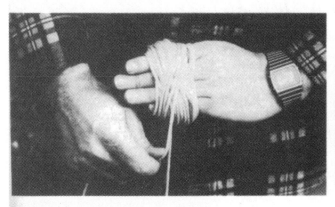

Fig 5-42—Chuck, K8CH, demonstrates how Ben Hassell, W8VPC, prepares a line for throwing. When the weight is thrown, the line should come freely out of the middle of the ball.

Fig 5-43—One method for securing the downhaul line to a tree. Excess line is neatly stored out of the way.

4-Band Tree Vertical

This article by Mark Weaver appeared in November 1995 *QST*. Here's what Mark said.

If the thought of a high-visibility HF antenna leaves you cold, it's time to branch out and get to the root of the problem… I live in a townhouse on a small lot in a neighborhood where no outdoor antennas are allowed. That's a fairly typical situation these days. So if I want to operate on the HF bands, am I resigned to an attic dipole or some other indoor compromise? No way! Believe it or not, I'm the proud owner of a four-band full-sized vertical antenna, and it's sitting right in my front yard. And the best part of all is the fact that my antenna is virtually invisible. No Klingon or Romulan cloaking devices here—just old-fashioned ingenuity.

The Concept

I tried an attic dipole and had nothing but problems. RF got into everything! It got into the TV and the kids howled. It got into the telephone and my wife howled. The antenna also picked up every kind of noise from my computer, TNC and any other electronic devices in the house.

One day while staring out my front window, dreaming of 100-foot towers and stacked Yagis, my gaze fixed upon a solitary 20-foot tree in my front yard. Wait a minute! I can run a 15-foot hunk of wire up the side of that tree! That's almost a quarter wavelength on 20 meters! But what about 40 meters, one of my favorite bands? I decided to worry about that later. Thus was born my four-band "tree" vertical.

My idea isn't new, although the application may be unique. The antenna is comprised of three quarter-wave-length wires (for 10, 20 and 40 meter), snaking up the side of the tree, more-or-less in parallel, all soldered together at the bottom to the center conductor of the coax (see **Fig 5-44**). Several radials are then soldered to the ground braid of the coax. But how do you get a quarter wavelength wire for 40 meters into a 20-foot tree? That's over 30 feet of wire! Easy. Bend the wire at the halfway point and run it to an upstairs window of your house, or some other convenient sup-

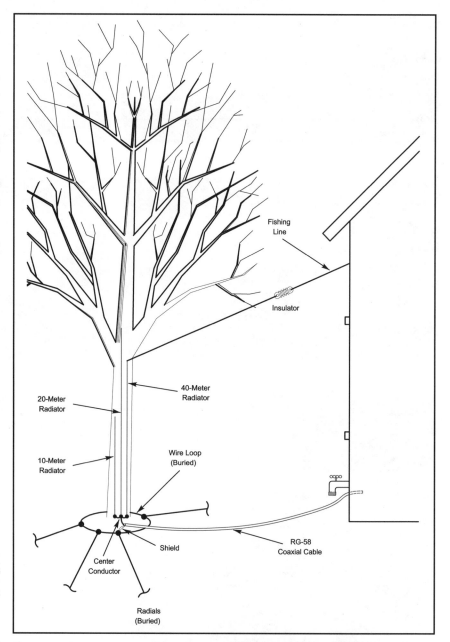

Fig 5-44—Run the three antenna wires along the trunk and then, if necessary, bend them along the branches. My 40-meter wire is so long that it leaves the tree altogether and attaches to my window frame. Use at least six radials for your ground system, more if you have the space and the patience to place them beneath the soil.

port. When you're finished you'll have an inverted L on 40 meters, a vertical with the top bent over so it looks like an upside down L. The 40-meter inverted L also works on 15 meters, where it's a ³/₄ wavelength.

Construction

Cut three pieces of wire at quarter wavelengths on 10, 20 and 40 meters using the formula:

$$\text{Length (feet)} = \frac{234}{f_{\text{MHz}}}$$

Choose frequencies that are in the middle of the bands or your favorite band segments. I recommend #26 enameled wire available at RadioShack. It's strong and difficult to see.

Examine your chosen tree and the surrounding area. Make absolutely certain that you're not near any power lines. If you see power lines running through the branches, find another tree.

Once you've selected your tree, run the wires up the side of the trunk. If you're an experienced tree climber, work your way up the branches taking the wire along as you go. The alternative is to use a ladder, but make sure you have someone on the ground hold it for you. If inquiring minds want to know what you're doing, explain that you're trimming the tree and/or inspecting the leaves. You can attach the wires to the tree with loops of fishing line, or any other low-visibility means.

The idea is to get the wires as high as possible. You'll probably have to bend the 20 and 40-meter antenna wires, depending on the height of your tree (and your desire to climb it!). The tree in my yard is about 20 feet from the house, so the end of my 40-meter antenna reaches to an upstairs bedroom window. If you use your house as a support, you need to insulate the antenna wire so it won't come in contact with metal siding, storm windows or whatever. I loosened a screw in my metal window frame, tightened it down on a piece of insulated wire and tied the antenna to the wire.

Now build your ground system. Take bare copper wire, preferably something thick like #14, and loop it around the bottom of the tree at ground level. Solder several radial wires to this loop and run them out into the yard. I only used six radials at various lengths, making each one as long as possible. Bury the radials about an inch beneath the soil. (Do this at night if you live in an antenna-restricted area. If anyone asks, just tell him/her you're checking the lawn for grubs.) The radial wires don't have to travel in straight lines. Zigzag them as much as necessary to fit the available space.

Now install the transmission line. My townhouse, like many, has a water spigot on the front. That means there is a hole through the house for the water pipe to pass through. There was enough extra room in this opening to pass a length of RG-58 coaxial cable. You may need to bury this coax between the tree and the house, so make sure to buy cable that is made specifically for burial in soil.

Back out at the tree, solder all three antennas to the center conductor of the coax and solder the coax braid to the copper radial loop. Weatherproof the coax connections. I used RadioShack "Outdoor RF Connector Sealant" (part no. 278-1645). Cover the copper radial loop with mulch or soil so it won't be visible. I planted pansies around mine and it looks very nice.

Testing

An SWR meter is all you need for testing. If you measured the antenna lengths correctly, the SWR will probably be no higher than 2:1. If you want it lower, add a few inches of wire to the antenna, or trim it as the case may be. If you have an antenna tuner, you don't have to bother with tuning unless the SWR is grossly out of whack. Simply adjust the tuner for a flat 1:1 SWR. Because your transmission line is likely to be short, an elevated SWR isn't as bad as it seems. On 15 meters you're using the 40-meter antenna on the third harmonic. This means that your SWR might be high, but the tuner should be able to take care of it.

Results

Is this antenna "optimal?" Far from it. No doubt there is some RF absorption by the tree, and the radiation patterns probably look like abstract art. I'm sure that some RF is being used to heat the coax when the SWR is high.

The point, however, is that this antenna solved my problems. It works well and is far enough from the house that I no longer have complaints about TVI and telephone interference. Signals from my computer and TNC are but distant memories.

Many operators are astonished when I describe my antenna. They can't believe that my signal is so strong. When conditions are decent, I even work a fair amount of DX. I've also managed to use the system on 30 and 17 meters with good success.

As far as visibility is concerned, you can't spot the antenna unless you walk right up to the tree. Even then, you need to know what you're looking for. So far it's been completely disregarded by the spies from the homeowner's association.

Take it from me: If you live in an apartment, townhouse or condo, you can get on the HF bands with a full-sized antenna. If you can see a tree anywhere on your lot, you've just found a home for your next antenna—and it will probably outperform any indoor design. I must admit, however, that I still stare out the window and dream of 100-foot towers and stacked Yagis!

6 More Simple and Fun Antennas for VHF and UHF

**This chapter is a collection of ideas for your consideration.
We believe you'll find something of interest here!**

The Simplest Ground Plane on 446 MHz

In Chapter 1, I related how Sylvia, K8SYL, (my wife) and I had made a simple ground plane for 2 meters to extend the range of our hand-held transceiver. What I didn't tell you there was how we later wanted to get on 70 centimeters. For that, I built another simple ground-plane antenna. See **Fig 6-1**.

Dimensions shown in **Fig 6-2** are for 446 MHz. (For 223 MHz, make the lengths 12.6 inches.) The antenna works well across the FM portion of the band, which is from 442 to 450 MHz.

I used #12 copper wire I stripped from a 9-inch length of Romex (house wiring). Because this antenna is about one-third the size of the 2-meter model, the elements are significantly stiffer in this 70-centimeter model. I still have the leftover lengths of brazing rod from the stiffened 2-meter ver-

sion in Chapter 1, and one day I'll probably use those to make a 70-centimeter antenna.

I formed the end loops by mak-

Fig 6-1—The simplest ground plane on 446 MHz.

ing a single-turn wrap around a ¼-inch rod. Solder closes the loop and leaves no sharp edges to poke or snag.

It's really that simple, and it works well. Mounting options are discussed in Chapters 1 and 4.

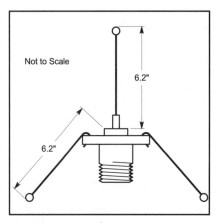

Not to Scale

6.2"

6.2"

Fig 6-2—Dimensions for the 70-centimeter (446 MHz) simple ground-plane antenna. See text.

The Simple Sixer

This VHF dipole by Jim Augusteijn, KE6LDX, which appeared in the September 1999 issue of *QST*, is proof that you don't need a complicated antenna to work exciting 6-meter DX. Build this rotatable dipole and use it outdoors or in your attic. It's also a good "take along" antenna for portable operating! See **Fig 6-3**.

They don't call 6 meters the

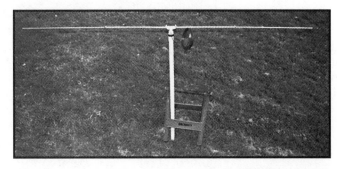

Fig 6-3—The Simple Sixer.

"Magic Band" for nothing. It can be silent for hours, then suddenly burst wide open for DX from hundreds or even thousands of miles away. When we are near the peak of the solar cycle, you can even expect episodes of global DX! (We've already seen some transatlantic and transpacific openings.)

A big beam on a tall tower is a definite asset for 6-meter work, but the other "magical" aspect of the band is that just about any antenna will send your signal bouncing around the continent or the world when conditions are right. If you don't have the budget for a tower or roof-mounted beam, something as basic as a dipole will let you enjoy much of the fun. Although a wire dipole is adequate, I prefer something more rugged. My Simple Sixer meets this requirement with its aluminum and PVC design. It assembles easily, and comes apart just as easily. If you're going roving during a VHF contest, you can toss this antenna in the trunk of your car and get on the air from any location within minutes.

Cutting and Soldering

Begin by cutting a ⅝-inch notch in each of the two pieces of ½-inch diameter, 1½-inch long schedule-40 PVC tubing (see **Table 6-1**). A bench clamp will help hold them in place while you make the cuts. With a hacksaw cut two lateral slits about ¾ inches long in the ends of each of the two ½ × 24-inch pieces of aluminum tubing.

To prepare the coax, strip about 2½ inches of the outer insulation from one end. RG-58 is fine for most applications, but consider low-loss cable if you plan to install the antenna more than about 50 feet from your radio. Separate the braid from the center conductor, strip ½ inch of insulation from the center conductor and apply some solder to the center conductor and the braid.

Assembly

Insert the notched pieces of the 1½-inch long PVC tubes into the PVC T (see **Fig 6-4**) and secure with PVC cement. After they are dry, slide the ⅜-inch wood dowel into the unslit end of one of the pieces of ½-inch diameter aluminum tubing. Push this tube and dowel through either of the notched pieces of 1½-inch long PVC and continue

Table 6-1
Bill of Materials
2 pieces ½-inch × 24-inch aluminum tubing—0.058 inch wall
2 pieces ⅜-inch × 36-inch aluminum tubing—0.058 inch wall
2 ¾-inch diameter stainless steel hose clamps
2 ½-inch diameter stainless steel hose clamps
1 ½-inch diameter PVC T
2 pieces of ½-inch diameter, 1½-inch-long schedule-40 PVC tubing
1 ⅜-inch-diameter wood dowel
1 metal, wood or PVC mast

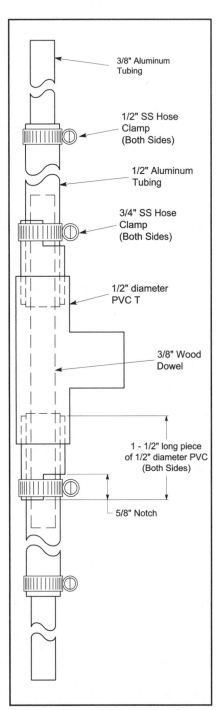

3/8" Aluminum Tubing

1/2" SS Hose Clamp (Both Sides)

1/2" Aluminum Tubing

3/4" SS Hose Clamp (Both Sides)

1/2" diameter PVC T

3/8" Wood Dowel

1 - 1/2" long piece of 1/2" diameter PVC (Both Sides)

5/8" Notch

Fig 6-4—The construction diagram of the Simple Sixer.

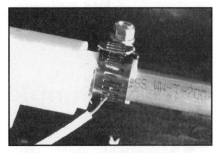

Fig 6-5—Use hose clamps to secure the aluminum tubing to the PVC T *and* to attach the coax conductors.

Fig 6-6—Tape the coax to the mast below the T to keep the connections from flexing in the wind. The remaining coax is shown rolled up and attached to the antenna in preparation for portable operation.

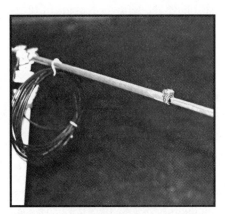

Fig 6-7—Complete the Simple Sixer by sliding in the narrower aluminum tubes and tightening the hose clamps.

pushing until the dowel goes through the PVC T and out the other side (the dowel should protrude about an inch or so). Now slide the other ¹/₂-inch aluminum tube onto the protruding end of the dowel.

Use stainless-steel hose clamps on either side of the T to secure the aluminum tubes in place. As you're tightening the clamps, insert the coax center conductor and braid to opposite sides of the T and make sure the clamp will hold them in contact with the aluminum tubing when it's fully tightened (**Fig 6-5**). If you intend to use the Simple Sixer for a permanent outdoor installation, I recommend attaching the coax to the tubes with something more durable, such as soldered ring terminals secured with sheet metal screws, and carefully water-

proofing the connections. In either case you should tightly tape the coax to the mast just below the T to prevent the connections from flexing in the wind (**Fig 6-6**).

Finally, slide the ³/₈-inch aluminum tubes into the slit ends of the ¹/₂-inch aluminum tubes. Use two more stainless steel hose clamps to hold these tubes in place (**Fig 6-7**).

Tune-up

This is the easiest part of the whole project. With an accurate VHF SWR meter, slide the ³/₈-inch aluminum tubes in or out as necessary to obtain the lowest possible SWR. Make sure you move both tubes equal distances prior to each measurement. You can adjust the

Simple Sixer while using a chair or step ladder to support the antenna's mast, but keep it well away from large pieces of metal such as vehicles or aluminum siding—if they are too close, they will detune the antenna.

A 10-Meter Version

You can convert the Simple Sixer into the Simple Tener by adding two 48-inch long, ¹/₄-inch diameter, aluminum tubes to each end of the antenna. Cut slots in the ends of the Simple Sixer's ³/₈-inch aluminum tubes and use hose clamps to hold the extensions in place. Adjust the tubes until both legs of the dipole are about 8 feet long. Now attach your SWR meter and fine-tune the antenna for resonance!

Broadband Half-Wave 6-Meter Vertical

Fredrick T. Smith, W6DV, was the designer and author of this project that first appeared in *The ARRL Antenna Compendium, Vol 5.*

The purpose of this antenna is to provide a vertically polarized antenna that covers both ends of the 6-meter band. I have used this antenna for about four years, to cover repeaters at the top end and local SSB nets at the low end of the band.

Design

The broad bandwidth is obtained by using a large-diameter, low-Q radiating element that is λ/2 long. This broadbanding technique is discussed in *The ARRL Antenna Book.* An L network is used to match the 50-Ω coax line to the high impedance at the bottom end of the λ/2 element.

I have previously used L networks to feed 12 and 2-meter λ/2 vertical antennas. The design technique is essentially a modification of the J-pole antenna. The λ/4 matching section of the J-pole is similar to a resonant parallel-tuned circuit. Connecting the inner conductor of the coax part way up from the bottom end of the λ/4 matching section corresponds to tapping a parallel circuit inductor several turns up from the bottom to obtain the desired impedance match.

The L network replaces the resonant parallel tuned circuit. A length of

RG-58 coax about seven inches long is used to provide the required capacitance in the L network. This eliminates the requirement for a weatherproof container for L-network components.

Formulas for computing the capacitive and inductive reactance values are given in the 1992 edition of *The ARRL Handbook.* The L network consists of the coax capacitor and an inductor connected between the bottom end of the antenna and the coax shield, as shown in **Fig 6-8**. The output impedance R2 at the bottom end of the antenna is transformed to R1 = 50 Ω at the input of the network.

The length of the antenna is computed from formulas found in *The ARRL Antenna Book,* using a coefficient C = 0.85, a frequency of 52 MHz, and multiplying by two for a λ/2 antenna. This yields an antenna length of 96.5 inches. This length is not precise, but small values of capacitive or inductive reactance resulting from the computed length differing slightly from the true resonant length will have a very small effect on the computation of network component values.

From curves found in Dr H. Jasik's book, *Antenna Engineering Handbook,* First Edition, the resistive component is 710 Ω, and the capacitive reactive component is −100 Ω. Again, these values are approximations. The formulas in the *Handbook* assume that

the load resistance R_2 is non-reactive. Whatever small reactance is present can be compensated for during final tuning. The equations for inductive and capacitive reactance are:

$$X_L = R_2 \sqrt{\frac{R_1}{R_2 - R_1}}$$

$$X_C = \frac{R_1 R_2}{X_L}$$

The computed values for L and C are:

L = 0.60 µH
C = 16.9 pF

The air-wound inductor was made by winding seven turns of #12 wire, 1¹/₄-inches long, on a ³/₄-inch diameter form. The form was then removed.

Construction

The construction details of the antenna are shown in Fig 6-8. The antenna consists of a length of ⁷/₈-inch diameter aluminum tubing. The antenna element is mounted to a piece of 2 × 2-inch wood support with aluminum clamps fastened to standoff insulators. The standoff insulators are spaced about 12 inches apart on the wooden support. At my installation, the wood support is about 3 feet long with a piece of 1¹/₂ × 1¹/₂-inch aluminum angle bolted to the bottom 6 inches of the wood support. The aluminum angle is secured

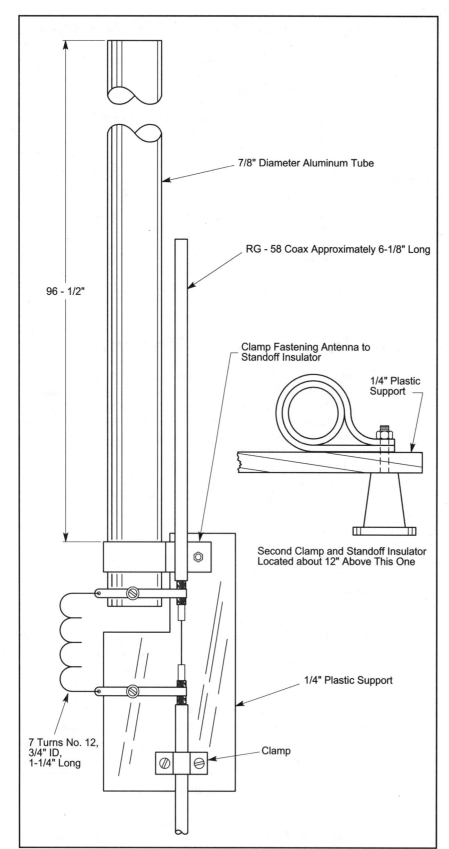

7/8" Diameter Aluminum Tube

RG - 58 Coax Approximately 6-1/8" Long

96 - 1/2"

Clamp Fastening Antenna to
Standoff Insulator

1/4" Plastic
Support

Second Clamp and Standoff Insulator
Located about 12" Above This One

1/4" Plastic Support

7 Turns No. 12,
3/4" ID,
1-1/4" Long

Clamp

Fig 6-8—Construction details for the 6-meter broadband vertical.

to a $1^1/_2$-inch pipe mast by two hose clamps.

A 3-inch long by $1^3/_4 \times {}^1/_4$-inch piece of plastic is mounted on the lower standoff insulator and provides the mounting for one end of the inductor and the end of the coaxial line to the antenna. A pair of solder lugs fastened to the bottom of the antenna provides connections for the shield of the coax capacitor and the other end of the inductor.

A second pair of solder lugs fastened to the lower end of the plastic support connects the end of the inductor to the shield of the coax transmission line feeding the antenna. The inner conductors of the coax capacitor and the coax transmission line are soldered together. The coax capacitor is taped to the antenna with black electrical tape, and the end of the coax is sealed, after adjustments are completed. A 3-inch diameter coaxial choke coil using four turns is located as close as possible to the bottom of the $^1/_4$-inch plastic support and taped to the wood support.

Adjusting for Minimum SWR

The network component values are adjusted by mounting the antenna about six feet above the ground on some form of support. The frequency for minimum SWR is determined. This should be close to 52 MHz. The turns of the inductor are compressed or expanded to minimize the SWR. Next, $^1/_8$ inch is clipped off the coax capacitor, and the coil turns again adjusted for minimum SWR. This process is repeated until a minimum SWR value of 1.1 or less is obtained. If the SWR at each end of the 6-meter band is less than or equal to 1.5, then the adjustment process is completed.

A Vertical 6-Meter Wire Extended Double Zepp

This project is by Wayde S. Bartholomew, WA3WMG. It was published in *The ARRL Antenna Compendium, Vol 4*.

I needed a low-cost gain antenna with vertical polarization for 52.525 MHz. The concept of an Extended Double Zepp looked interesting. I constructed a mock-up antenna at my QTH to compare it with a quarter-wave vertical at a height of 50 feet. The Extended-Double Zepp typically outperformed the vertical by two to three S units for both receive and transmit. This was with a power output of 25 W, talking with stations 30 to 100 miles distant. This encouraged me to construct the final version, which was placed at the 100-foot level on a commercial tower 1800 feet above sea level.

Construction is fairly straightforward. See **Fig 6-9**. The upper and lower legs of the dipole sections are supported by $1^1/_2$-inch PVC pipe. The 1:1 balun and matching section are placed inside another piece of $1^1/_2$-inch PVC pipe for support and weather protection.

Spacing from the tower has a definite effect on directivity. **Fig 6-10** shows the effect on the azimuthal and elevation patterns of spacing the antenna 5 feet away from a tower, compared to a 10-foot spacing from the tower. In this case the bottom of the antenna is at the 50-foot level on a 100-foot high tower. The front-to-back ratio is about 9 dB for the 5-foot spacing.

Although it is still distorted, the pattern for the 10-foot spacing is more omnidirectional in nature than the 5-foot spacing. Of course, the larger spacing does present more of a construction problem when using PVC pipe.

Tuning of the antenna is simple. The legs are temporarily stretched out on the tower with the bottom of the antenna a few feet off the ground. The ladder line is purposely made a little long at installation (3 feet is a good starting point), and then trimmed a little at a time for the lowest SWR. This should be close to 1:1.

Once the feed line is trimmed, the ends of the PVC pipe should be sealed with RTV sealant. A small hole should be drilled in the bottom of the PVC to drain off any condensation that may form inside. A small screen should be placed over the drain hole to keep out spiders and wasps—they seem to like antennas for homes!

Results have been impressive. During band openings the antenna is an excellent performer, and during marginal band conditions it has the gain to

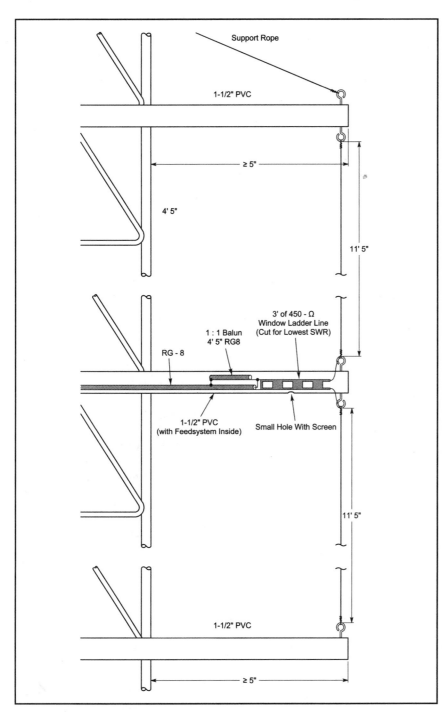

Fig 6-9—Mounting dimensions for the 6-meter Extended Double Zepp antenna. The 450-Ω "window" ladder line is cut long initially at 3 feet and trimmed for best SWR at installation. The feed system, including the 1:1 coax balun and window line, is placed inside 1½-inch PVC pipe for support and weather protection.

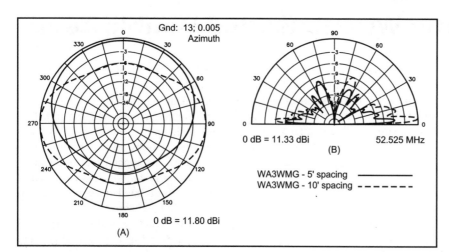

Fig 6-10—Patterns for vertical 6-meter EDZ mounted parallel to metal tower. At A is a comparison of computed azimuthal patterns for 5 and 10-foot spacings from tower; at B is a comparison of elevation patterns. The larger spacing yields coverage that is more omnidirectional.

Gnd: 13; 0.005 Azimuth

0 dB = 11.33 dBi
(B)

52.525 MHz

WA3WMG - 5' spacing ————
WA3WMG - 10' spacing – – – – – –

0 dB = 11.80 dBi
(A)

still be effective. In the three months time from November 1991 to January 1992, I worked 25 states. Three other Extended Double Zepps were constructed for repeater use, with excellent results.

A 5/8-Wave VHF Antenna

This project is by Don Norman, AF8B. It appeared in *The ARRL Antenna Compendium, Vol 2*.

This antenna grew out of a series of experiments with feed-line decoupling. Ralph Turner, W8HXC, and I began exploring feed-line decoupling after Ralph discovered considerable RF on the feed line of a popular commercial 2-meter vertical antenna. I built a $5/8$-λ antenna and began a series of experiments with feed-line decoupling.

Since this was a homemade antenna, the radials were attached to the mast with a homemade ring clamp and could be repositioned very easily. A series of tests and measurements proved to my satisfaction that $1/4$-λ radials do not belong near the matching network on a $5/8$-λ antenna. Quarter-wave radials positioned $3/8$ λ below the matching network worked quite nicely and yielded excellent feed-line decoupling.

I believe that a $5/8$-λ antenna with $1/4$-λ radials placed $3/8$ λ below the matching point acts in the same manner as the venerable extended double Zepp antenna. In fact, the antenna works well when the matching network is removed and it is center fed with 300-Ω balanced line. The balanced line must be led away from the antenna at right angles for more than 1 λ.

When the decoupling experiments were finished, there were a large number of odds and ends on hand and a search was begun for a design of an antenna that the average amateur could

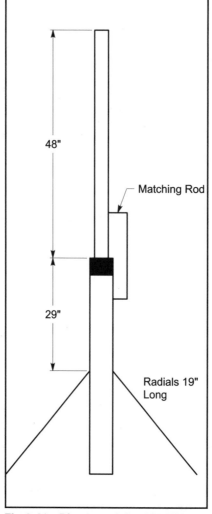

Fig 6-11—Diagram of the 147-MHz $5/8$-λ antenna. It is designed to be built with readily available parts and ordinary hand tools.

48"

Matching Rod

29"

Radials 19" Long

build with ordinary hand tools and hardware store and RadioShack items. A sketch of the antenna is presented in **Fig 6-11**.

The radiator is cut from $3/4$-inch OD aluminum tubing and the supporting mast is a $1 1/4$-inch OD television antenna mast. The matching rod and radials are made from hard-drawn aluminum clothesline wire. The center insulator is made from a pipe coupling for the sort of semi-flexible plastic water pipe that is joined with molded plastic fittings and stainless steel hose clamps. **Fig 6-12** shows three views of the plastic pipe fitting.

Fig 6-12A is a sketch of the coupling before anything is done, 12B is a cutaway of the coupling inside the mast, and 12C is the radiator inside the insulator. The $3/4$-inch aluminum radiator is a loose fit inside a l-inch pipe coupling, and the l-inch pipe coupling is a loose

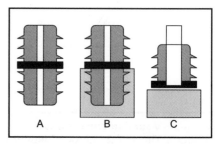

A   B   C

Fig 6-12—Three views of the plastic pipe fitting inside the center insulator.

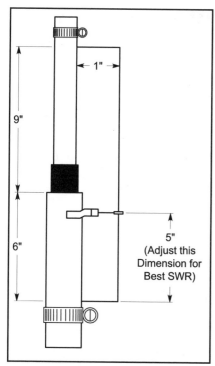

Fig 6-13—Detailed view of the matching network.

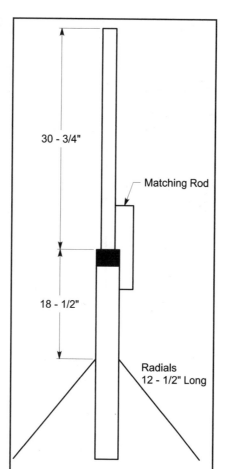

Fig 6-14—Diagram of the 220-MHz version of the antenna.

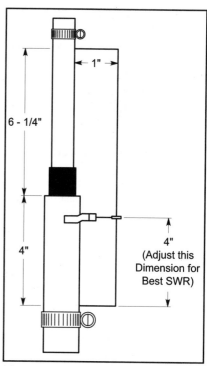

Fig 6-15—The matching network for the 220-MHz version.

fit inside the TV antenna mast. These loose fits are tightened with shims cut from aluminum beverage cans. The radiator is installed in the insulator by inserting the tubing halfway through the coupling and drilling a hole and installing a self -tapping sheet-metal screw. The radials are attached to the mast with self-tapping sheet-metal screws.

Fig 6-13 is a sketch of the matching network of the ⅝-λ antenna. The matching rod is bent up from a 19-inch length of hard-drawn aluminum wire. Measure 2 inches from one end and make a right-angle bend. Make another right-angle bend 1 inch from that one. Measure 2 inches from the other end and make a right-angle bend. Make another right-angle bend 1¼ inches from the end. You should now have a U-shaped piece of wire with the U 1-inch deep at one end and ¾ inch deep at the other.

Drill a ⅜-inch hole through the mast and insulator between two of the mast attachment screws. Fish the coax through this hole. Attach the matching rod to the radiator and mast with stainless steel hose clamps according to the dimensions in Fig 6-13. (Be sure to file any paint or anodizing off the mast and radiator.) Ground the coax shield to the mast under one of the mast attachment screws. Attach the coax center conductor to the matching rod with a homemade clamp. Adjust the coax tap position on the matching rod for best SWR.

The same design works well at 220 MHz. A 220 antenna was designed, constructed and tested in 1982, but only recently became popular locally. **Fig 6-14** gives overall dimensions for the 220 antenna. Materials and construction of the 220-MHz version are the same as for the 147-MHz version; only the lengths are different.

Fig 6-15 is the matching detail for the 220-MHz antenna. The antenna may be built for center frequencies other than 147 and 220 MHz. Formulas are

(all dimensions in inches, f = center frequency)

Radiator—7056/f
Radials—2793/f
Radial attachment point below top of mast—4263/f
Matching rod—2205/f
Matching rod attachment point above top of mast—1323/f

The matching rod is spaced 1 inch from the radiator for both the 2-meter and 1¼-meter bands.

This antenna design works well, whichever frequency it is constructed for. We have found that matching is easier if the feed line is cut in multiples of a half wavelength at the most common operating frequency. A half wavelength in inches is determined by the equation

$$L \text{ (inches)} = 5904/f \times VF$$

where

f = frequency in MHz
VF = velocity factor of the particular cable.

Build a Weatherproof PVC J-Pole Antenna

There have been many versions and variations of J-poles published in the ham literature in recent years. This one by Dennis Blanchard, K1YPP, was published in July 1995 *QST*. I selected it because of its weatherproof construction and because Dennis tells you how to build one for the 50, 144 or 222-MHz bands.

The twinlead J-pole antenna has been around for quite some time. It was brought into the limelight by an excellent article written by John S. Belrose, VE2CV, in the April 1982 *QST*. While Jack provided an excellent theoretical discussion of the J-pole, his article did not offer great detail on precisely how to build this wonderful VHF/UHF antenna.

J-poles are easy to build—which is why you see so many versions in use. (And so many articles in print!) Even so, several misconceptions exist concerning the J-pole. One common mistake is to assume that all you have to do is attach a piece of coaxial cable to a length of twinlead, short the bottom section and cut a notch. Not quite!

Another misconception is that once the antenna is built and tuned, you can stuff it inside a PVC tube and expect it to work flawlessly. Unfortunately for many amateurs, the PVC treatment often results in a failed antenna—unless you do it right.

Understanding J-Pole Construction

The J-pole antenna comprises two parts (see **Fig 6-16**): a $^{1}/_{4}$-wavelength matching section, which is the entire portion below the notch; and the radiating section, which is the $^{1}/_{2}$-wavelength section above the notch. The portion of the antenna below the notch is most affected by the type of insulation that surrounds it. It also has the most influence on the resonance of the antenna. The radiating section is not as greatly affected by the insulation or the type of wire used. (We'll discuss this effect in a moment.)

When installed inside a PVC tube, the J-pole is a rugged and weather resistant antenna. If you place a J-pole inside PVC, however, you must center the antenna within the tube. One way

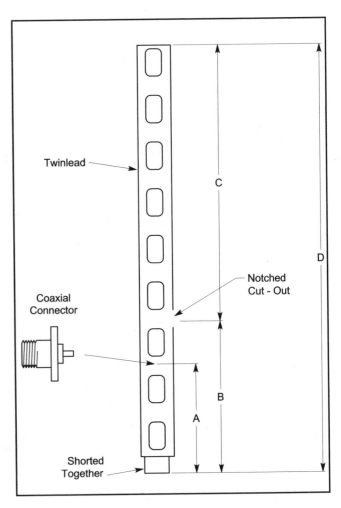

Fig 6-16—The critical lengths for the J-pole (see Table 6-2). Note the notch that's cut into one of the twinlead wires. The wires at the bottom are shorted together.

Twinlead

Coaxial Connector

Notched Cut - Out

Shorted Together

to do this is to place the antenna inside a piece of foam insulation, preferably the type used to insulate hot-water pipes, before you slide it into the tube. If you choose a 1.5-inch PVC tube, this insulation is often a perfect fit (see **Fig 6-17** and **Fig 6-18**).

Building a JM -Pole Antenna

STEP ONE: The Decision Phase

Choose a frequency for your J-pole. In the case of 144 or 222 MHz bands, the antenna bandwidth is many megahertz, so this isn't a critical decision. Simply use the middle of the band, 146 MHz and 223 MHz, respectively. However, on 50 MHz the antenna will not cover the entire band without readjustment. On 50 MHz the bandwidth will be approximately 2 MHz. This means you'll need to select a frequency that corresponds to your favorite portion of the band.

Table 6-2 gives you the cutting lengths for the antenna sections. But before you can start cutting, you need to consider the velocity factor of the twinlead you're using. Despite what you may have heard, RF energy does not flow through a cable at the speed of light in a vacuum. The wire and even the insulation act to slow the speed of the wave. So, the time required for the signal to travel through a length of cable is longer than the time required to travel the same distance in free space. This means that the full wavelength of the signal exists in a physically shorter length of cable. If you cut the cable for the wavelength of the signal in free space, you'll be off the mark!

Cable manufacturers test for the velocity factor and specify it as a decimal percentage of the speed of light. The lengths shown in Table 6-2 are based

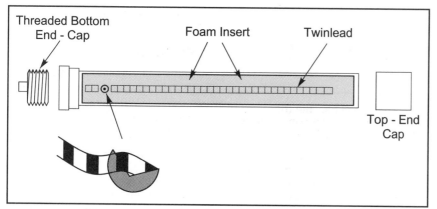

Fig 6-17—In this cut-away view you can see that a foam insert keeps the antenna centered within the PVC tube. End caps keep out moisture and an M-359 right-angle connector makes it easy to attach the coax.

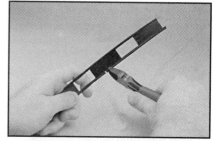

Fig 6-19—Cut the notch in only one of the twinlead wires. The twinlead shown in these photographs is 450 Ω. However, the same techniques apply to 300-Ω twinlead.

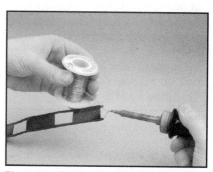

Fig 6-20—Strip the insulation from the end of the twinlead and twist the conductors together. A little solder ensures a good electrical connection.

Table 6-2
Section Lengths (See Figure 6-16)

Frequency (MHz)	D, Total Length (in.)	A(in.)	B(in.)	C(in.)
50.00	160.4	3.2	48.2	112.2
51.00	157.2	3.1	47.2	110.0
52.00	154.2	3.1	46.3	107.9
53.00	151.3	3.0	45.5	105.9
54.00	148.5	3.0	44.6	103.9
146.00	54.9	1.1	16.5	38.4
222.00	36.1	0.7	10.9	25.3

on windowed 300-Ω twinlead with a velocity factor of 0.85. If other twinlead is used, you may need to increase or decrease the lengths proportionally. For example, if a section length is $16^{1}/_{2}$ inches long and you're using TV twinlead with a typical velocity factor of 0.83, reduce the length by 2%, to $16^{3}/_{16}$ inches. (A velocity factor of 0.83 is roughly 98% of 0.85. Putting it another way, it's 2% less than 0.85.)

Next, decide how the antenna will be used: indoors or outdoors, fixed station or portable. If the antenna is to be used indoors, weather sealing will not be needed. If you're going to use

it outdoors, apply a sealant to cover the exposed metal (the coaxial cable connection and the copper wire in the twinlead).

To limit possible RF absorption, use schedule-40 PVC. Make sure it is ultraviolet resistant as well.

Applying a sealant directly to the twinlead will change the resonant frequency of the antenna. At first this may seem a bit odd. But, believe it or not, the sealant does affect the velocity factor of the twinlead. If the velocity factor changes, the resonant frequency of the antenna changes. Usually it will be lower than calculated. For example, an

antenna cut for 146 MHz may resonate at 142 MHz after the exposed conductors are coated with sealant—a 4% change!

STEP TWO: Cutting the Wire

Select a good grade of 300-Ω twinlead, one that is tough and will withstand abuse. Avoid TV-grade twinleads that tend to crack easily. Windowed 300-Ω twinlead is available from several *QST* advertisers.

Measure a length of twinlead that is approximately 10% longer than the amount needed. Measure it so that the

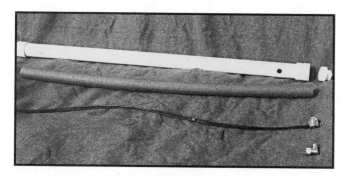

Fig 6-18—The disassembled J-pole antenna. The twinlead antenna core is shown at the bottom with the M359 right angle connector removed. It's placed within a foam insert (middle) that keeps the antenna centered within the PVC tube (top). This is the construction technique used by the JADE Products "JADE-POLE" antenna. (*Photo by Dennis Blanchard, K1YPP.*)

Fig 6-21—The center pin (not shown) of the SO-239 coaxial connector is soldered to the wire that runs the full length of the antenna. You can use a file to notch the pin. This will make it easier to solder. Then, attach a solder lug to the exterior of the SO-239 using the appropriate screw and nut. Strip away enough insulation to expose the wire on the opposite side of the twinlead and solder the lug in place

notch will be cut where there is insulation all the way across between the two conductors, not at a "window."

Cut the notch. See **Fig 6-19**. Cut only one wire; the other will run the full length of the antenna. The notch can be a small V or square. Make it at least a $^1/_4$ inch long. Measure from the notch to the bottom of the antenna cut off the excess wire. Strip about $^1/_2$ inch of insulation off each of the wires at the bottom. Twist the conductors together and solder. See **Fig 6-20**. Now measure from the bottom to the top of the antenna and cut off the excess. Using a razor knife or other sharp knife, remove the insulation where the coax will be connected.

STEP THREE: Connect the Coax

You have two choices: You can solder the coaxial cable directly to the twinlead, or install a UHF or BNC co-axial connector. A connector is highly recommended because it allows quick connections and disconnections. It also provides some strain relief, so the connection is less likely to break.

If you decide to use a connector, first file a slot in the center conductor of the connector and set the antenna wire into the slot. For the other connection, mount a solder lug on one of the holes on the connector. Wrap the lug around the wire, or slot the lug and slip the wire into it. Solder both conductors. See **Fig 6-21**. One word of caution: Make sure the center conductor is connected to the wire that runs the full length of the antenna and that the braid side of the coax is connected to the notched side.

After you install your J-pole in a PVC tube, an M-359 right-angle coax connector comes in handy. It makes it much easier to bring the coax connection outside the tube. You can create a flat spot on the tube with a heat gun. Heat the PVC carefully until it softens then press down with a narrow piece of wood. By creating this flat surface and using a small rubber gasket, you'll have a waterproof seal for the coax connector.

STEP FOUR: Test the Antenna

You can tune the antenna with an SWR analyzer, if you have one, or just an accurate SWR meter. The resonant frequency of your J-pole is where you'll find the lowest SWR. The 144- and 222-MHz versions have a bandwidth almost twice as wide as the bands themselves, so tuning should not be necessary. The 50-MHz version may require minor tuning to make it resonant at the correct frequency (see the sidebar, *Tuning Your 6-Meter J-Pole*). Place the antenna in the foam core and PVC before you check for resonance.

If you find that you need to tweak your J-pole, make the matching section at the bottom slightly longer. Usually this will not be necessary.

STEP FIVE: Installation

You can install your PVC J-pole on a mast, or against a flat nonconductive wall. Plastic clamps for 1.5 and 1.0-inch PVC are available from JADE Products, PO Box 368, East Hampstead, NH 03826. Consider drilling a tiny hole in the bottom of the tube to allow any water to escape.

Conclusion

Jack Belrose, VE2CV, recommends placing a choke near the coaxial connection. To fashion a simple choke, take a cylindrical ferrite (Amidon 2X-43-251) and attach it to the coax at the feed point.

The J-pole antenna does not need radials, so it has a very narrow profile and low wind resistance. This is particularly important if you live in an area where icing is a problem. If the PVC enclosure has a threaded bottom, the antenna can be attached to a short piece of mating PVC and mounted above surrounding surfaces.

7 More HF Dipoles

Chapter 2 dealt with the basic dipole and showed how to increase its versatility and usefulness. This chapter picks up that theme and carries it forward. Each project will give you more ideas on how to increase the utility of a dipole.

K8SYL's 75 and 10-M Dipole

Sylvia, K8SYL, wanted antennas for 75 and 10-meter operation. With help from her OM, K8CH, she put together a 120-ft center-fed dipole and installed it about 35-feet high. This allowed her to join the other members of The Auto State YL Net (TASYLs) on their weekly 75-meter net.

That was okay, but what to do for 10 meters? The OM had a partially built 10-meter ground-plane antenna in the basement (described in Chapter 5 of this book), but that ground plane wasn't going to do much good until it was finished. Sylvia wasn't going to wait. One afternoon she was tuning across the 10-meter band when she came across KP4NU calling CQ from Caguas, Puerto Rico. She really wanted to have a QSO in Spanish, so she did what most of us would do—she called José using her 75-meter dipole. (First she engaged the internal antenna tuner in her transceiver.) Sylvia had a nice QSO. Was it luck, good conditions, or what? She asked her OM (me, K8CH).

We both knew that a dipole will work on odd harmonics (3rd, 5th, 7th, etc.), but 28 MHz is 8 times 3.5 MHz. That's true, but Sylvia's dipole is cut for the high end of the band—closer to 4 MHz. Hmm, 4 times 7 is 28, and harmonic resonances are higher than one would expect. In other words, while you

would expect that a 75-meter antenna that was resonant at 3.94 MHz would have a 7th harmonic resonance at 27.58 MHz, it will actually be over a MHz higher than that.

Now we both understood the theory, but to better answer her question, I next connected my MFJ-259B analyzer to the antenna feed line. The analyzer showed a resonance just below 29 MHz with an SWR of less than 3:1. I then modeled Sylvia's antenna in *EZNEC*, which confirmed what the analyzer had already shown. At this point there were two options. The first was to leave well enough alone and use the transceiver's automatic antenna tuner.

The second option was to make the 75-meter antenna useable on 10 meters without the need of an antenna tuner. That's what we opted to do.

The Design

There were two issues that we had to deal with. The first was to improve the 10-meter match without upsetting the situation on 75-meters. The second was to move the dipole's 10-meter resonance a bit lower in the band.

At resonance on 10 meters, the feed-point impedance is about 120 Ω. I used a calculator to confirm that a quarter-wave transformer made with 75-Ω coax would take care of the 10-meter impedance match. At the same time, the

length of this coaxial transformer is short enough to have no significant effect on the antenna's 75-meter operation.

I used RG-11 to build the stub. For low-power operation, RG-59 will substitute. The physical length of the stub depends on the velocity factor. My RG-11 (Belden 8238) has a 66% velocity factor and that means that the stub is 5 feet, 9 inches long. If you use 75-Ω coax with a 78% velocity factor (such as Belden 8213 or 8212), you'll need to make your stub 6 feet, 9.5 inches long.

Sylvia built her antenna to cover the upper end of the 75-meter band. We thought about lengthening the dipole to move the 10-meter resonance to the vicinity of 28.4 MHz. It would require 4.5-inch extensions to each dipole leg. The downside to this is that it moves the 75-meter resonance to 3.89 MHz, and that's lower than what Sylvia was looking for. Could we find a method to lower the 10-meter resonance without substantially moving the 75-meter resonant frequency?

In Chapter 2, I described adding capacitance hats on a 40-meter dipole to move the 3rd harmonic resonance lower in the 15-meter band. We can use a similar technique to lower the 7th harmonic resonance of the 75-meter dipole. In the case of K8SYL's antenna, it took only the little bit of loading provided by a pair of short (three-inch)

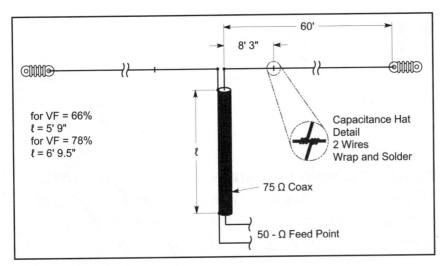

for VF = 66%
ℓ = 5' 9"
for VF = 78%
ℓ = 6' 9.5"

Capacitance Hat
Detail
2 Wires
Wrap and Solder

75 Ω Coax

50 - Ω Feed Point

Fig 7-1—K8SYL's 75 and 10-meter dipole. Capacitance hat wires ended up being 3 inches extended from the main dipole wire. This drawing is not to scale.

K8SYL Dipole = Solid Line
10 - m GP = Dashed Line

Max Gain = 10.82 dBi   Freq = 28.4 MHz

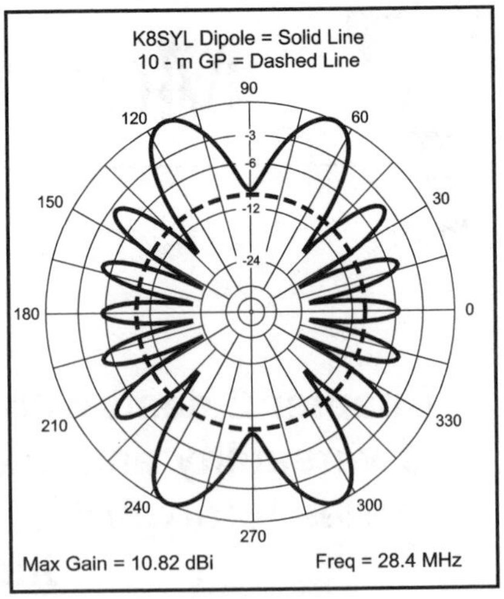

Fig 7-2—Azimuthal radiation pattern on 28.4 MHz of K8SYL's dipole at an elevation angle of 12 degrees, compared to the response of a 10-meter ground-plane antenna.

wires on each leg of the dipole. You'll find details and dimensions in **Fig 7-1**.

Tuning the Antenna

With the quarter-wave transformer section in place, tune the antenna first for (fundamental) resonance in the upper part of the 75-meter band. You'll need to choose a frequency above about 3.89 MHz or you'll lose 10-meter coverage.

Next, check the 10-meter resonant frequency. (For Sylvia's dipole it was just below 29 MHz.) If you need to lower that frequency, add the capacitance hats as shown in Fig 7-1. You may want to make the wires a bit longer to start with. Check the resonant frequency again—it will be lower. To raise the frequency you can trim the fingers of the capacitance hat or you can just bend them a bit. It's that easy.

Sylvia and I have been using the dual-band dipole with good results. I've also completed that 10-meter ground-plane antenna. In comparisons, sometimes the ground plane works better, and sometimes the dipole comes out ahead. The radiation pattern, which is shown in **Fig 7-2**, graphically depicts the reason why. In any case, it's always good to have a choice between the two antennas.

A Dipole for 80 and 30 Meters

When Sylvia, K8SYL, asked me why her 75-meter dipole worked on 10 meters, it took little time for me to answer. That's because I'd already been thinking about that same topic. The dual-band 40 and 15-meter dipole that was described in Chapter 2 had triggered my thinking about other possible combinations of the same basic idea. In

particular, I had been thinking about the possibility of a dual-band 80 and 30-meter dipole.

In a conversation, I mentioned this to Dean Straw, N6BV, and he said that it should work. I thanked him and said that I'd have to model it the next week when I'd have some time. Later that same day, I received an *EZNEC* file via

e-mail from Dean. The file was the design for the antenna that we had talked about on the phone. You'll find Dean's design in **Fig 7-3**. The dimensions given are for the low end of the 80-meter band (centered around 3.525 MHz), and will cover the entire 30-meter band.

As far as I know, no one has built one of these. Nevertheless, it should work and it would be a handy thing for the CW operator. For those reasons and to illustrate what is possible, I've included this yet unproven design in this chapter.

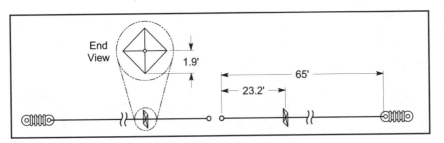

End View

1.9'

65'

23.2'

Fig 7-3—N6BV's design for an 80 and 30-meter dipole. This drawing is not to scale.

A Roll-Up Dipole

This next project is more than a variation on the theme. Robert H. Johns, W3JIP, wrote the following under the title, "Roll Your Own Dipole," for January 1999 *QST*. This is a nifty way to build a portable antenna.

Although superstitious hams may tell you that coiling wire at the ends of dipole or V antenna legs is somehow taboo, winding the excess wire on small spools is a convenient and effective way to make antennas that are physically and electrically adjustable.

To make a dipole antenna that can be easily lengthened or shortened, simply wind the unused wire at the ends of the elements onto spools. If you use insulated antenna wire, the coils act as high-impedance chokes that have little effect on the antenna. Uninsulated "end coils" are "blobs of conductor"—small capacitance hats at the ends of the wire elements.

Fig 7-4 shows a portable dipole with a center insulator and two spools of wire, each containing about 65 feet of insulated, stranded copper wire. By unwinding the proper lengths, a dipole for any band from 6 through 80 meters can be produced. And by configuring the system as an inverted V—with the ends close to the ground—it's easy to change bands. "End spooling" also makes it easy to adjust feed points and leg lengths for off-center-fed dipoles.

Construction

Insulated wire is preferred for portable antennas. In addition to increased electrical safety, the insulation minimizes the effects of wet bushes or trees that antenna wires must often pass through. The spools in the photo are from Home Depot, which sells #12 and #14 stranded copper wire in 50 and 100-foot lengths. Smaller spools are available from RadioShack. I prefer the larger spools because they're easier to wind. Three-quarter-inch wooden dowels make good handles and axles, and a short nut-and-bolt makes a crank handle on the outer edge of a spool. A loop of bungee cord wrapped around the spool, as shown in Fig 7-4, will prevent the wire from unwrapping.

It's convenient to mark the spooled wires so it's easy to determine exactly

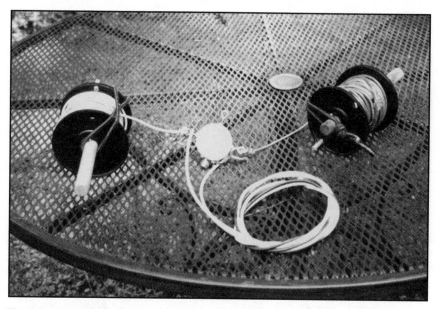

Fig 7-4—A portable dipole or inverted V antenna. The wire is unrolled from the spools as needed while the rest of the wire remains coiled at the ends. A short transmission-line matching section is connected to the center insulator.

how much wire has been unwound. I mark each foot with a permanent marker pen, place a black electrical tape "flag" every five feet and a bright yellow numbered flag every 10 feet.

Any reasonable center insulator will do. The one in the photo was made from a small PVC cap.

Inverted V center insulators use a rope or line to support the weight of the antenna elements and the feed line. I use $1/8$-inch nylon or polypropylene rope for the main support line (and for the guy lines at the ends of the antenna). I simply throw a line over a high tree branch or other available support to raise the center insulator skyward. Of course, scout the area carefully beforehand and make sure there aren't power lines nearby.

Be sure to attach the guy ropes several feet in from the ends of the antenna elements to allow for easy adjustments and length changes. **Fig 7-5** shows an easy knot to tie for just such an installation. **Fig 7-6** shows variations on what to do with the extra wire. You can stretch it out along the guy rope, fold it back and hang it from the antenna, or run it off to some bush or tree in another direction. The idea is

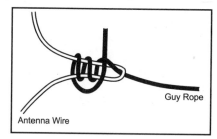

Fig 7-5—A knot to attach guy ropes to antenna wires.

to have it readily accessible from the ground.

Harmonics

For portable operations it'd be nice to have a lower-frequency antenna that can work effectively at higher frequencies. Thanks to the harmonic nature of antennas and amateur bands, these double-duty combos can work on 40 and 15 meters, or 75 and 10 meters, for example. This is possible because half-wave dipoles are resonant at odd multiples of their fundamental frequencies.

There are, however, two difficulties in using a 40-meter dipole on

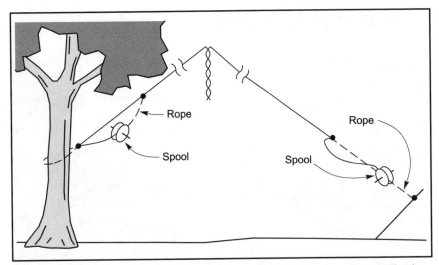

Fig 7-6—There are several ways to support the element ends. Two methods are shown here.

Table 7-1

Leg Lengths and Resonant Frequencies of Inverted V antennas with Element Ends Approximately Six Feet Above Ground. Numbers in Parentheses are SWRs at the Indicated Frequencies.

Leg Length	Frequency MHz (SWR)			
(feet)	Fundamental	3rd Harmonic	5th Harmonic	7th Harmonic
21	10.1 (1.2)	33.0 (1.3)		
23	9.3 (1.3)	28.7 (1.6)		
30	7.2 (1.2)	22.2 (1.7)		
31	7.0 (1.3)	21.5 (1.4)		
48	4.5 (1.1)	14.0 (1.2)	23.6 (1.0)	34.3 (1.2)
53	4.0 (1.0)	12.6 (1.2)	21.4 (1.0)	31.1 (1.2)
56	3.8 (1.1)	12.0 (1.4)	20.5 (1.2)	28.4 (1.1)
64	3.4 (1.1)	10.9 (1.3)	18.3 (1.2)	26.4 (1.2)

15 meters. The 15-meter resonant frequency will be slightly above the band, and the SWR there will be about 2 to 1. An inverted V with adjustable end coils takes care of the first problem. Simply lengthen the antenna a bit when going from 40 to 15 meters.

Fixing the high SWR is also possible. A short segment (about 6 feet) of transmission line can be added between the antenna and the 50-Ω coax feed line. Its impedance is somewhere between that of the coax and the higher impedance of the $^3/_2$-wavelength antenna on 15 meters. This transmission line is shown in Fig 7-4. It's a twisted pair of # 14 or # 12 stranded insulated copper wires with an SO-239 coax connector at the lower end. At the top, each wire is connected to one dipole leg at the center insulator.

I have used many different kinds of wire for these transformer sections, and the insulation type isn't critical. This simple addition reduces the SWR of HF dipoles and Vs while operating on odd harmonics.

Operation

Table 7-1 shows leg lengths for three inverted Vs with fundamental frequencies in or near the 30, 40, and 80-meter bands. The frequencies of the odd harmonics are also shown, as are the SWRs (in parentheses) measured by an MFJ Model 249 Antenna Analyzer. Table 7-1 is useful for determining leg length changes necessary when switching between fundamental and harmonic frequencies.

For example, if you've been operating in the 40-meter phone band (with your 40-meter V or dipole), you would add one foot to each leg to operate on 15 m. The lengths in the table are a starting point. Height and ground conditions at your location will influence your results.

Notice that an 80-meter inverted V provides access to five bands with only minor changes in leg length, plus the ability to move anywhere in the 75/80-meter band. The bandwidths of the harmonic bands are very broad.

So, instead of cutting and testing several dipoles for Field Day or your next radio outing, why not "roll your own" truly versatile antenna?

Five Band Dipole

This project by Bill Wright, GØFAH, was published in June 1995 *QST* under the title, "Five Bands, No Tuner." Wright's purpose was to allow you to enjoy some of the advantages of a multiband, ladder-line-fed antenna without an antenna tuner. Here's what he had to say.

Reading "The Doctor is IN" (*QST*, January 1995) reminded me that the search continues for a simple backyard antenna. A wire dipole antenna fed at the center with 450-Ω ladder line is a good choice. The ladder line keeps your losses low—even at moderately high SWRs. All you need is an antenna tuner and you're in business. No coils or traps necessary.

But can you do away with the tuner and still keep the ladder line? That would certainly make life simpler. To achieve this, your transceiver needs to see an impedance that looks reasonably close to 50 Ω on as many bands as possible. Without an antenna tuner acting as the middleman between the 450-Ω ladder line and your 50-Ω radio, this could be a problem.

Can It Be Done?

A few years ago I attempted to design an antenna that would work on several HF bands from 80 to 10 meters. Full details were published in the spring 1992 edition of *SPRAT*, the journal of the G-QRP club.

My inspiration was the venerable G5RV. I took a 94-foot-long dipole and fed it with ladder line (see **Fig 7-7**). By cutting the ladder line to a specific length and using a 1:1 balun to make the transition to coaxial cable, I found that I could get close to 50-Ω (and thus achieve reasonably low SWRs) on at least five bands: 40, 20, 17, 12 and 10 meters (see **Table 7-2**).

The on-air results were better than I expected. My radio was happy and I didn't need to meddle constantly with an antenna tuner.

Of course, you'll need an antenna tuner to work the bands where the SWR exceeds 3:1.

A simple tuner will do the job, though. Because you're using unbalanced coax ahead of the balun, you won't need one of the more expensive tuners designed for balanced feed lines.

For best results, put your antenna as high as possible. If the ends must bend downward to accommodate the size of your lot, don't worry. Run the ladder line to your balun and take your coax from there to your radio. Keep the coax portion as short as possible.

Conclusion

By eliminating the antenna tuner completely, you lose the flexibility of loading your ladder-line-fed antenna on virtually any band. In return, however, you gain the convenience of operating on several bands without making tuner adjustments each time you change frequency. Your losses in 50-Ω coaxial cable are held to a minimum, which means that most of the power your radio generates is radiated by your antenna. Not a bad compromise! Of course, the results I achieved will vary when used at other locations. Still, it's a simple, fun project in the experimental spirit of Amateur Radio.

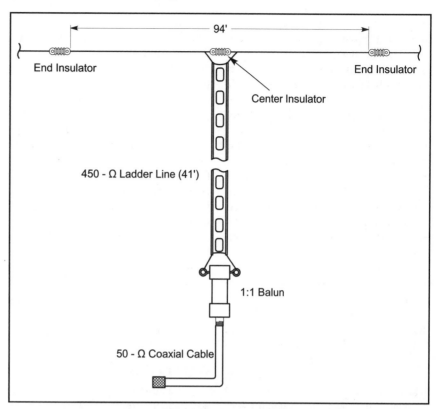

Fig 7-7—The wire dipole antenna is 94 feet in length. If you don't have 94 feet of open space, don't hesitate to droop the ends of the dipole to make it fit. Feed the antenna with 41 feet of 450-Ω ladder line that is connected to a 1:1 balun. From the balun to your radio, use 50-Ω coax.

Table 7-2

Calculated SWRs for a 94-foot Dipole Fed with 41 Feet of 450-Ω Ladder Line

Note: Although the antenna is cut for the CW portions of the band, expect similar results at other frequencies.

Frequency	SWR
3.56	7.6:1
7.1	2.4:1
14.2	1.5:1
18.1	2:1
24.9	1.5:1
29	2.4:1

A Four-Band, Off-Center-Fed Dipole

If you notice a similarity between this and the previous project that's probably because they were both brought to us by Bill Wright, GØFAH. This project was published in February 1996 *QST* under the title, "Four Bands, Off Center." Because of the inherent imbalance of off-center feed, you may experience difficulties with common-mode currents on your feed line. That means that your results may not match someone else's experience. Nevertheless, a great number of folks give glowing reports of their off-center fed antennas. Bill Wright makes a convincing case for experimenting with this type of antenna.

Have you ever wondered why you're required to attach your feed line to the center of a dipole antenna? The middle is a good place for a half-wavelength antenna because the feed impedance is low, typically it's close to 50 Ω when the antenna is cut to resonance at the operating frequency. This makes for a good match for 50-Ω coaxial cable, and a good match for your radio. But could you get a more versatile antenna by moving the feed point away from the middle?

Like many amateurs, I often ask other hams to describe the antennas they're using. Most of the time the answer is a wire antenna like the classic half-wavelength dipole. On occasion, however, some European amateurs tell me that they're operating with "FD3" antennas. Being more than a little unfamiliar with this design, I was eager to find out more.

After some research I learned that the FD3 is a single-wire antenna, with the feed point not in the middle, but one third the way from one end. It's coax fed with a 6:1 balun at the feed point. It actually resembles the Windom antenna with the single-wire feed that was popular in the early 1930s.

Studying the FD3 gave me an idea for the antenna shown in **Fig 7-8**. This off-center-fed dipole works on four bands: 40, 20, 15 and 10 meters. And, as a bonus, you don't need an antenna tuner! This antenna is similar to the 1950s Windom antenna that was fed with 300-Ω twinlead.

Construction

Imagine that you have 69 feet of #12 copper wire. If you were to cut this wire in two equal halves and feed it with 50-Ω coax, you'd probably find that it is resonant at the bottom end of the 40-meter band. (This depends, of course, on how high the antenna is above ground and so on.)

For your nonimaginary antenna, use 69 feet of bare copper wire, but don't cut it into equal halves. Instead, cut one length at 23 feet and the other at 46 feet. Rejoin the two sections with an insulator in between. This off-center feed point will have an impedance close to 300 Ω when you apply a 40-meter signal. This same feed point will also present a 300-Ω impedance on the 20 and 10-meter bands, at a typical height of 40 feet or more.

Connect ladder line, either the 300 or 450-Ω variety, at the feed point. At our one-third feed point, the impedance will be very high on the 15-meter band. But if you make the ladder line a quarter wavelength long at 15 meters, it will transform the high impedance at the feed point down to a low impedance near your radio. (See Fig 7-8.)

A quarter wavelength of 300-Ω ladder line is about 10 feet for 21 MHz. This is probably going to be a little short to reach your radio. You can make it longer on one condition: The overall length must be an odd multiple of the 21-MHz $1/4$ wavelength. For best SWR on all four bands, I recommend either 55 or 111 feet of 450-Ω line (or 50 or 110 feet of 300-Ω line). One of these lengths should get the ladder line to your radio with room to spare.

Now that we have a low impedance at the end of the feeder, we use a 4:1 or 1:1 balun to make the transition to 50-Ω coax. Use a 4:1 balun for 40, 20 and 10 meters, and a 1:1 balun for 15 meters. At my station I have 4:1 and 1:1 baluns that I can plug in as required when I change to and from the 15-meter band. You can purchase 1:1 and 4:1 baluns from a number of *QST* advertisers.

Conclusion

How well does the off-center dipole work? I enjoy the convenience of hopping from one band to another without having to fiddle with a tuner. I found that changing the balun when moving to the 15-meter band wasn't all that cumbersome. By choosing the correct line length, the balun was right next to my radio. Best of all, the SWR never exceeded 2:1 on any of the four bands.

Not only is the antenna easy to use, it rewards me with plenty of contacts. Off center, yes, but spot-on performance!

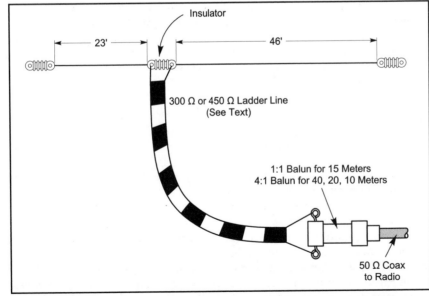

Fig 7-8—This off-center fed dipole offers four-band performance without an antenna tuner. Just cut the wires and the ladder line to the proper lengths. You'll need to swap baluns when you want to operate on 15 meters.

A Compact Rotary 20-Meter Dipole

David G. Byrd, KD7VA, described this portable 20-meter antenna that's easy to assemble and easy on your wallet in June 2001 *QST* under the title, "The Arkansas Catfish Dipole." See **Fig 7-9** and **7-10**. David turned his intelligence and creativity to the task of designing this antenna. The results are worth reading in his own words:

Two of my favorite pursuits are Amateur Radio and fried catfish. As a matter of fact, as I prepare this article, the odor of frying Arkansas Catfish envelops me from the nearby kitchen. That wonderful smell—and my favorite "fishing pole"—had a lot to do with the title of this article.

This past winter, I spent most of December and January in southern Arkansas helping to care for my wife's parents. Although we didn't have much warning before departure, I did pack my backup HF transceiver and 2-meter hand-held. I also took my MFJ-259B Antenna Analyzer so I could worry about the antennas after I had arrived and surveyed possible antenna sites.

Eight hours after we arrived, southern Arkansas was hit with the worst ice storm in more than 30 years. Because most of the tree limbs were broken and on the ground, all thoughts of hanging wire antennas from the remaining ice-burdened limbs went south (further south) for the winter. I decided to construct a 20-meter antenna that could be assembled indoors (during the bad weather) and erected later with minimal effort.

Necessity . . .

With no ham store in Magnolia, Arkansas, on-site hardware pickings were slim. The local RadioShack stocked a few CB antennas and 50-foot lengths of RG-58 coax, but nothing ham-specific. The store normally carried 20-foot telescoping steel masts, but even these were out of stock. I would have to gather any remaining components from Ace Hardware and Wal-Mart.

I purchased the #20 enamel wire and the two 14-foot cane poles at Wal-Mart. The cane poles were varnished and separated into three five-foot (or less) sections for transport. The remaining parts were purchased at Ace Hard-

Fig 7-9—The completed "Catfish Dipole" was tied to the chimney with nylon rope and was rotatable from ground level.

Fig 7-10—The center section of the dipole showing assembly details of the plastic pipe, compression T, mast, clamps and coaxial RF choke.

ware but should be available at most hardware stores. There are many mast choices with widely varying lengths and costs; but after the ice storm had wiped out hundreds of TV antennas the previous week, I had to get creative and use a telescoping pool cleaning pole.

Assembly

See **Fig 7-11**. Insert the four-foot piece of plastic pipe through both sides of the compression T (see the parts list in **Table 7-3**) and center it. Make 2-inch cuts in each end of the plastic pipe to allow it to clamp down on the poles. Put a 1-inch hose clamp loosely on each end of the pipe. Insert the butt end of each fishing pole approximately 6 inches into the plastic pipe and tighten the clamp. Assemble the remaining sections of the fishing pole. This will provide an assem-

bly with 15.5 feet on each side of center, or 31 feet total. Put a sheet metal screw into the plastic pipe about 1 inch on each side of the T support. The screws will be used to attach the wire elements to the feed line.

Each fishing pole has a loop at the tip to guide the fishing line. I used it as a tie point for the end of each side of the dipole. Feed the #20 wire through the loop and twist a couple of turns to secure it. Wind the wire in a slow spiral for the full length of the element. This spiral forms a distributed loading coil so don't overdo it. I used about one turn per foot over the length of the cane pole and added five closer-spaced turns around the plastic pipe on each side of center. Scrape the enamel from the wire and attach it under the sheet metal screw near the center T. Make the coax

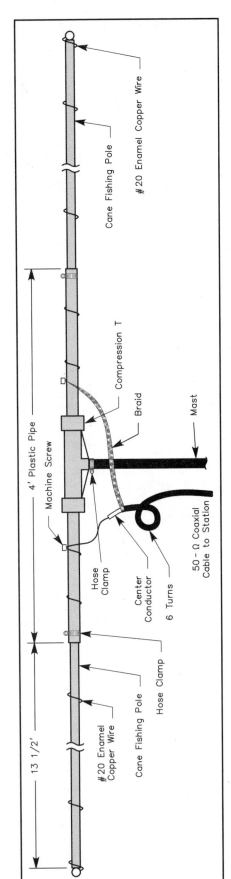

Table 7-3
Parts

Qty	Description	Cost
2	14-foot cane fishing poles	$ 9.90
2	25 feet of #20 enamel copper wire	$ 4.50
1	4 feel of 1-inch-OD schedule-40 plastic pipe	$ 2.00
1	Compression Ts (1×1×3/4-inch pipe thread)	$ 2.95
1	Galvanized pipe nipple (3/4×3-inch)	$ 0.69
3	1-inch screw-type hose clamp	$ 2.25
1	(optional mast) 16-foot pool-cleaning pole (telescoping)	$19.95
Total cost		$42.24

connections under the same two sheet metal screws and tighten. Do not over-tighten. I removed the close-spaced turns (ultimately all of them) one at a time until the resonant frequency was 14.2 MHz.

Wind six or seven turns of the feed line coax into an RF choke near the feed point. This will decouple the unbalanced feed line from the balanced dipole. Fig 7-10 shows a poorly wound coaxial RF choke. I later rewound it on a four-inch cardboard form and taped it up for improved appearance and performance. Tape the coil securely to the mast and weather proof the coax connections.

Performance

The expected input impedance at the center of a ½-wavelength wire dipole is 72 Ω and should result in an SWR of 1.5:1 when fed with 50-Ω coax. I used the MFJ-259B Antenna Analyzer to measure the resonant frequency and SWR. The measured SWR at 14.2 MHz was 1.4:1, and didn't exceed 1.5:1 anywhere in the 20-meter band.

In the day after completion, I made contacts with hams in Aruba, Slovenia

and Chile—and even acted as net control station for the "Microcomputer Network" with coast-to-coast US stations, all with S-7 or better reports, while using a 100-W transceiver.

Future Plans

This antenna certainly served its purpose as an inexpensive temporary antenna, and it would be ideal for Field Day-type activities. For future projects, consider the following:

- Make the antenna even more portable by soldering the element wires to the metal ferrule, that connect/separate the sections of the fishing pole. Taking the pole apart would also break down the wire elements.

- Wind multiband dipoles on the same pole (any frequency between 20 and 6 meters) and feed them from the same feed line.

- Build a half-size 40-meter dipole by adding loading coils on each side of the center plastic pipe.

- Add a suitably lightweight boom and another fishing pole assembly to make an inexpensive two-element Yagi.

- "Ruggedize" the design by switching to fiberglass fishing pole elements. You're moving into uncharted territory, but the thought is interesting, considering that inexpensive fiberglass poles are available at every Wal-Mart.

Fig 7-11—Construction diagram of the Catfish Dipole. Note that the #20-wire is loosely wound along each side of the antenna at about 1 turn per foot with somewhat tighter turns as you reach the center.

An Improved 80-40-17-10-Meter Trap Antenna

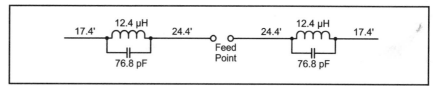

Fig 7-12—An improved 80, 40, 17 and 10-meter trap dipole.

A trap antenna is a compromise that offers the advantage of multiband operation. However, sometimes that advantage comes at a price. In July 1996 *QST*, Al Buxton, W8NX, described this antenna that features traps with lower loss, higher Q, increased power-handling capability and four-band coverage.

This improved multiband trap dipole introduces a new trap design and a change in trap location. The antenna features *double-coaxial-cable-wound traps* having lower reactance and a higher quality factor (Q) than earlier coax-cable traps. Because trap loss resistance is determined by trap reactance divided by Q, these enhancements provide a substantial reduction in such losses. Of as much significance, the new traps have a *fourfold increase in power-handling capability* over that of other coax cable traps (more on that later). Weatherproof performance and the ease of construction of coax-cable traps is retained.

This antenna is a rewarding and inexpensive project for those of you who like to homebrew your own equipment. The dipole (see **Fig 7-12**) operates on 80, 40, 17, and 10 meters; four of our more popular bands. The dipole is made of #14 stranded copper wire radiating elements, a 1:1 balun, a pair of insulators and a pair of the new traps. Notice the change in trap location. The traps are at the ends of 24.4-foot elements rather than 32-foot elements as in a conventional 80 and 40-meter trap dipole. Trap resonance on the four bands is nonexistent. Because there is no open-switch divorcement action by the traps, the full length of the antenna radiates on the four bands. Avoiding trap resonance lowers the possibility of trap-voltage breakdown. True resonant-current feed is obtained on the four bands, making the antenna compatible with either 50 or 75-Ω coaxial-cable feed lines. Fundamental-frequency operation is provided on 80 and 40 meters, and long-wire, odd-harmonic operation on 17 and 10 meters.

Trap Construction

Trap construction is relatively easy, even for those with few manual

Fig 7-13—Close-up of a completed trap.

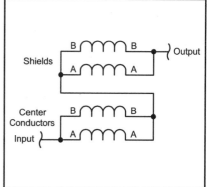

Fig 7-14—Double-coax trap schematic.

skills and tools. **Fig 7-13** is a photograph of a trap; **Fig 7-14** is the trap schematic. Double-coax-wound traps have two parallel windings of coax cable (A and B) rather than a single-cable winding. The two shield windings and center conductors are each connected in parallel. The series loss resistance of the trap—dominated by skin effect—is essentially halved by the parallel connection. The surface area for convection and heat conduction away from the trap is essentially doubled. Power losses in the polyethylene dielectric of the trap are almost negligible because of the relatively low frequencies involved.

The SWR performance of the antenna at my location, using a 50 to 75-Ω transformer and a 75-Ω feed line, is shown in **Fig 7-15**. The antenna is installed as an inverted V with a 40-foot apex height. Notice the very good performance on 40 meters, where the SWR is less than 2:1 across the entire band. The antenna favors the low end of 10 meters, where most of the activity seems to be concentrated. On 17 meters, the SWR is close to 3:1 across the band, requiring an antenna tuner to keep the rig happy. The 2:1 SWR bandwidth on

80 meters is 75 kHz, centered on 3.79 MHz. A good antenna tuner can extend the operating bandwidth on 80 meters well into the CW portion of the band or into the General class phone portion.

I measured the Q of these traps at two widely separated low frequencies and extrapolated the results to the higher operating frequencies. This two-frequency extrapolation method solves an otherwise impossible problem of directly measuring the Q of coaxial-cable traps. This approach separates the dielectric losses and the skin-effect ohmic losses of the trap; it assumes the skin-effect losses vary as the square root of frequency, and the dielectric losses vary as the first power of frequency. The results are shown in **Fig 7-16**, where the Q of an RG-59 double-coax trap is compared with the Q of a common RG-59 coax trap. The Q of a common RG-58 coax trap is also shown. The superiority of the double-coax configuration is clearly evident. The superiority of RG-59 over RG-58 is also demonstrated. All traps are tuned to a nominal 5.16 MHz and are of the optimum Q and length/diameter ratio. As you can see, the double-coax RG-59 configuration

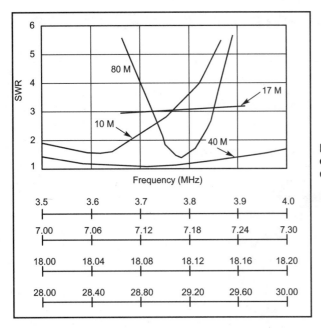

Fig 7-15—SWR plot of the improved trap dipole.

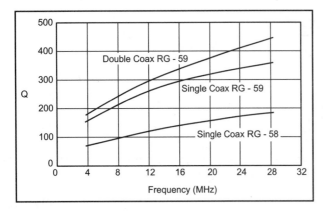

Fig 7-16—Trap quality factor, Q, versus frequency.

Table 7-4
Trap Loss Summary

Band (meters)	Freq MHz	Radiation Efficiency, %	Trap Loss, dB	Trap Dissipation, W
80	3.8	68.2	1.66	119.4
40	7.15	99.2	0.04	3.1
17	18.1	99.9	0.001	0.04
10	28.5	99.9	0.000	0.01

has a Q about 18% higher than the common singly wound coax configuration.

I calculated the trap losses for the bands covered using Roy (W7EL) Lewallen's *EZNEC* program. The results are shown in **Table 7-4**. The antenna was assumed to be horizontally mounted, 40 feet above real ground and using the legal power-output limit of 1500 W PEP. The stray capacitance of

the outer shields of the coax traps was simulated as a 1.5-foot length of #14 wire hanging down from the outboard end of the traps. The ratio of PEP to average power is assumed to be 2:1, corresponding to ideal two-tone single-sideband modulation. Notice the very high radiation efficiency and negligible trap dissipation on 40, 17 and 10 meters. On 80 meters, however, the antenna's

low height and its shortened length reduce the antenna-input resistance to 51.8 Ω, making trap loss significant. On 80 meters, the trap Q is 171. The combined loss from both traps equals a mere 1.66 dB on this band. The input-resistance component chargeable to trap loss becomes significant to the extent of dissipating 24.9% of the input power in the traps as heat. At this power level, there is an average dissipation of 119.4 W in each trap. The voltage drop across the traps is 2984 V, which is below the 3400-V rating of the cable.

My operating experience indicates that common coaxial-cable traps can dissipate 35 W or more without failure. Therefore, I believe that the double-coax traps can dissipate 140 W or more without failure, indicating that the 119.4-W dissipation per trap at the 1500-W PEP level can be handled successfully. Because I lack the necessary amplifier, I haven't confirmed such operation. So far, I've operated this antenna only at the 600-W PEP output level of my Yaesu FL-7000 amplifier. (During subsequent ARRL Lab tests, these traps successfully handled a two-tone 1500-W PEP signal for 10 minutes with no signs of stress. —*Ed.*) If any amateur has a theoretical basis for calculation of trap power-dissipation capability, please let me know about it.

Details of the trap construction and its connections to the antenna segments are shown in **Fig 7-17** and **Fig 7-18**. Before commencing construction, study the trap details in these figures as well as Figs 7-13 and 7-14. The trap resonant frequency is 5.16 MHz. Trap resonant-frequency tolerance is 50 kHz, permitting selection of a resonant frequency anywhere between 5.11 and 5.21 MHz. The band most sensitive to trap-frequency error is 80 meters, where a trap-frequency error of 50 kHz causes an antenna resonant-frequency error of 30 kHz of the same sign. Thus, if you have a General class ticket and want to be above 3.85 MHz on 80 meters, it's better to have the trap resonant frequency err on the high side rather than on the low side of 5.16 MHz. Indeed, General class ticket holders may want to shorten the trap windings by an eighth of a double-turn to set the 80-meter antenna frequency above 3.85 MHz. In that case, increase the trap frequency to

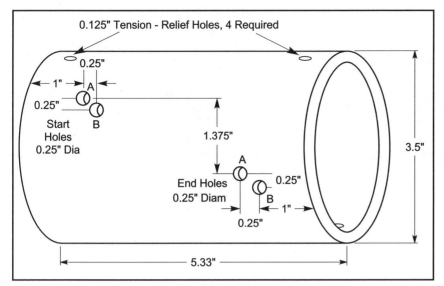

Fig 7-17—Hole positioning for the trap coil form.

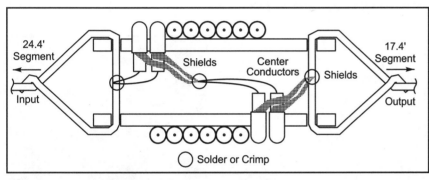

Fig 7-18—Cross-sectional view of a double-coax trap.

about 5.35 MHz. The trap frequencies should be checked with a dip meter and an accurate frequency reference before installing the traps in the antenna. Errors and changes in the trap's resonant frequency have much smaller effects on the 40, 17, and 10-meter bands than on the 80-meter band.

Making the Traps

Describing how to make the traps is more difficult than making them! See Figs 7-17 and 7-18. Each trap consists of 6.88 *double* turns of seven-foot lengths of RG-59 (Belden 8241) coaxial cable (A and B) wound on a PVC form. Make sure the coax you use has a polyethylene (not foam) dielectric. A foam dielectric allows the center conductor to migrate. Each form is a 5.33-inch length of 3.5-inch-OD schedule-40 PVC pipe (three-inch *ID* PVC pipe). Confirm the 3.5-inch OD of the PVC because trap frequency is sensitive to

form diameter. Drill two 0.25-inch-diameter holes at the windings' start and end. See Fig 7-17. The center of the starting hole for winding A is one inch from the end of the form. Stagger the two starting holes relative to each other, using the hole for winding A as the reference location. The B winding starting hole is delayed 0.25 inch longitudinally and 0.25 inch along the circumference relative to the B winding starting hole. The 6.88 fractional number of double-coax turns is ¹/₈ of a turn less than a full seven turns. Therefore, the ending-turn holes are drilled ¹/₈ of the circumference (1.375 inches) shy of seven full turns. The 0.25-inch staggered relationship at the start of the windings is repeated at the end of the windings. Thus, the end winding hole for winding A lags 1.375 inches along the circumference behind the start winding hole for winding A.

Chamfer the hole edges with a

sharp utility knife or rattail file to permit the cable to feed easily through the holes. The cable's 0.242-inch OD makes for a snug fit in the 0.25-inch-diameter holes.

The seven-foot cable lengths leave four inches at each winding end to make the trap pigtails that extend inside the PVC form. Wind the A and B turns simultaneously. Use locking pliers inside the PVC form to firmly hold the two pigtails at the start of the windings. Clamp the far end of the windings in a vise to maintain firm and equal tension on the two cables as you wind them around the form. Avoid gaps between turns. After placing the turns, insert the cable ends through the end holes. While maintaining tension on the cables, use your fingers and needle-nose pliers to push and pull the cables into the inside of the form.

Using a sharp utility knife, strip away the last three inches of polyvinyl cover from the pigtails. Avoid cutting the shield braid. Separate the pigtail's shield braid from the dielectric and its inner conductor. Balloon the shield braid to an increased diameter by pushing it toward the end of the polyvinyl cover. Use a sharp pick to spread the braid and form a large hole close to the polyvinyl cover through which you can pull the cable's dielectric and center conductor. Again, be careful to avoid damaging the braid. The three-inch pigtail has now become two smaller pigtails—a shield pigtail and a center-conductor pigtail—each somewhat less than three inches long. Remove about two inches of the dielectric to expose the inner conductor. Convert all four ends of the cable windings into similar pigtail pairs.

The center conductors at the start of the winding connect together; forming the trap *input* terminals for attachment to the 24.4-foot antenna wire. You may prefer to use crimp connectors rather than solder connections. Access to the inside of the traps—where the connections must be made—is somewhat awkward. The center conductors at the far end are fed back through the interior of the form, where they are connected to the shield braid at the start of the windings. The far-end shield braids connect together to form the *output* terminal of the trap for attachment to the 17.4-foot antenna segment. It's important to avoid reversing the input and output terminals of the traps! Reversal detunes the antenna a small amount by misplacing about 4 pF of stray capacitance of the trap shield braid. Build the second trap identical to the first.

Summary

Use a high-quality 1:1 balun for the antenna's center support and feed terminals. The 24.4-foot antenna segments attach to the balun's output terminals. Attach the trap-input pigtails to the far end of the 24.4-foot segments. Check the 24.4-foot segment lengths, measuring from the balun eyelets to the trap strain-relief terminals. The trap-output terminals connect to the near end of the 17.4-foot antenna segments. Check the 17.4-foot-segment lengths. Terminate the far ends of these segments in good-quality end insulators capable of withstanding the high RF voltage present at the antenna end points. The tension on the antenna may be loose, allowing considerable antenna sag. Install the antenna as high as possible—at least 35 feet above the ground at the center—and with the ends at least 15 feet high. Feed the antenna with either 50 or 75-Ω coaxial cable, the higher value being preferred to lower the feed-line SWR on 17 and 10 meters.

That done, go and have some fun!

Two 80-40-20-15-10 or 80-40-17-12-Meter Trap Dipoles

Al Buxton, W8NX, gave us the details of another coax trap design that he used in two multiband antennas; one covering 80, 40, 20, 15 and 10 meters, and the other covering 80, 40, 17 and 12 meters. He described this in the article that he wrote for August 1994 *QST*. See **Fig 7-19** and **Fig 7-20**.

Over the last 60 or 70 years, amateurs have used many kinds of multiband antennas to cover the traditional HF bands. The availability of the 30, 17 and 12-meter bands has expanded our need for multiband antenna coverage. A fortunate few have the space and resources for multiband antennas like rhombics or long Vs, but many hams have employed inverted-L long wires or parallel dipoles. Old-timers will recall the off-center-fed Windom of the '30s—the first version using a single-wire transmission line, and the later design using two-wire feed line. Over the years, random-length dipoles with open-wire feeders and associated tuners have been used successfully as multiband antennas. The G5RV multiband antenna is a specialized example of this approach.

The log periodic array represents a kind of brute-force approach to the goal of achieving coverage of multiple HF ham bands. It seems inefficient because of the large gaps between our relatively narrow amateur HF bands.

Over the last few decades, two factors have affected the development of multiband antennas—the popularity

Fig 7-19—Photos of W8NX trap.

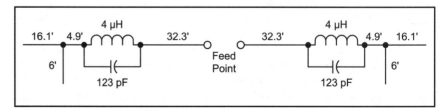

Fig 7-20—A W8NX multiband dipole for 80, 40, 20, 15 and 10 meters. The values shown (123 pF and 4 µH) for the coaxial-cable traps are for parallel resonance at 7.15 MHz. The low-impedance output of each trap is used for this antenna.

of low-impedance (usually 50-Ω) coaxial feed lines, and the appearance of untuned, 50-Ω solid-state amplifiers. The impedance of an antenna is relatively low only at its fundamental frequency and at odd-order harmonics. Although antenna tuners are often necessary to resonate an antenna system, the quest for expanded multiband coverage with simple antennas continues. This article discusses in detail an innovative trap design employed in two multiband dipoles.

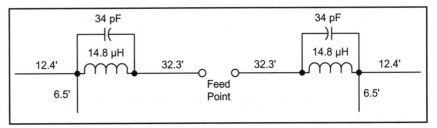

Fig 7-21—A W8NX multiband dipole for 80, 40, 17 and 12 meters. For this antenna, the high-impedance output is used on each trap. The resonant frequency of the traps is 7.15MHz.

One W8NX Trap Design—Two Multiband Dipoles

Two diffferent antennas are described here. The first covers 80, 40, 20, 15 and 10 meters, and the second covers 80, 40, 17 and 12 meters. Each uses the same type of W8NX trap—connected for different modes of operation—and a pair of short capacitive stubs to enhance coverage. The new W8NX coaxial-cable traps have two different modes: a high and a low-impedance mode. The inner-conductor windings and shield windings of the traps are connected in series in the conventional manner for both modes. However, either the low or high-impedance point can be used as the trap's output terminal. For low-impedance trap operation, only the center conductor turns of the trap windings are used. For high-impedance operation, all turns are used, in the conventional manner for a trap. The short stubs on each antenna are strategically sized and located to permit more flexibility in adjusting the resonant frequencies of the antenna.

Fig 7-20 shows the configuration of the 80, 40, 20, 15 and 10-meter antenna. The radiating elements are made of #14 stranded copper wire. The element lengths are the wire span lengths in feet. These lengths do not include the lengths of the pigtails at the balun, traps and insulators. The 32.3-foot-long inner 40-meter segments are measured from the eyelet of the input balun to the tension relief hole in the trap coil form. The 4.9-foot segment length is measured from the tension relief hole in the trap to the 6-foot stub. The 16.1-foot outer-segment span is measured from the stub to the eyelet of the end insulator.

The coaxial-cable traps are wound on PVC pipe coil forms and use the low-impedance output connection. The stubs are 6-foot lengths of $1/8$-inch stiffened aluminum or copper rod hanging perpendicular to the radiating elements. The first inch of their length is bent 90° to permit attachment to the radiating elements by large-diameter copper crimp connectors. Ordinary #14 wire may be used for the stubs, but it has a tendency to curl up and may tangle unless weighed down at the end. I recommend that you feed the antenna with 75-Ω coax cable using a good 1:1 balun.

This antenna may be thought of as a modified W3DZZ antenna (shown for many years in various ARRL publications) with the addition of capacitive stubs. The length and location of the stubs gives the antenna designer two extra degrees of freedom to place the resonant frequencies within the amateur bands. This additional flexibility is particularly helpful to bring the 15 and 10-meter resonant frequencies to more desirable locations in these bands. The actual 10-meter resonant frequency of the W3DZZ antenna is somewhat above 30 MHz, pretty remote from the more desirable low frequency end of 10 meters.

Fig 7-21 shows the configuration of the 80, 40, 17 and 12-meter antenna. Notice that the capacitive stubs are attached immediately outboard after the traps and are 6.5 feet long, which is 0.5 foot longer than those used in the other antenna. The traps are the same as those of the other antenna, but are connected for the high-impedance output mode.

Since only four bands are covered by this antenna, it is easier to fine tune it to precisely the desired frequency on all bands. The 12.4-foot tips can be pruned to a particular 17-meter

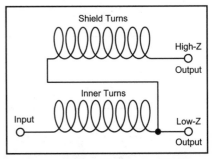

Fig 7-22—Schematic for the W8NX coaxial cable trap. RG-59 is wound on a $2^3/8$-inch OD PVC pipe.

frequency with little effect on the 12-meter frequency. The stub lengths can be pruned to a particular 12-meter frequency with little effect on the 17-meter frequency. Both such pruning adjustments slightly alter the 80-meter resonant frequency. However, the bandwidths of the antennas are so broad on 17 and 12 meters that little need for such pruning exists. The 40-meter frequency is nearly independent of adjustments to the capacitive stubs and outer radiating tip elements. Like the first antennas, this dipole is fed with a 75-Ω balun and feed line.

Fig 7-22 shows the schematic diagram of the traps. It explains the difference between the low and high-impedance modes of the traps. Notice that the high-impedance terminal is the output configuration used in most conventional trap applications. The low-impedance connection is made across only the inner conductor turns, corresponding to one-half of the total turns of the trap. This mode steps the trap's impedance down to approximately one-fourth of that of the high-impedance level. This is what allows a single trap

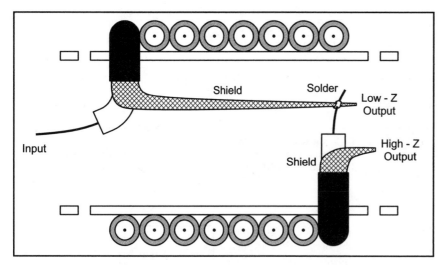

Fig 7-23—Construction details of the WBNX coaxial cable trap.

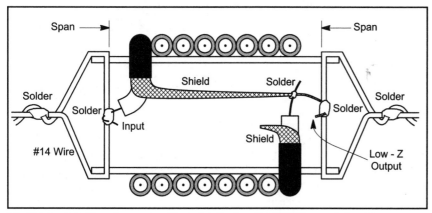

Fig 7-24—Additional construction details for the W8NX coaxial-cable trap.

design to be used for two different multiband antennas.

Fig 7-23 is a drawing of a cross-section of the coax trap shown through the long axis of the trap. Notice that the traps are conventional coaxial-cable traps, except for the added low-impedance output terminal. The traps are 8³/₄ close-spaced turns of RG-59 (Belden 8241) on a 2³/₈-inch-OD PVC pipe (schedule 40 pipe with a 2-inch ID) coil form. The forms are 4¹/₈ inches long.

Trap resonant frequency is very sensitive to the outer diameter of the coil form, so check it carefully. Unfortunately, not all PVC pipe is made with the same wall thickness. The trap frequencies should be checked with a dip meter and general coverage receiver

and adjusted to within 50 kHz of the 7150 kHz resonant frequency before installation. One inch is left over at each end of the coil forms to allow for the coax feed-through holes and holes for tension-relief attachment of the antenna radiating elements to the traps. Be sure to seal the ends of the trap coax cable with RTV sealant to prevent moisture from entering the coaxial cable.

Also, be sure that you connect the 32.3-foot wire element at the start of the inner conductor winding of the trap. This avoids detuning the antenna by the stray capacitance of the coaxial-cable shield. The trap output terminal (which has the shield stray capacitance) should be at the outboard side of the trap. Reversing the input and output terminals of the trap will lower the 40-meter

frequency by approximately 50 kHz, but there will be negligible effect on the other bands.

The title-photos in Fig 7-19 show a coaxial-cable trap. Details of the trap installation are shown in **Fig 7-24**. This drawing applies specifically to the 80, 40, 20, 15 and 10-meter antenna, which uses the low-impedance trap connections. Notice the lengths of the trap pigtails: 3 to 4 inches at each terminal of the trap. If you use a different arrangement, you must modify the span lengths accordingly. All connections can be made using crimp connectors rather than by soldering. I find that access to the trap's interior is attained more easily with a crimping tool than with a soldering iron.

Antenna Patterns

The performance of both antennas has been very satisfactory. I am currently using the 80, 40, 17 and 12-meter version because it covers 17 and 12 meters. (I have a tribander for 20, 15 and 10 meters.) The radiation pattern on 17 meters is that of ³/₂-wave dipole. On 12 meters, the pattern is that of a ⁵/₂-wave dipole. At my location in Akron, Ohio, the antenna runs essentially east and west. It is installed as an inverted V, 40 feet high at the center, with a 120° included angle between the legs. Since the stubs are very short, they radiate little power and make only minor contributions to the radiation patterns. The pattern has four major lobes on 17 meters, with maxima to the northeast, southeast, southwest, and northwest. These provide low-angle radiation into Europe, Africa, South Pacific, Japan and Alaska. A narrow pair of minor broadside lobes provides north and south coverage into Central America, South America and the Polar Regions.

There are four major lobes on 12 meters, giving nearly end-fire radiation and good low-angle east and west coverage. There are also three pairs of very narrow, nearly broadside, minor lobes on 12 meters, down about 6 dB from the major end-fire lobes. On 80 and 40 meters, the antenna has the usual figure-8 pattern of a half-wavelength dipole. I have some pattern distortion and input impedance effects from aluminum siding on my house. Nevertheless, DX is easily workable on either of these antennas using a 100-W transceiver, when the high-frequency bands are open.

Both antennas function as electrical half-wave dipoles on 80 and 40 meters with a low SWR. They both function as odd harmonic current-fed dipoles on their other operating frequencies, with higher, but still acceptable, SWR. The presence of the stubs can either raise or lower the input impedance of the antenna from those of the usual third and fifth harmonic dipoles. Again, I recommend that 75-Ω rather than 50-Ω feed line be used because of the generally higher input impedances at the harmonic operating frequencies of the antennas.

The SWR curves of both antennas were carefully measured. A 75 to 50-Ω transformer from Palomar Engineers was inserted at the junction of the 75-Ω coax feed line and my 50-Ω SWR bridge. The transformer prevents an impedance discontinuity, with attendant additional undesired line reflections appearing at the 75 to 50-Ω junction. The transformer is required for accurate SWR measurement if a 50-Ω SWR bridge is used with a 75-Ω line. No harm is done to any equipment, however, if the transformer is omitted. Most 50-Ω rigs operate satisfactorily with a 75-Ω line, although this requires different tuning and load settings in the final output stage of the rig or antenna tuner. I use the 75 to 50-Ω transformer only when making SWR measurements and at low power levels. The transformer is rated for 100 W, and when I run my 1-kW PEP linear amplifier the transformer is taken out of the line. (I hope my absent-mindedness doesn't catch up with me some day!)

Fig 7-25 gives the SWR curves of the 80, 40, 20, 15 and 10-meter antenna. Minimum SWR is nearly 1:1 on 80 meters, 1.5:1 on 40 meters, 1.6:1 on 20 meters, and 1.5:1 on 10 meters. The minimum SWR is slightly below 3:1 on 15 meters. On 15 meters, the stub capacitive reactance combines with the inductive reactance of the outer segment of the antenna to produce a resonant rise that raises the antenna input resistance to about 220 Ω, higher than that of the usual $^3/_2$-wavelength dipole. An antenna tuner may be required on this band to keep a solid-state final output stage

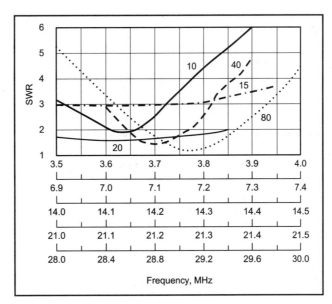

Fig 7-25—Measured SWR curves for an 80, 40, 20, 15 and 10-meter antenna, installed as an inverted-V with 40-ft apex and 120° included angle between legs.

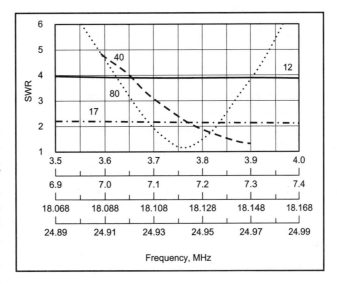

Fig 7-26—Measured SWR curves for an 80, 40, 17 and 12-meter antenna, installed as an inverted-V with 40-ft apex and 120° included angle between legs.

happy under these load conditions.

Fig 7-26 shows the SWR curves of the 80, 40, 17 and 12-meter antenna. Notice the excellent 80-meter performance with a nearly unity minimum SWR in the middle of the band. The performance approaches that of a full-size 80-meter wire dipole. The short stubs and the very low inductance traps shorten the antenna somewhat on 80 meters. Also, observe the good 17-meter performance, with the SWR being only a little above 2:1 across the band.

But notice the 12-meter SWR curve of this antenna, which shows 4:1 SWR across the band. The antenna input resistance approaches 300 Ω on this band because the capacitive reactance of the stubs combines with the inductive

reactance of the outer antenna segments to give resonant rises in impedance. These are reflected back to the input terminals. These stub-induced resonant impedance rises are similar to those of the other antenna on 15 meters, but are even more pronounced.

Too much concern must not be given to SWR on the feed line. Even if the SWR is as high as 9:1, no destructively high voltages will exist on the transmission line. Recall that transmission-line voltages increase as the square root of the SWR in the line. Thus, 1 kW of RF power in 75-Ω line corresponds to 274 V line voltage for a 1:1 SWR. Raising the SWR to 9:1 merely triples the maximum voltage that the line must withstand to 822 V. This voltage is well

Table 7-5
Trap Q

Frequency (MHz)	3.8	7.15	14.18	18.1	21.3	24.9	28.6
High Z out (W)	101	124	139	165	73	179	186
Low Z out (W)	83	103	125	137	44	149	155

Table 7-6A
Trap Loss Analysis: 80, 40, 20, 15, 10-Meter Antenna

Frequency (MHz)	3.8	7.15	14.18	21.3	28.6
Radiation Efficiency (%)	96.4	70.8	99.4	99.9	100.0
Trap losses (dB)	−0.16	−1.5	−0.02	−0.01	−0.003

Table 7-6B
Trap Loss Analysis: 80, 40, 17, 12-Meter Antenna

Frequency (MHz)	3.8	7.15	18.1	24.9
Radiation Efficiency (%)	89.5	90.5	99.3	99.8
Trap losses (dB)	−0.5	−0.4	−0.03	−0.006

below the 3700-V rating of RG-11, or the 1700-V rating of RG-59, the two most popular 75-Ω coax lines. Voltage breakdown in the traps is also very unlikely. As will be pointed out later, the operating power levels of these antennas are limited by RF power dissipation in the traps, not trap voltage breakdown or feed-line SWR.

Trap Losses and Power Rating

Table 7-5 presents the results of trap Q measurements and extrapolation by a two-frequency method to higher frequencies above resonance. I employed an old, but recently calibrated, Boonton Q meter for the measurements. Extrapolation to higher frequency bands assumes that trap resistance losses rise with skin effect according to the square root of frequency, and that trap dielectric losses rise directly with frequency. Systematic measurement errors are not increased by frequency extrapolation. However, random measurement errors increase in magnitude with upward frequency extrapolation. Results are believed to be

accurate within 4% on 80 and 40 meters, but only within 10 to 15% at 10 meters. Trap Q is shown at both the high and low-impedance trap terminals. The Q at the low-impedance output terminals is 15 to 20% lower than the Q at the high-impedance output terminals.

I computer-analyzed trap losses for both antennas in free space. Antenna-input resistances at resonance were first calculated, assuming lossless, infinite-Q traps. They were again calculated using the Q values shown in Table 7-5. The radiation efficiencies were also converted into equivalent trap losses in decibels. **Table 7-6A** summarizes the trap loss analysis for the 80, 40, 20, 15 and 10-meter antenna and **Table 7-6B** for the 80, 40, 17 and 12-meter antenna.

The loss analysis shows radiation efficiencies of 90% or more for both antennas on all bands except for the 80, 40, 20, 15 and 10-meter antenna when used on 40 meters. Here, the radiation efficiency falls to 70.8%. A 1-kW power level at 90% radiation efficiency corresponds to 50-W dissipation per trap. In my experience, this is the trap's survival

limit for extended key-down operation. SSB power levels of 1 kW PEP would dissipate 25 W or less in each trap. This is well within the dissipation capability of the traps.

When the 80, 40, 20, 15 and 10-meter antenna is operated on 40 meters, the radiation efficiency of 70.8% corresponds to a dissipation of 146 W in each trap when 1 kW is delivered to the antenna. This is sure to burn out the traps—even if sustained for only a short time. Thus, the power should be limited to less than 300 W when this antenna is operated on 40 meters under prolonged key-down conditions. A 50% CW duty cycle would correspond to a 600-W power limit for normal 40-meter CW operation. Likewise, a 50% duty cycle for 40-meter SSB corresponds to a 600-W PEP power limit for the antenna.

I know of no analysis where the burnout wattage rating of traps has been rigorously determined. Operating experience seems to be the best way to determine trap burnout ratings. In my own experience with these antennas, I've had no traps burn out, even though I operated the 80, 40, 20, 15 and 10-meter antenna on the critical 40-meter band using my AL-80A linear amplifier at the 600-W PEP output level. I have, however, made no continuous, key-down CW operating tests at full power purposely trying to destroy the traps!

Summary

Some hams may suggest using a different type of coaxial cable for the traps. The dc resistance of 40.7 Ω per 1000 feet of RG-59 coax seems rather high. However, I've found no coax other than RG-59 that has the necessary inductance-to-capacitance ratio to create the trap characteristic reactance required for the 80, 40, 20, 15 and 10-meter antenna. Conventional traps with wide-spaced, open-air inductors and appropriate fixed-value capacitors could be substituted for the coax traps, but the convenience, weatherproof configuration and ease of fabrication of coaxial-cable traps is hard to beat.

8 Dual-Band VHF/UHF Antennas

In this chapter you'll find a couple of projects that will give you 2-meter and 70-centimeter coverage. They do that with a single feed line—a useful feature for today's multiband radios.

Dual-Band Mobile Whip for 146/446 MHz

This nifty project by Wayde Bartholomew, WA3WMG, is taken from the pages of *The ARRL Antenna Compendium, Vol 5*. His mobile antenna won't take long to build, works well and only requires one feed line for the two-band coverage. Here's what Wayde said.

I needed a dual-band antenna for my brand-new dual-band handheld. However, I was not really impressed with the cost-to-benefit ratio for several commercial antennas I tried, so I decided to make one myself.

On HF I have enjoyed success using a single radiator with a decoupling stub. On-the-air results were good for DX, indicating to me that I was achieving low angles of radiation. This inspired me to try this design on VHF/UHF.

I used a commercial NMO-style base and magnetic mount. For the radiator and decoupling stub, I used brazing rod, which was coated with a rust inhibitor after all the tuning was done. I started out with a 2-meter radiator that was 20.5 inches long. This is an inch longer than normal so that it could be pruned for best SWR.

I then tacked on the 70-cm decoupling stub, which was 6.5 inches long. I trimmed the length of the 2-meter

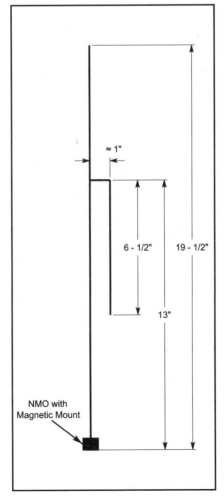

NMO with Magnetic Mount

≈ 1"

6 - 1/2"   19 - 1/2"

13"

radiator for best SWR at 146 MHz and then tuned the 70-cm stub on 446 MHz, moving it up and down for best SWR. There was no interaction between the adjustments for either frequency.

See **Fig 8-1** for the final dimensions I used. The SWR in the repeater portions of both bands was less than 2:1.

I'd like to thank my father Wayne, WA3WLD, who ran all around the local area with this antenna on his minivan to check the performance.

Adapting WA3WMG's Mobile Antenna for Fixed-Station Use

Ever since I saw Wayde Bartholomew's mobile antenna in print, I've thought about mounting two of them base-to-base to form a dual-band dipole. It should work well. Just follow Wayde's tuning instructions.

Mount this vertical, and you'll need a common-mode choke on the dipole. Current flowing on the outside of the coaxial feed line could ruin the vertical radiation pattern and thus destroy the effectiveness of the antenna.

Fig 8-1—Diagram of WA3WMG's dual-band 146/446-MHz mobile whip. Brazing rod was employed for the 2-meter radiator and for the 70-centimeter decoupling stub.

A 146 and 445-MHz Antenna

I remember when the October 2000 *QST* arrived at my house. There were a number of good things in that issue—one of my favorites is this project by Andrew S. Griffith, W4ULD. Here's what he said.

Getting on 146 and 445-MHz with a single J-pole antenna can be done inexpensively. I did it by building the dual-band J pole shown in **Fig 8-2** and **Fig 8-3**. The total materials cost about $21, and only commonly available hand tools are required for assembly. Interested?

Some Background

A vertical J-pole or dipole designed for use at 146 MHz will reso-

Fig 8-2—Photo of W4ULD's completed dual-band antenna.

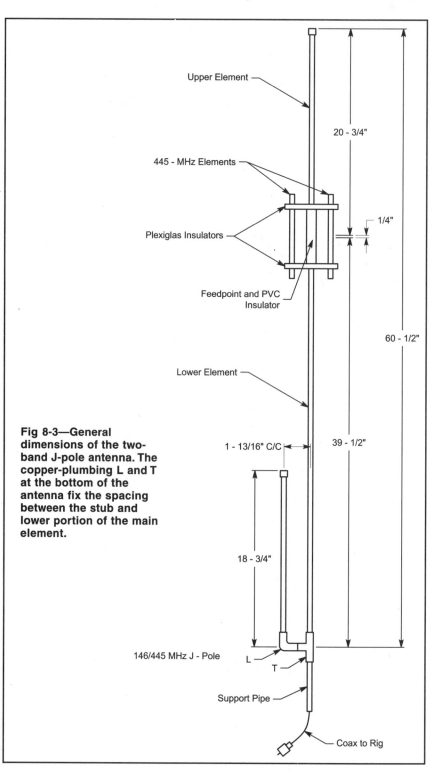

Fig 8-3—General dimensions of the two-band J-pole antenna. The copper-plumbing L and T at the bottom of the antenna fix the spacing between the stub and lower portion of the main element.

nate at 440 MHz because it's about $^3/2\ \lambda$ long at that frequency. However, according to *EZNEC*, most of the 445-MHz radiation is at an elevation angle of about 45° instead of a lower angle desired for repeater and ground-wave communication. Also, the antenna's input impedance at 445 MHz is about two and a half times that of the 146-MHz value. For dual-band operation, both of these hurdles can be overcome by simply placing two 445-MHz elements close to the feed point of the 146-MHz $^1/2$-λ element. The vertical radiation pattern of the resulting antenna at 445 MHz is shown in **Fig 8-4**. The 445-MHz elements have little effect on 2-meter operation. Once the antenna is adjusted for 2-meter operation, the 445-MHz antenna input impedance can be adjusted to equal the 2-meter impedance by adjusting the spacing of the 445-MHz elements from the main element. Increasing the spacing between the elements increases the impedance at 445 MHz and vice versa. The length of the 445-MHz elements primarily affects the resonant frequency and to some extent, also affects the input impedance. The

length of each 445-MHz element is less than $^1/2\ \lambda$ at 445 MHz. At a true $^1/2\ \lambda$, the impedance and resonant frequency appear to be insensitive to spacing and length adjustments.

At 146 MHz, this antenna's input impedance is about 65 Ω, delivering an SWR of about 1.3:1 at resonance. Placing a $^1/4$-λ Q section in the feed line at the feed point can lower the SWR between 144 and 148 MHz. The Q-section impedance is about 59 Ω. Because the Q-section length is about $^3/4\ \lambda$ at 445 MHz, it also works at this frequency.

How It Works

The antenna's main vertical element (see Fig 8-3 and the title page photo) is about $^1/2\ \lambda$ long at 146 MHz and employs a $^1/4$-λ stub at the bottom to decouple the main element from the mast and feed line. The antenna is similar to a standard J-pole antenna except that it's fed at the center of the main element instead of tapping the feed line partway up the stub. The coaxial cable feed line passes through the main element. Two elements, almost $^1/2\ \lambda$ long at 445 MHz, are placed near the

antenna's feed point and parallel to the main element. These elements are parasitic and don't need a separate feed line; they are excited by the main vertical element. The antenna is quite efficient because no lossy matching networks or coils are used. The gain on both bands is about the same as a vertical dipole or single-band J pole.

As described later, the Q-section is made by replacing 13$^5/8$ inches of the coaxial-cable feed line shield braid with 13$^5/8$ inches of $^3/8$-inch copper tubing.

Construction

The antenna elements are made of $^1/2$-inch copper water pipe and soldered fittings. The center insulator (see **Fig 8-5**) is made from $^1/2$-inch PVC pipe and the standoff insulators (see **Fig 8-6**) for the 445-MHz elements are made of $^1/4$-inch-thick Plexiglas. You can purchase the $^1/2$-inch copper pipe, copper fittings and $^1/2$-inch PVC pipe from a building supply outlet. (If you're going to build two antennas, you can purchase the copper pipe much cheaper in 20-foot lengths at a plumbing supply.) The Teflon-silver PL-259 connector

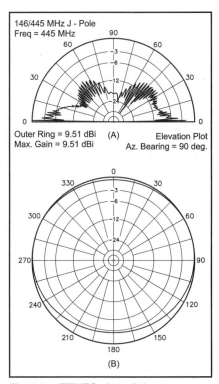

Fig 8-4—*EZNEC* plot of the antenna's vertical (A) and azimuthal (B) radiation patterns at 445 MHz.

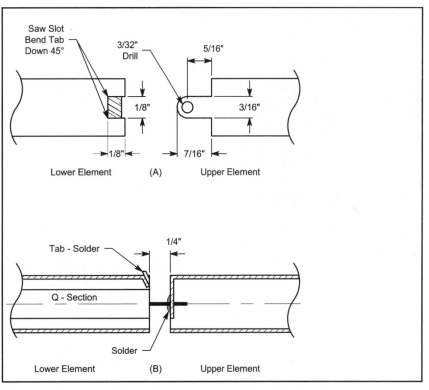

Fig 8-5—Feed-point detail. The tab on the upper portion of the main element accepts the center conductor of the coax of the Q section. See Fig 8-11.

and RG-8 coax are available from RadioShack. (You can find good buys on such connectors at hamfests.) Short lengths of ³/₈-inch-diameter tubing can be purchased at a hardware store. Small pieces of ¹/₄-inch-thick Plexiglas can be found as scrap at a glass shop usually. Broken golfcart windshields are another source of Plexiglas.

In any 445-MHz antenna construction project, it's important to adhere to the given dimensions. A dimension deviation of even ¹/₁₆ inch is considerable at 445 MHz, especially at the feed point. It's practically impossible to construct a feed point connection at 445 MHz without introducing some transformation of the antenna impedance. Therefore, you should closely follow the dimensions and feed point detail described. I built a second antenna using the plans provided here and it performs exactly like the prototype. I used type M pipe (it's lighter than type L), because I intended to suspend the antenna from a support.

If you intend to mount the antenna on a mast, you may want to use type L copper pipe for the elements. If you do use type L, the dimensions will need to be changed. This is covered in the appendix to this article.

Before soldering, polish all mating pipe pieces with #0000 steel wool. I recommend using a propane torch for soldering the joints. The trick in soldering copper pipe and fittings is to get the copper hot enough to melt the solder before applying solder. The solder then flows into the joint without leaving drips that require cleanup.

First, cut two pieces of copper pipe to make the stub and the 39¹/₂ inch lower element. Cut these pieces to their final lengths after soldering each piece to the respective L and T at what will be the bottom ends of the stub and lower element. Measure the length of these pieces from the center of the T and L connection. Cut the stub pipe to a length of 18¹¹/₁₆ inches allowing about ¹/₁₆ inch for placement of a cap at the top of the stub. Use a 1-inch length of pipe to join the T and L. The T and L butt together to fix the 1¹³/₁₆ inch center-to-center spacing between the stub and lower element. The mounting/support section below the lower element can be any length, but should be at least 12 inches

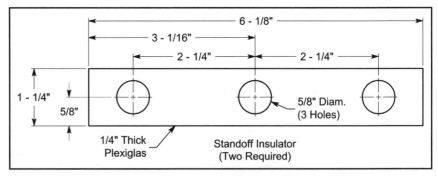

Fig 8-6—Two standoff insulators made of ¼-inch-thick Plexiglas sheet or ½-inch PVC pipe are required to hold the 445-MHz elements adjacent to the main element.

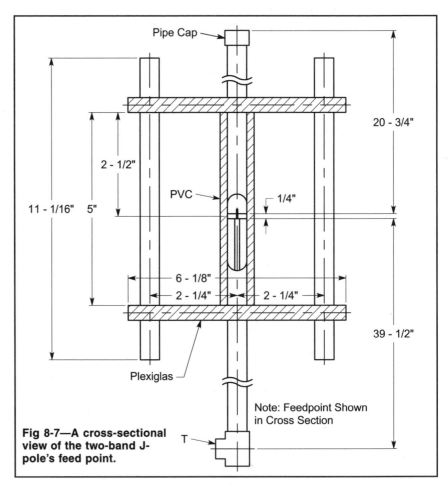

Fig 8-7—A cross-sectional view of the two-band J-pole's feed point.

to allow clamping to a mast.

Make two hacksaw slots in the top of the lower element as shown at the left in Fig 8-5A. Bend the tab between the slots about 45° toward the center of the pipe.

Before cutting the upper element to length, some work must be done. At what will be the bottom of the upper element, cut a tab as shown at the right in Fig 8-5A. Drill a ³/₃₂-inch-diameter

hole through the end of the tab. (It is at this tab where the center conductor of the feed-line coax will later be attached.) Dress the tab with a file and tin the tab using a propane torch or high-power soldering iron. Bend the tab 90° toward the pipe center as in Fig 8-5B. Once the tab is bent, cut the upper element to a length of 20³/₄ inches allowing about ¹/₁₆ inch for placement of a cap on the upper-element top.

You can fabricate the standoff insulators shown in Fig 8-6 from $^1/_4$-inch-thick Plexiglas or $^1/_2$-inch PVC pipe. Plexiglas is easier to use because the $^5/_8$-inch-diameter holes can be made using a hand-held drill and a common wood spade bit. Drill at a low speed to prevent melting the Plexiglas. If you use PVC pipe for the standoffs, use a drill press to keep the holes properly aligned. Cut the two 445-MHz elements to a length of $11^1/_{16}$ inches (see **Fig 8-7**). Make the center insulator from a 5-inch length of $^1/_2$-inch PVC pipe (see **Fig 8-8**). Cut a longitudinal slit the entire length of the pipe; I used a hacksaw to do this.

The coaxial-cable feed line extending from the antenna's feed point to just below the support section can be any convenient length, but use RadioShack RG-8 (RS278-1312) to get the proper velocity factor and impedance for the Q section. The Q-section details are shown in **Fig 8-9**. The Q-section consists of a $13^5/_8$-inch length of $^3/_8$-inch copper tubing (Fig 8-9A) slid over the center insulation of the top end of the feed line (Fig 8-9B).

On the Q section, fashion a tab on the end of the tubing similar to that at the bottom of the upper element (see Fig 8-9A). Following Fig 8-9B, cut the end of the feed line with a sharp knife to expose $^7/_{16}$ inch of the center conductor. (**Fig 8-10** shows the finished feed point end of the Q section.) Remove $13^1/_4$ inches of the coaxial cable feed line's outer cover and the shield to expose the dielectric. Then remove an additional $^5/_8$ inch of the coaxial cable's outer covering exposing the shield braid. Clean and tin the tab and the opposite end of the Q-section tubing. Slide the tubing over the coax and under the shield so that the end of the tubing with the tab is even with the end of the center dielectric (Fig 8-9B). Using a high-power soldering iron or low torch flame, solder the shield to the tubing, allowing the solder to flow through the braid. Dress the joint so that it passes through the lower element.

Assembly

Clamp the lower element and stub assembly horizontally in a vise about 14 inches from the top of the lower element. Slide the Q section and feed line into and through the support section

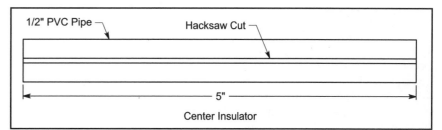

1/2" PVC Pipe
Hacksaw Cut
5"
Center Insulator

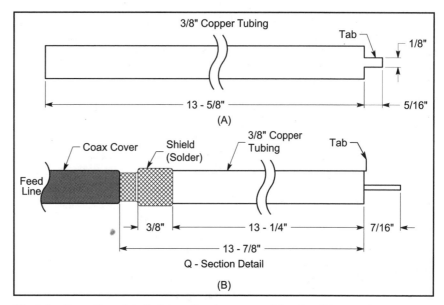

3/8" Copper Tubing
Tab
1/8"
13 - 5/8"
5/16"
(A)

Coax Cover
Shield (Solder)
3/8" Copper Tubing
Tab
Feed Line
3/8"
13 - 1/4"
7/16"
13 - 7/8"
Q - Section Detail
(B)

Fig 8-9—Q-section detail. A length of copper tubing is slid over the coaxial cable's dielectric and soldered to the shield braid at one end; see text.

until the Q section is exactly even with the top of the lower element. While keeping the Q section in the center of the lower element (Fig 8-5B); bend the tab on the Q section over the tab on the lower element. Solder the tabs together. Snip off the excess tab length of the Q-section and file the joint flush with the surface of the lower element.

Slide one standoff onto the lower element until it is about 10 inches from the feed point. Open the slit in the center insulator and hold open the slit by inserting two pennies (or something similar) side by side at four points within the slit. Slide the center insulator over the lower element until it touches the standoff. Bring the upper element into place passing the center conductor of the coax into the hole in the tab according to Fig 8-5B. To hold the feed point in place, clamp the lower and upper elements to a strip of wood using hose clamps. Solder the coax center conductor to the upper-element tab

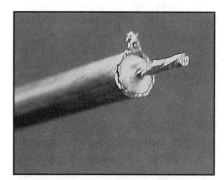

Fig 8-10—Feed-point end of the Q section prior to final assembly.

by heating the upper element near the base of the tab and letting the heat flow down the tab.

Remove the hose clamps and wood strip around the feed point. Slide the center insulator up until it is centered over the feed point and remove the pennies. The center insulator will clamp tightly around the feed point. As shown

Fig 8-11—This cutaway view shows the tabs of the Q section and lower element soldered together.

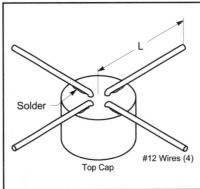

Fig 8-12—Technique for lowering the antenna's resonant frequency. See text.

L

Solder

#12 Wires (4)

Top Cap

Table 8-1
Materials Required
10 feet of copper water pipe (type L or M; see text)
5 inches of $^1/_2$ inch PVC pipe
1 each $^1/_2$ inch copper T
1 each $^1/_2$ inch copper L
2 each $^1/_2$-inch copper pipe caps
15 inches of $^3/_8$-inch OD copper tubing (0.331-inch ID)
2 pieces of $1^1/_4$ in × $6^1/_8$ in × $^1/_4$-inch-thick Plexiglas
5 ft of RadioShack RG-8 coax (RS 278-1312)
1 Teflon-silver PL-259 connector

in Fig 8-7, assemble the 445-MHz elements and upper standoff. Use silicone cement or caulking to hold the 445-MHz elements in place. Seal the top, bottom and slit of the center insulator with silicone cement or caulking. Install the cap on the top of the upper element.

If you intend to suspend the antenna by its top in a tree, install a top insulator made from PVC pipe and provide a support for the feed line at the bottom of the support section.

Evaluation

I found that the SWR and frequency range of the antenna are about the same when the antenna is mounted on a 20-foot mast as when it's suspended by its top at 40 feet. With 50 feet of CQ-4XL cable ("poor man's hardline" available from The Wireman), the SWR measured 1.3:1 or less from 144 MHz to 148 MHz and 1.5:1 or less from 438 MHz to 450 MHz. Because I don't have a tower, I suspended the antenna in a tall pine tree. With the top at about 40 feet, I got the expected signal reports on 2 meters from repeaters within a 40-mile radius. The only repeater available to me in the 440-MHz band is about 30 miles away and at an elevation of only 100 feet, with its antenna on the side of the tower opposite my location. Six of seven bars on my LCD S meter lit up and I received good reports from stations that I worked. I've concluded that the radiation patterns and gain predicted by *EZNEC* are close to those that are realized on the air.

Appendix—The Author's Follow-up Comments

I received a good response from my article, "A 146 and 445-MHz J-Pole Antenna," in the October 2000 issue of *QST*. The antenna worked fine for most builders. However, three builders who used the heavier Type L copper pipe found that the antenna resonated from 143 to 145 MHz, instead of about 146 MHz and had a very high SWR in the repeater portion of the 440 MHz band. Other builders wanted the minimum SWR in the 440 MHz band to be in the 440 to 450 MHz range rather than at 436.5 ± 1.5 MHz for the original design.

I have constructed several antennas since writing the article. I find that those constructed from the lighter Type M pipe are fairly uniform with the 2 meter resonant frequency at 146 ± 1.5 MHz and the 440 band resonant frequency at 437.5 ± 1.5 MHz. However, antennas constructed from Type L pipe appear to be non-uniform and tend to resonate lower in frequency. One resonated at 430 MHz causing unacceptable SWR near 450 MHz.

If an antenna constructed from Type M pipe resonates at about 146 MHz, the 440 band resonant frequency can be raised to about 441 MHz by simply shortening the 440 band elements to $10^1/_8$ inches from the specified $11^1/_{16}$ inches The elements must be re-centered opposite the feed point. This will not change the 2-meter resonant frequency, and the SWR at the antenna should be 1.5:1 or less from 435 MHz. to 450 MHz.

The resonant frequency of both

bands for Type M construction can be increased by limited shortening ($1^1/_2$ inches maximum) of the upper element. A reduction of $^7/_8$ inch will raise the 2-meter resonant frequency by 1 MHz and the 440 band resonant frequency by 2.7 MHz. This must be done before shortening the 440 MHz elements. The 440 band resonant frequency can be raised further by shortening the 440 band elements by about $^3/_{16}$ inch per MHz.

If the resonant frequency of an antenna constructed from Type L pipe is 143 to 145 MHz, use the following procedure. Shorten the upper element to $20^1/_8$ inches, shorten the lower element to $38^7/_8$ inches, and shorten the 440 band elements to $10^1/_8$ inch. The stub and Q-section should not be changed. If the resonant frequency is now too high, solder four 3-inch long #12 bare copper wires to the top of the cap on the upper element (see **Fig 8-12**). The four wires should be at right angles and horizontal to the ground. Trim each wire to $2^1/_2$ inches from the center of the cap to the end of the wire. Check the resonant frequencies. They should be too low. Finally, trim the wires equally to obtain the desired resonant frequency. Each reduction of $^9/_{16}$ inch in the length of the wires will increase the 2-meter resonant frequency by 1 MHz and the 440 band resonant frequency by about 2.85 MHz. One of my modified Type L antennas did not require top wires, one required 1-inch wires, and one required $1^3/_4$ inch wires.

9 An HF Vertical That Needs No Radials

Try the HVD

Looking for an effective antenna that's easy to build and install? One that requires only a little bit of real estate? I was. As you probably know, horizontal dipoles work well, but they usually require two, or even three, supports. I wanted an antenna for 15 meters that didn't require a tower, mast or tree for support. The solution to my problem is the *Half-wave Vertical Dipole*, or HVD for short.

The HVD is simply a dipole that is constructed from tubing, supported vertically from the lower end. This antenna doesn't need support from above the antenna. Early in the planning stages of this book, Dean Straw, N6BV, had urged me to build an HVD. I was skeptical, and said so. Wouldn't a good horizontal dipole beat it? I certainly thought it would. Nevertheless, it made sense to try one, so I agreed and we added it to the contents page. After all, wouldn't some of you folks be in situations that would allow installation of an HVD but not of a horizontal dipole? Besides, I'd never tried an HVD; and it would be easy to build and fun to check the results. It was, and it is, but more on that later.

THE DESIGN ANALYSIS

Summer finally arrived and the time came to build a 15-meter HVD. But first, I turned to my computer and fired up *EZNEC 3.0*. It wasn't long before I had a model of the antenna entered into the program. The model comprises only one "wire" (to use modeling terminology) of 0.875-inch diameter and 22-feet long. In the first model, I placed the bottom end of the HVD 8 feet above ground. The analysis looked mostly promising. Imagine SWR better than 1.5 from band edge to band edge. Sounds great, doesn't it?

What about gain? Right, what about it? This is not a simple question. The numbers confirm that the HVD does not posses the S-Unit of ground-reflection gain that the horizontal dipole does. Ouch! However, the gain question comes down to this: Gain in which direction(s)? That means both horizontal (azimuth) and vertical (elevation). Don't forget that to achieve gain in one direction, you have to lose it in another.

I had decided to mount the 15-meter HVD on the peak of my garage roof. That's 14 feet above the ground. I planned to guy the antenna to the corners of the roof with $^3/_{16}$-inch Dacron line, and to run the feed line along one of those guys. *EZNEC* confirmed that this should work well.

How well would it work? I decided to compare with a computer-modeled horizontal dipole both at the height of the HVD center and at the height of the HVD upper tip. Except for low angles, the dipoles win. Or at least they appear to win. Research by N6BV shows that almost all long-distance communications on 15 meters, is supported by takeoff (vertical) angles under 24°. In fact, most of the time the best takeoff angle is less than 12°.

The peak gain of the HVD may be nearly an S-unit below a horizontal dipole. However, my HVD has its peak gain at 14°—well below the peak from a similar-height dipole. This could be interesting, but enough analysis—it was time to build my HVD. Testing, comparisons and further analysis could wait until the HVD was built and installed.

CONSTRUCTION

Throughout this book, I have used 6-foot lengths for aluminum tubing. While 12-foot lengths are available, they must be shipped by freight. By contrast, the 6-foot lengths will ship by UPS.

The 15-meter HVD consists of four 6-foot lengths of 0.875-inch aluminum tube with 0.058 wall thickness. In addition there are two 1-foot lengths of 0.75-inch tubing (used for splicing the 0.875-inch tubing pieces together), and two one-foot lengths of 0.75-inch fiberglass rod for insulators. See **Table 9-1** for dimensions.

Start by cutting off 1 foot from a 6-foot length of 0.875-inch tubing. Next, insert six inches of one of the 1-foot-long 0.75-inch tubes into the machine-cut end of your tubing and fasten the tubes together. Now, slide an end of another 6-foot length of 0.875-inch tube over the protruding end of the 0.75-inch tube and fasten them together. Repeat this procedure with the remaining tubing.

You should now have two 11-foot-long elements. As you can see in **Fig 9-1**, when I built my HVD, I was temporarily out of aluminum pop rivets, so I used sheet metal screws. Either will work fine, but pop rivets can easily be drilled out and the antenna

Table 9-1
HVD Dimensions
Length using 0.875-inch aluminum tubing

MHz	Feet	Inches
18.11	33	11
21.2	22	0
24.94	18	9
28.4	16	5

These lengths should divided by two to determine the length of the dipole legs.

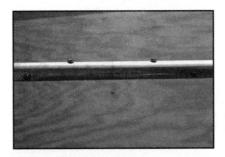

Fig 9-1—Element splice uses a 1-foot length of 0.75-inch tubing inserted into the 0.875-inch sections to join them together. Self-tapping sheet-metal screws are used in this photo, but aluminum pop rivets or machine screws with washers and nuts can also be used.

Fig 9-4—Guys are made of Dacron line that is attached to the HVD by a stainless-steel worm-screw-type hose clamp. A self-tapping sheet-metal screw (not visible in the photo) prevents the clamp from sliding down the antenna.

disassembled if you ever want to make changes.

Because my hand-made cuts using a hacksaw are not perfectly square, I decided to put those element ends at the center of the antenna. You may want to do the same. Slip these cut ends over the ends of a 1-foot length of 0.75-inch fiberglass rod. This rod serves as the center insulator. Leave about a 1-inch gap at the center. Drill aluminum and fiberglass for #8 hardware as shown in **Fig 9-2**.

Now, slip half of the remaining 1-foot length of 0.75-inch fiberglass rod 6 inches into one end the dipole. (This end will be the bottom end or base.) Drill and secure with #8 hardware. See **Fig 9-3**.

The final step is to secure the guy wires to your vertical. You can see how I did that in **Fig 9-4**. I started by drilling a pilot hole and then driving a sheet metal screw into the antenna about a foot above the center. The purpose of that screw is to prevent the clamp and guys from sliding down the antenna.

The guys are clean lengths of $^3/_{16}$-inch Dacron line. (The Dacron serves a dual purpose: it supports the antenna vertically, and it acts as an insulator.) Tie secure knots into the guy ends and secure these knotted ends to the antenna with a stainless-steel worm-screw-type hose clamp. Take care to not overtighten the clamps. You don't want the clamp to slip (although the knots and the sheet-metal screw will help), but you especially don't want to cut your guy lines. Your antenna is ready for installation.

Fig 9-2—The center insulator of the 15-meter HVD is a 1-foot length of 0.75-inch fiberglass rod. Insulator and elements have been drilled to accept #8 hardware.

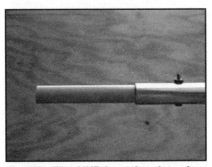

Fig 9-3—The HVD base insulator is a 1-foot length of 0.75-inch fiberglass rod.

INSTALLATION

Installation requires two things. First, a place to sit or mount the base insulator. Second, you need anchors for the support guys.

I used a piece of 2 × 6 lumber to make a socket to hold the HVD base securely in place. I drilled a ¾-inch-deep hole with a ¾-inch spade bit. A

couple of pieces of 2 × 2 lumber at the ends of the base form a saddle, which nicely straddles the ridge at the peak of my garage roof. You can see how I did this in **Fig 9-5**. The dimensions are not critical, but you should paint your base to protect it from the weather.

Choke Balun

This antenna needs a common-mode choke to ensure that stray RF doesn't flow on the shield of the coax. This device is also known as a *choke balun*. Unlike a horizontal dipole, don't consider it an option to omit the common-mode choke when building and installing an HVD.

I used 8 feet of the RG-213 feed line wound into 7 turns for a balun, resulting in a coil about 6 inches in diameter. I secured the turns together with electrical tape, and secured the feed line and balun to one of the guy lines with UV-resistant cable ties.

Because the feed line slants away from the antenna, I wanted to do *all* that I could to eliminate common-mode currents from the feed line. For that reason, I made another balun about 11.5 feet from the first one. This balun also comprises 8 feet of the RG-213 feed line wound into 7 turns. See **Fig 9-6** and the sidebar *Effects of Feed-Line Dress on Vertical Half-wave Dipole*.

My wife Sylvia, K8SYL, held the antenna in place while I secured the guys to the screw eyes that I had previously installed for that purpose. The only hard part of this operation was waiting for a time when there was very little breeze. (The wind is seldom calm

Fig 9-5—At K8CH, the HVD base insulator sits in this saddle-shaped wooden fixture. This was photo was taken before the fixture was painted—a necessary step to protect against the weather.

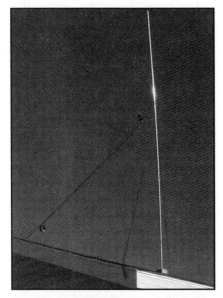

Fig 9-6—The HVD installed at K8CH. An eye screw that is used for securing one of the guy lines is visible in the foreground. You can also see the two choke baluns that are used in the feed system (see text).

around these parts, especially atop our hill.)

RESULTS

The skeptic has become a convert! I was resigned to accept an S-unit lower performance from the HVD. Isn't that a fair trade-off for convenience of no special (tall) supports needed and no radials required?

I have had a variety of horizontal dipoles (with and without baluns) to use for comparison. Mainly, I used the three-band dipole described in Chapter 2 as the reference antenna. On 15 meters, this works as a three half-waves dipole. As I had expected, there are times when one or more of the dipoles has an S-unit edge over the HVD. What I had not expected was for the HVD to beat the dipoles most of the time, usually having an edge of one to two S-units.

Why? That was the question. The short answer is that the HVD performance at low elevation angles compares well to a dipole at a similar height. It does slightly better against an inverted V. You can read more about this in the sidebar *Comparing the HVD with an Inverted-V Dipole*.

Don't sell your monoband Yagi to put up an HVD. Don't even sell your triband Yagi. However, you may want to try one of these instead of a horizontal dipole. Better yet, put up both. When you're using simple antennas, it's good to have choices. Well, it's good to have choices in any Amateur Radio installation, but all the more so when you're using simple antennas!

POSSIBLE ENHANCEMENTS

10/12-Meter Coverage

I have considered adding 10 and 12-meter coverage to my 15-meter HVD. It would be fairly easy to support wires for those bands using plexiglass supports. You'll find this technique illustrated in **Fig 9-7**. You can expect edge-to-edge coverage of the narrow 12-meter band. On 10-meters, you'll find adequate, but less than full-band coverage.

If you add these bands to the 15-meter HVD, you'll need to add another set of guys to the structure. That's because of the increased wind load that these wires will create. My HVD has withstood 50-mph wind gusts, but it flexes quite a bit.

Another potential concern with the multiband unit is the angle at which the feed line comes away from the antenna. To minimize common-mode currents, this angle should be as close to 90° as you can make it. In the single band (15-meter) version, there are two common-mode chokes placed a quarter wavelength apart. These will not be a quarter wavelength apart on either 10 or

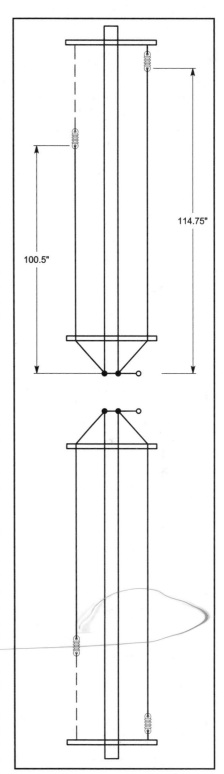

Fig 9-7—Plexiglas pieces can be used to support wires for adding 12 and 10-meter coverage to the HVD.

EFFECTS OF FEED-LINE DRESS ON A VERTICAL HALF-WAVE DIPOLE

Ever since my experience in November 1998 in Jamaica at the 6Y2A contest operation, I've been intrigued by half-wave vertical dipoles. I described the 6Y2A antennas in some detail in an article I wrote for *The ARRL Antenna Compendium, Vol 6,* "Antennas Here are Some Verticals on the Beach…"

A vertical half-wave dipole has some operational advantages compared to a more-commonly used vertical configuration – the quarter-wave vertical, used with some sort of above-ground counterpoise or an on-ground radial system. See **Fig A1** and A2, which show the two configurations modeled here. In each case, the lowest part of each antenna is 8 feet above ground, to prevent passersby from being able to touch any live wire. Each antenna is assumed to be made of ⁷/₈-inch aluminum tubing to simulate an actual 20-meter vertical made of telescoping tubing.

Elevating the half-wave vertical dipole antenna so that the bottom is 8 feet off the ground has another advantage—it brings the feed-point impedance close to 50 Ω. The closer the bottom approaches ground, the higher the feed-point impedance rises—to the theoretical limit of about 95 Ω for a thin-wire antenna approximation.

Fig B compares elevation patterns for the half-wave vertical dipole and the quarter-wave ground-plane antenna for "average ground." You can see that the half-wave dipole has about 1.5 dB higher peak gain, since it compresses the vertical elevation pattern down somewhat closer to the horizon than does the quarter-wave ground plane. Another advantage to using a half-wave radiator besides higher gain is that less horizontal "real estate" is needed compared to a quarter-wave vertical with its horizontal radials.

The obvious disadvantage to a vertical half-wave dipole is that it is taller than a quarter-wave ground plane. This requires a higher support (such as a taller tree) if you make it from wire, or a longer element if you make it from telescoping aluminum tubing.

Another problem is that theory

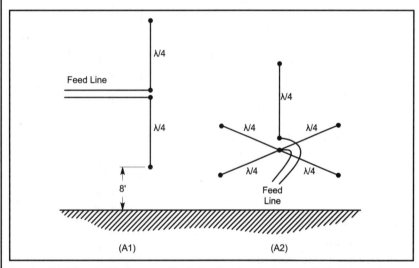

Fig A—At A1, a half-wave vertical dipole elevated a small distance above the ground. The feed line is run perpendicularly away from the dipole. At A2, a "ground plane" type of quarter-wave vertical, with four elevated resonant radials. Both antennas are mounted 8 feet above the ground to keep them away from passersby.

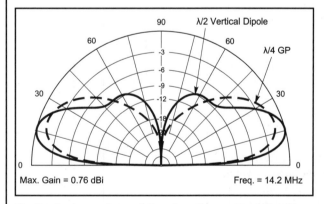

Fig B—A comparison of the elevation patterns for the two antennas in Fig A. The peak gain of the vertical half-wave dipole is about 1.5 dB higher than that for the quarter-wave radiator with radials.

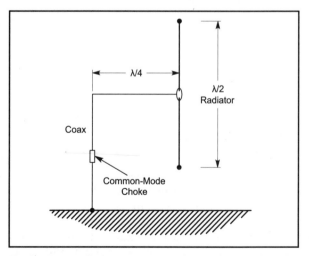

Fig C—The coax feed line has been supported so that as much of it as possible is horizontal, perpendicular to the vertical half-wave dipole.

says you want to dress the feed line so that it is perpendicular to the half-wave radiator. This means you must support the coax feed line above ground for some distance before bringing the coax down to ground level. A question immediately arises: How far must you go out horizontally with the feed line before going to ground level to eliminate common-mode currents radiated onto the coax shield? Such common-mode currents will affect the feed-point impedance as well as the radiation pattern for the antenna system. See **Fig C**, which shows the layout for a vertical dipole and 40.9 feet of coax feed line, dressed so that as much as possible is horizontal before going vertically down to ground level. Why did I choose a length of 40.9 feet for the feed line? This places the vertical portion of the coax—the only one onto which the vertical half-wave radiator actually radiates current because of symmetry—a quarter-wavelength away.

This setup will create quite a bit of distortion in the azimuthal

pattern, if no choke baluns are used to suppress common-mode currents radiated onto the coax shield. **Fig D** shows the non-circular azimuthal pattern that results from these common-mode currents. A single common-mode choke, however, placed in the center of the vertical section of coax will suppress these spurious currents and results in a mere 0.04 dB departure from a perfectly circular azimuthal pattern.

Constructing such a common-mode choke is very simple. You could do it the way K8CH did by winding the feed-line coax into a choke coil, or you could slip three large ferrite beads over the coax (before the connectors are soldered on or else they won't fit!) and tape the beads in place.

The only problem with the scheme shown in Fig D is that an additional support (some sort of "skyhook") is required to support the coax horizontally at the left-hand end. Let's try to simplify the installation by slanting the feed line coax down to ground from the feed point. See **Fig E**.

Note that the bottom end of the coax is grounded to a ground rod. This serves a couple of purposes—it serves as a mechanical connection to hold the coax in place, and it provides some protection against lightning strikes. Again, the common-mode chokes would use ferrite beads, just as above.

Now, as a purely practical matter, just how picky am I being here? What if we skip the second common-mode choke in Fig E and use just one choke at the feed point? The computer models predicts that there will be some distortion in the azimuthal pattern—about 1.1 dB worth. Is this enough to be concerned about? I doubt it. However, you may find other problems with the resulting common-mode currents on the coax shield; problems such as RF in the shack or variable SWR readings depending on the way coax is routed in the shack. I think the addition of three extra ferrite beads to suppress the common-mode currents is a good idea. —*N6BV*.

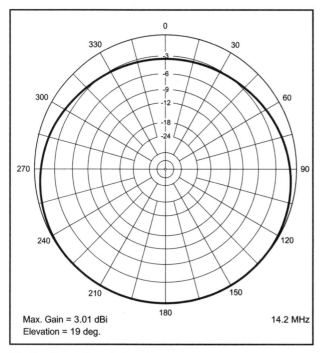

Max. Gain = 3.01 dBi
Elevation = 19 deg.

14.2 MHz

Fig D—The azimuthal pattern resulting from the layout of coax feed line in Fig C. This is a worst-case plot, when no common-mode choke is used on the feed line, allowing small amounts of common-mode current to be radiated onto the coax shield.

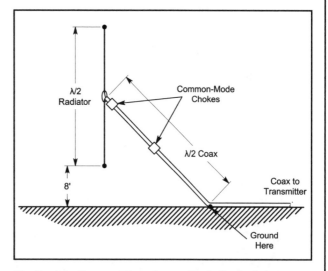

Fig E—A half-wave 20-meter vertical dipole (whose bottom is 8 feet off the ground), fed with a half-wave length of RG-213 coax (33 feet long). This system uses one common-mode choke at the feed point and another ¼-λ down the line. The resulting azimuthal radiation pattern is within 0.4 dB of being perfectly circular. The resonant feed-point impedance is 57 Ω, resulting in a low SWR. The total "wingspan" of the antenna system is 27 feet from radiator to the point where the coax comes to the ground.

12 meter, and for that reason they will not be as effective at suppressing common-mode currents on those bands.

Another way to convert the 15-meter HVD to multiband use is to feed the antenna with ladder line. For best performance, you'll need to bring the feed line away perpendicular from the antenna. You'll also need a balanced antenna tuner to match this system to your transceiver. The configuration is shown in **Fig 9-8**. You should have good results with this antenna on 20, 17, 15, 12 and 10 meters.

An HVD Beam

This antenna can also be used as part of a 15-meter vertical beam. You only need to add a reflector. While that will about double the cost of material, you may find the enhanced performance well worth the price. It certainly

---

COMPARING THE HVD WITH AN INVERTED-V DIPOLE

At K8CH, the 15-meter HVD is mounted atop the garage. This puts the base at 14 feet above the ground, and puts the center at 25 feet.

For a comparison antenna I use a 40-meter dipole with capacitance hats to make the antenna resonant in the 15-meter band. This second (comparison) antenna is described in Chapter 2. This dipole has its apex at 29 feet, and the ends droop slightly, creating an inverted V with an approximately 140° included angle between the dipole legs.

Several weeks of observations and tests, including a couple of casual contest operations, reveal

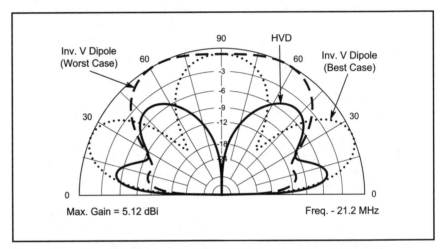

Fig F—Elevation patterns for the HVD (solid line) and the Inverted V comparison antenna in its best case (dashed line) and worst case (dotted line). See sidebar text for discussion.

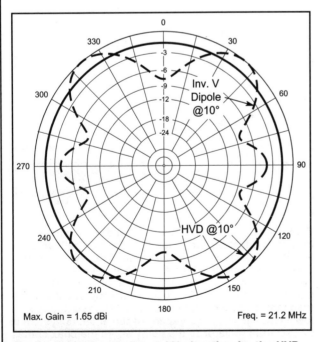

Fig G—Azimuth patterns at 10° elevation for the HVD (solid line) and inverted V (dashed line). See text.

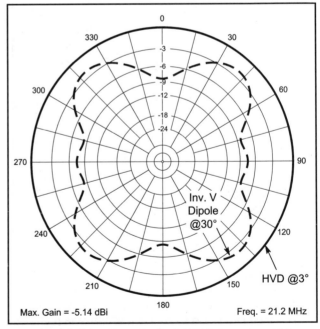

Fig H—Azimuth patterns at 3°elevation for the HVD (solid line) and the inverted V (dashed line). See text.

could make sense on a dB gain per dollar spent basis. The beam will favor one direction, but it will be stronger in that direction and you'll receive less noise and interference off the back. Details are given in the sidebar *Converting the HVD into a Beam*.

Finally, **Fig 9-9** shows the elevation patterns for three antennas, compared with elevation-angle statistics from K8CH's location to all of Europe. The three antennas are the HVD, an HVD 2-element beam, and a 40/15-meter inverted V dipole whose apex is 29 feet above ground—the height of K8SYL's inverted V. For this inverted-V dipole, two elevation patterns are shown. They represent the best case and the worst-case azimuths, while the basic HVD is omnidirectional. The elevation angle for the 2-element HVD

Table A
15-Meter Elevation-Angle Percentages, Summary from Cleveland

Elev	To EU	To SAm	To Af	To JA	To OC	To AS	Avg	At or Below
1	0.8	4.3	13.5	23.4	20.5	22.1	14.10	14.10
2	10.7	6.7	22.6	15.9	18.2	17.8	15.32	29.42
3	12.8	11.5	9.1	7.5	31.8	10.6	13.88	43.30
4	9.7	18.1	4	7.5	4.5	18.8	10.43	53.73
5	11.7	13.3	12.4	2.8	4.5	12	9.45	63.18
6	7.4	5.4	11.7	9.3	13.6	3.4	8.47	71.65
7	6.1	4.6	8.4	9.3	2.3	7.2	6.32	77.97
8	4.3	4.8	4	9.3	0	6.7	4.85	82.82
9	5.9	5.4	7.7	4.7	4.5	1.4	4.93	87.75
10	7.9	9.6	4.4	1.9	0	0	3.97	91.72
11	4.3	6.1	1.5	1.9	0	0	2.30	94.02
12	5.9	2.6	0.7	4.7	0	0	2.32	96.33
13	1.5	0.9	0	1.9	0	0	0.72	97.05
14	1	1.1	0	0	0	0	0.35	97.40
15	1.3	1.3	0	0	0	0	0.43	97.83
16	2.3	2.4	0	0	0	0	0.78	98.62
17	1.5	0.9	0	0	0	0	0.40	99.02
18	2	0.4	0	0	0	0	0.40	99.42
19	0.8	0.4	0	0	0	0	0.20	99.62
20	0.5	0.2	0	0	0	0	0.12	99.73
21	0	0	0	0	0	0	0.00	99.73
22	0.8	0	0	0	0	0	0.13	99.87
23	0.5	0	0	0	0	0	0.08	99.95
24	0.3	0	0	0	0	0	0.05	100.00

EU = all of Europe, SAm = deep South America (ZP), Af = southern Africa (9J), JA = Japan, OC = Oceania (VK3), AS = south Asia (VU).

have a problem with my inverted V?

Thinking that perhaps something was wrong, I double-checked the coax and connectors, but everything seemed to be okay. Maybe the explanation had something to do with the elevation angles that were supporting propagation to the stations that I was in contact with or to which I was listening.

It was time for some more analysis. Dean Straw, N6BV, has compiled elevation angle statistics for more than 150 locations and has included them on the supplemental CD to *The ARRL Antenna Book* 19th edition. I used his Cleveland data tables and compiled the 15-meter data shown in **Table A**.

To the destinations included in the data from my part of the United States, over 90% of the time the band is open you'll be using elevation angles of 10° or less! Nearly half the time, you'll be using elevation angles of 3° or less. I realized that I had not been looking closely enough at those very low angles.

Before going on, I want you to realize that the table is interesting and informative, but it is not exhaustive. In other words, higher angles may be useful on some other paths that are not shown. Nevertheless, this is useful data—especially for the DXer.

Finally, I compared the azimuth patterns for the HVD and inverted V antennas at elevation angles of 10° (**Fig G**) and at 3° (**Fig H**). As you can plainly see, my mystery was solved.—*K8CH*.

that the HVD beats the inverted V most of time. That raised the question, "Why?" The answer would come from a careful inspection of computer models of my antennas. In particular, we need to look at the far-field patterns for these antennas. (I'd already modeled both antennas in *EZNEC* as part of the design work.)

The analysis begins as we look at the elevation patterns shown in **Fig F**. In the case of the inverted V, I chose best-case and worst-case azimuth angles. If we look only at the best-case pattern, we might be lead to believe that the inverted V would usually win. Doesn't it appear to beat the HVD at all but the very low angles? Could most of the signals that I was hearing and working be coming in the direction of the nulls in the inverted V's pattern? Or did I

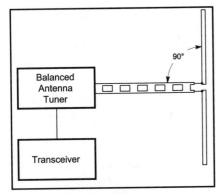

Fig 9-8—Configuration for the ladder-line-fed version of the HVD.

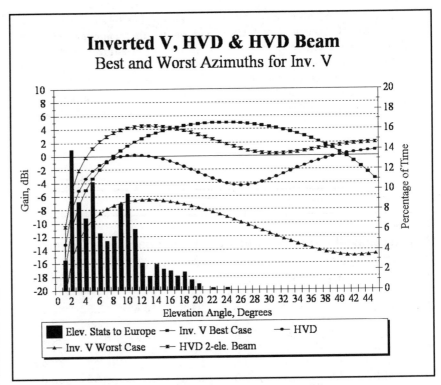

Fig 9-9—Comparison of elevation-angle responses for an HVD, a 2-element HVD beam and a 40/15-meter Inverted-V dipole whose apex is 29 feet above ground. The elevation patterns for the best-case and the worst-case azimuthal directions of the Inverted-V dipole are shown for comparison.

beam is the direction of its peak azimuthal response.

At the low elevation angles needed to communicate effectively with Europe from Michigan, the 2-element HVD beam is very effective indeed—some 5 dB better than the Inverted V at its best and about 10 dB better than the Inverted V at its worst. The 2-element HVD is better than the basic HVD by about 3 dB, which is equivalent to doubling your transmit power.

CONVERTING THE HVD INTO A BEAM

After I had used the 15-meter HVD in the 2000 IARU HF Championship Contest, I was feeling good. The antenna had proved to be better than my expectations and I had the proof. I told Dean Straw, N6BV, that he was a very clever fellow for having talked me into building such a fine antenna. In typical style, he responded, "You think that's good? Put a reflector behind it and it'll knock your socks off."

Dean's comment may contain some hyperbole, but it's not a bad idea. Hmm, if you add a parasitic element, in this case a reflector, to an HVD, would you call it an HVB (*half-wave vertical beam*)? Why not? I modeled the idea in *EZNEC*, and in consultation with Dean, developed a set of dimensions that provide good gain, clean pattern and excellent SWR (less than 1.5:1) across the 15-meter band. The elevation pattern of the main lobe is shown in **Fig I**. The rest of the potential of this design can be seen by looking at the azimuths patterns of the HVB at 10° elevation (**Fig J**) and at 3° elevation (**Fig K**).

The HVB is potentially a very worthwhile enhancement. HVB gain is significant if not great, and the

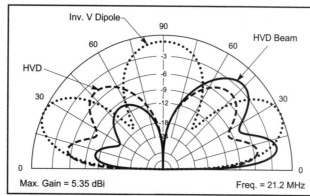

Fig I—Elevation pattern of the HVD Beam (solid line) compared with the HVD (dashed line) and the 40-meter inverted V in its best direction (dotted line).

half-power (3-dB) beam width of the HVB is approximately 150°. That means you'll have pretty broad coverage in the desired direction. Further, the nearly 10 dB front-to-back ratio of the HVB means less noise and interference from the back of the antenna.

BUILDING A 15-METER HVB

You'll start with an HVD (Half-wave Vertical Dipole), and then add a (longer) reflector 6.5 feet behind it. You can consider it an easy add-on, but you'll need to retune the driven element (HVD). That's caused by the presence of the reflector and the interaction of the two elements. The HVD design calls for an overall

length of 22 feet, but for the HVB, the driven element should be 21 feet, 4 inches. In other words, you'll have to remove 4 inches from each side of the original HVD.

The reflector is 24 feet long. You build it with four 6-foot lengths of 0.875-inch aluminum tubing, splicing them together with three 1-foot lengths of 0.75-inch tube (no center insulator in the reflector). Insert half of a 1-foot length of 0.75-inch fiberglass rod in one end to serve as a base insulator, in the same way as was done with the HVD.

It really is that simple. Wonder if I can fit one of these on my garage roof? I'll let you know.

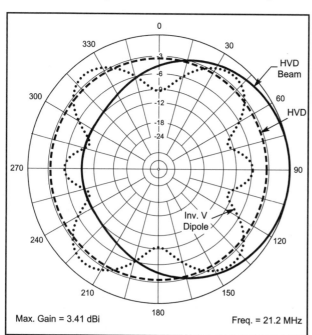

Fig J—Azimuth patterns at a 10° elevation angle for the HVD Beam (solid line), the HVD (dashed line) and the 40-meter inverted V (dotted line).

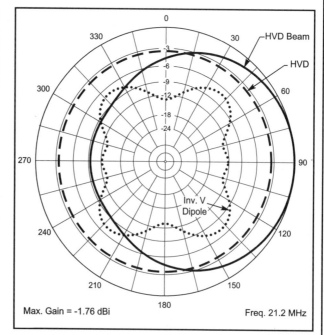

Fig K—Azimuth pattern at a 3° elevation angle for the HVD Beam (solid line), HVD (dashed line) and 40-meter inverted V (dotted line).

10 Yet More HF Dipoles

Dipoles, dipoles, dipoles!
Even more possibilities for your HF station

In Chapter 9, I described the construction of a 15-meter HVD (half-wave vertical dipole). That antenna's performance exceeded my expectations—so much so that I started to think about a possible multiband version. In Chapter 9, I also touched briefly on a couple of possibilities. Let's consider them again. I could make parallel dipoles for 12 and 10 meters that would be supported by the 15-meter HVD. It's a good idea, but mechanically a little bit more complicated; it adds to the wind load and it's not necessary. Why not just use the antenna as-is on other bands? Easy enough to check. Change bands on the transceiver and listen. Okay, it seems to work—at least I can hear stations.

So will the 15-meter HVD work on other bands? As you've probably guessed, the answer is, "Yes." In fact, it will work well on five bands.

A Five-Band Vertical Dipole

I used *EZNEC* and *TLW* to analyze the situation, and the results are shown in **Table 10-1**. (*EZNEC* is available from W7EL, and *TLW* is software bundled with the 19th Edition of *The ARRL Antenna Book*.) As you can see in the table, the original design when used with 75 feet of RG-213 feed line suffers significant loss on other bands.

However, if the feed line is changed to 75 feet of 450-Ω window ladder line, the situation looks much better. In fact, the 15-meter HVD will perform well on 20 through 10 meters when fed with the 450-Ω line. This five-band vertical dipole is shown in **Fig 10-1**.

The window ladder line costs about a quarter as much as RG-213. That's good news. Other good news is that the radiation pattern is very good on each one of these bands. See **Fig 10-2**, which overlays the elevation patterns for 20, 15 and 10 meters together on one plot. (In this scenario, the bottom of the HVD is placed 8 feet above ground, where it can't be touched accidentally by passersby.)

There are a couple of negatives about the all-band HVD fed with window

Table 10-1
SWR and Line Loss for the 15-Meter HVD

Frequency (MHz)	SWR (50 Ohm)	RG-213 Line Loss (dB)	SWR (450 Ohm)	Ladder-Line Loss (dB)
28.4	15	4	3.4	0.2
24.94	7.3	2.3	3.6	0.2
21.25	1.4	0.8	6	0.3
18.118	11.4	2.8	11	0.5
14.2	97	9	30	1.1
10.1	480	16	100	2.9
7.2	1200	21	300	4.9

Line loss is based on 75 feet of feed line.

ladder line that you should consider. First, you'll need a balanced-output antenna tuner. Second, ladder line requires care in routing and installation.

Antenna tuners with balanced-output can sometimes be found in ham-radio flea markets. If you find a Johnson Matchbox, you've located a treasure. The 250-W unit works just fine, and the high-power version has very low loss. You can probably locate other manufacturers' models, either new or used, that will work well. You might want to build your own, and if so you'll find a design for one of these later in this chapter.

Ladder line has many advantages—not the least of which is low loss. Be aware, however, that it has special requirements for installation. In Chapter 11 on ladder lines, Dean Straw has covered what you need to know about using ladder line. There you'll find helpful hints on how to route and install your line. For now, I'll tell you that it's best

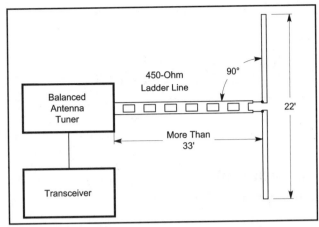

Fig 10-1—A five-band vertical dipole that covers 20, 17, 15, 12 and 10-meter bands. The dipole is fed with 450-Ω window ladder line and requires a balanced antenna tuner.

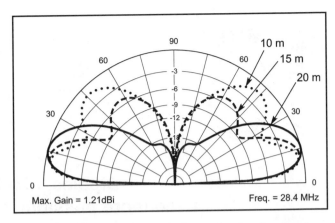

Fig 10-2—Vertical radiation patterns for the five-band vertical dipole mounted 8 feet above the ground. The solid trace is the pattern on 14.2 MHz, while the dashed line represents 21.2 MHz and the dotted line represents 28.4 MHz.

to keep the ladder line to a multi-band HVD at right angles to the vertical radiator, extending a distance horizontally for at least 33 feet (a half wavelength on 20 meters). This is shown in Fig 10-1 and is meant to prevent radiating RF back onto the feed line, which can distort the radiation pattern by re-radiation from the feed line.

Build A 135-foot Multiband Center-Fed Horizontal Dipole

I've often said that if I could only have one antenna for HF, I'd choose a 135-foot horizontal dipole, center-fed with ladder line and mounted as high and as flat as possible. This antenna covers all the bands from 80 through 10 meters, is simple and inexpensive. Oh yes, it's also a good performer. The antenna is illustrated in **Fig 10-3**. As you can see in the figure, you'll again need to use a balanced-output antenna tuner.

Over the years, countless hams have used one of these at home or on Field Day. You might call it *old fashioned*, but I prefer to call it a *classic*. Ben Hassell, W8VPC, introduced me to this, his favorite Field Day antenna, in the sixties. The 135-foot dipole was a lot easier to put up than a tower, rotator and beam. And the results were always gratifying.

I've used a 135-foot center-fed for many Field Days. However, my most memorable QSO with one of these antennas took place in December 1977. I had moved into a new location a few months earlier and was using the 135-foot center-fed for my HF antenna. On this day, I was tuning the 20-meter CW band when I heard a station signing STØRK. Oh yeah, sure! Someone's having some fun. Okay, I'm a DXer and the DXer's motto is WFWL (work first, worry later). But this can't be serious, can it? WFWL, but crank the output power down to 25-W output. One call and STØRK was in my log and I was in his log. It turned out to be a new counter for DXCC and was not a prank. Thank goodness the center-fed worked well!

That was my experience. You may not repeat it, but you'll have fun if you install a similar antenna. For best results

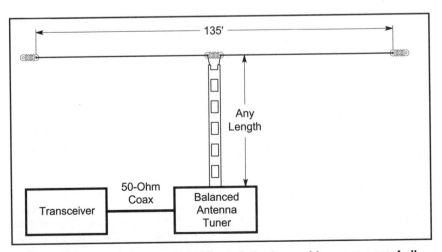

Fig 10-3—The versatile 135-foot center-fed dipole provides coverage of all Amateur Radio HF bands.

with this versatile antenna, place it as high as you can, and keep both antenna and ladder line clear of metal and other conductive objects. Despite significant SWR on some bands, system losses are low.

You can install the antenna as an inverted V, but expect compromised performance if you do. ARRL staff analyzed a 135-foot dipole at 50 feet above typical ground and compared that to an inverted V with the center at 50 ft, and the ends at 10 ft. The results show that on 80 meters, it won't make a really big difference which configuration you choose (see **Fig 10-4**.) The inverted V exhibits additional losses because of its proximity to the ground.

Fig 10-5 shows a comparison between a 20-meter flattop dipole and the 135-foot flattop dipole when both are placed at 50 feet above ground. At a 10°-elevation angle, the 135-foot dipole has a gain advantage. This advantage comes at the cost of two deep, but narrow, nulls that are broadside to the wire.

Fig 10-6 compares the 135-foot dipole to the inverted-V configuration of the same antenna on 14.1 MHz. As you can see in the figure, the inverted V pattern is essentially omnidirectional. In the favored directions, the convenience of mounting the antenna as an inverted V has a price of decreased gain—about 8 dB less than a horizontal flattop.

As you might expect, patterns become more complicated at 28.4 MHz. As you can see in **Fig 10-7**, the inverted V has the advantage of a pattern with only

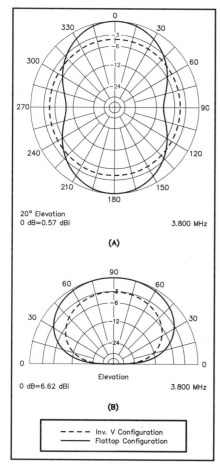

Fig 10-4—Patterns on 80 meters for a 135-ft, center-fed dipole erected as a horizontal dipole at 50 ft, and as an inverted V with the center at 50 ft, and the ends at 10 ft. The azimuth pattern is shown at A where conductors lie in the 90° to 270° plane. The elevation pattern is shown at B, where the conductors come out of the paper at right angles to the paper. At the fundamental frequency, the patterns are not markedly different.

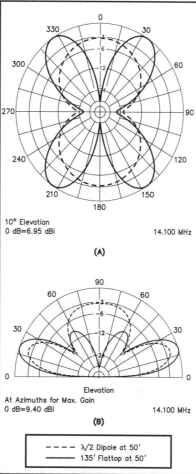

Fig 10-5—Patterns on 20 meters comparing a standard half-wave dipole and a multiband 135-foot dipole. Both are mounted horizontally at 50 feet. The azimuth pattern is shown at A, where conductors lie in the 90° to 270° plane. The elevation pattern is shown at B. The longer antenna has four azimuthal lobes, centered at 35°, 145°, 215° and 325°. Each is about 2 dB stronger than the main lobes of the half-wave dipole. The elevation pattern of the 135-foot dipole is for one of the four maximum-gain azimuth lobes, while the elevation pattern for the half-wave dipole is for the 0° azimuthal point.

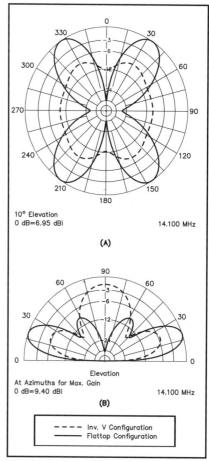

Fig 10-6—Patterns on 20 meters for two 135-foot dipoles. One is mounted horizontally as a flattop and the other as an inverted V with 120° included angle between the two legs. The azimuth pattern is shown at A, and the elevation pattern is shown at B. The inverted V has about 6 dB less gain at the peak azimuths, but has a more uniform, almost omnidirectional, azimuthal pattern. In the elevation plane, the inverted V has a fat lobe overhead, making it a somewhat better antenna for local communication, but not quite so good for DX contacts at low elevation angles.

slight nulls, but with reduced gain compared to the flattop configuration, averaging about 10 dB, almost two S units.

Still, in summary and no matter how you install it, the 135-foot center-fed dipole is a simple antenna that can work well from 3.5 to 30 MHz. Band switching is handled by the antenna tuner that is located at your operating position.

ALTERNATE LENGTHS

There are a number of good reasons to consider other lengths for a center-fed dipole. For example, you may have space limitations, and for that reason need a more compact antenna. If so, consider a 100-foot center-fed dipole. It will work about as well as the 135-foot version.

You may ask, "If a 100-foot dipole works nearly as well as a 135-foot dipole, why use the extra wire?" Good question. The advantage to the longer wire is that it is resonant, or nearly so, on 80 meters. That doesn't mean that it will radiate much better on that band. It does mean that it will be easier to match, however, and it will result in lower feed-line losses on 80 and 40 meters.

In the classic configuration, the 135-foot dipole is fed with 63 feet (or an odd multiple thereof) of open-wire line. This length of open-wire line serves as a quarter-wave transformer on 80 meters, which converts the low impedance at the dipole's feed point to a higher impedance at the antenna tuner at the other end of the feed line. The old-timers called this a *center-fed Zepp*. It became a classic because it performed well and it presented a high impedance on 80, 40, 20, 15 and 10 meters, which in turn simplified antenna-tuner design. If you were going to build one today, you might want to substitute 450-Ω win-

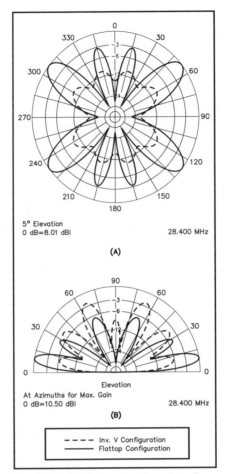

5° Elevation
0 dB=8.01 dBi   28.400 MHz

(A)

Elevation
At Azimuths for Max. Gain
0 dB=10.50 dBi   28.400 MHz

(B)

- - - - Inv. V Configuration
———— Flattop Configuration

Fig 10-7—Patterns on 10 meters for 135-foot dipole mounted horizontally and as an inverted V, as in Fig 10-6. The azimuth pattern is shown at A, and the elevation pattern is shown at B. Once again, the inverted-V configuration yields a more omnidirectional pattern, but at the expense of almost 8 dB less gain than the flat-top configuration at its strongest lobes.

dow ladder liner for the 600-Ω line the old-timers used. In that case the length should be 62 feet and 4 inches, or an odd multiple of that length.

What About Shorter Antenna Lengths?

The 135-foot dipole has lobes off the sides on 80 and 40 meters. On 30 meters strong secondary lobes exist, and on 10 meters there are multiple lobes (see Fig 10-7). On the other hand, a 40-foot long center-fed dipole has a single lobe off each side on the bands 30 through 10 meters.

If you're content with 20 through 10-meter coverage, you could use a 33.5-foot (20-meter half-wave) dipole. The 33.5-foot dipole will also work on 30 meters, but there will be a bit over 1 dB line loss in 100 feet of 450-Ω window ladder line.

You could build the shorter (33.5-foot) antenna as a rotary dipole, which can be rotated with a light or medium-duty rotator. That's a really good idea, because you can then steer a lobe towards a target area or a null towards a source of interference. You might be tempted to use coax instead of a balanced feeder. Don't! On 28.4 MHz, you'll experience 11.4 dB loss in 100 feet of RG-213. By contrast, the loss is only 0.8 dB if you use 100 feet of 450-Ω window ladder line.

Cover the Compass

If your situation allows, you might want to consider adding a second, and perhaps even a third, antenna to fill the gaps in the azimuth coverage of a single antenna. Additional antennas should be configured differently than the first antenna. By that I mean that you should install your antennas in different directions. You could make a detailed study of patterns, or install your antennas in a convenient pattern and experiment from there. Don't overlook the advantage of having a vertical antenna to choose from, as well as a horizontal antenna or two.

A Low-Power Link-Coupled HF Antenna Tuner

Here's a project that's been around for a while, and for that reason, you may have already seen it in *The ARRL Handbook* or *The ARRL Antenna Book*. (See **Fig 10-8**.) The circuit, shown in **Fig 10-9**, has been in use by hams for several decades to couple into balanced loads on the HF bands. In other words, this is a tried-and-proven technique for feeding balanced feed line from coax. I have personally built several variations of this basic circuit, and some of them were for high-power operation. All of them worked well.

The Circuit

The antenna tuner shown in Fig 10-9 is a band-switched, link-coupled unit. The unit described here is intended for power levels up to roughly 200 W. Balance was checked by ARRL Lab staff. They used two RF ammeters, one

Fig 10-8—Exterior view of the band-switched link-coupled antenna tuner. Alligator clips are used to select the proper tap positions on the coil.

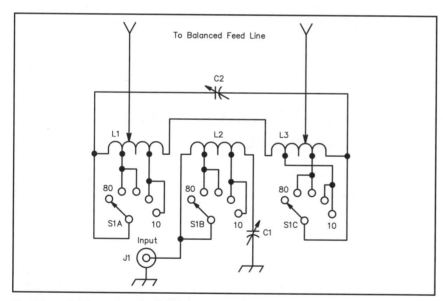

Fig 10-9—Schematic diagram of the link-coupled antenna tuner. The connections marked as "To Balanced Feed Line" are steatite or ceramic feed-through insulators. The arrows on the other ends of these connections are alligator clips.

C1—350 pF maximum, 0.0435-in. plate spacing or greater.
C2—100 pF maximum, 0.0435-in. plate spacing or greater.
J1—Coaxial connector
L1, L2, L3—B&W 3026 Miniductor stock, 2-in. diameter, 8 turns per inch, #14 wire. Coil assembly consists 48 turns, L1 and L3 are each 17 turns tapped at 8 and 11 turns from the outside ends. L2 is 14 turns tapped at 8 and 12 from the C1 end. See text for additional details.
S1—3-pole, 5-position ceramic rotary switch.

in each leg of the feed line to measure current in the legs. Results showed the balance to be well within 1 dB.

In the schematic, L2 is the link and C1 is used to adjust the coupling. S1B selects the proper amount of link inductance for each band. L1 and L3 are located on each side of the link and are the coils to which the antenna is connected. Alligator clips are used to connect the antenna to the coil because different impedances must be connected at different points (taps) along the coil. Also, with most antennas it will be necessary to change taps for operation on different bands. C2 tunes L1 and L3 to resonance at the operating frequency.

Switch sections S1A and S1C select the amount of inductance needed for the various HF bands. The inductance of each of the coils has been optimized for loads in the impedance range of roughly 20 to 600 Ω. Antenna systems that exhibit impedances well outside this range may require that some of the fixed connections to L1 and L3 be changed. Should this be necessary, remember to keep the L1 and L3 sections symmetrical—the same number of turns on each coil. This will help maintain system balance.

Construction

The unit is housed in a homemade aluminum enclosure that measures 9 × 8 × 3½ inches. As can be seen from the schematic, C2 must be isolated from ground. This can be accomplished by mounting the capacitor on steatite or ceramic standoffs or other suitable insulating material.

Make sure that the hole through the front panel for the shaft of C2 is large enough so that the shaft does not make contact with the chassis. Better yet, connect an insulated coupler to the shaft and use an extension to pass through the front panel. This technique can be seen in **Fig 10-10**.

Tune-Up

The transmitter should be connected to the input of the antenna tuner through an SWR meter or directional wattmeter. Set S1 to the band of operation, and connect the balanced line to the insulators on the rear panel of the coupler. Attach alligator clips to the mid points of coils L1 and L3, and apply power. Adjust C1 and C2 for minimum

Yet More HF Dipoles 5

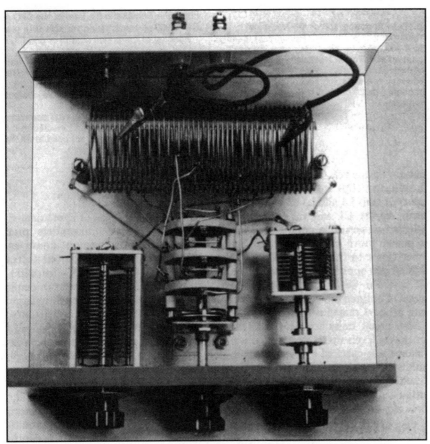

Fig 10-10—Interior view of the link-coupled antenna tuner, showing the basic positions of the major components. Component placement is not critical, but the unit should be laid out for minimum-length leads.

reflected power (best SWR). If a good match can't be obtained, move the antenna tap points either closer to the ends or center of the coils. (The tap points should be the same number of turn from the ends—or center—of L1 and L3.) Again apply power and tune C1 and C2 until the best possible match is obtained. Continue this procedure until you're able to reach a 1:1 match.

I find it handy to make a list of tap points and capacitor settings for the various bands. With that list at hand, it's a lot quicker and easier to change bands.

An Extended Double Zepp Antenna for 12 Meters

This article by John J. Reh, K7KGP, first appeared in the December 1987 issue of *QST*. Do you have a little over 50 feet of horizontal space to spare for a 24-MHz skywire? If so, this simple antenna will beat your half-wave dipole by about 3 dB—and you can phase two of them for even more gain and directivity. The sidebar by Bob Mandeville, N1EDM, explains how to adapt Reh's antenna for other bands.

According to *The ARRL Antenna Book*, *Zepp*—short for Zeppelin—is a term long applied to just about any resonant antenna end-fed by a two-wire transmission line. A bit further on in the *Antenna Book*, there's a discussion of the extended double Zepp (EDZ) antenna. This interested me because I have

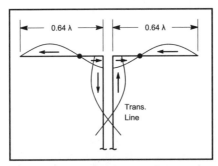

Fig 10-11—The extended double Zepp antenna consists of two 0.64-λ elements fed in phase.

always been intrigued by "old-fashioned" wire antennas—and because the old-fashioned extended double Zepp's 3-dB gain over a half-wave dipole would provide performance quite suitable for

modern times! The EDZ antenna consists of two collinear 0.64-λ elements fed in phase. **Fig 10-11** shows current distribution in an EDZ, and **Fig 10-12** shows the EDZ's horizontal directivity pattern in free space.

The extended double Zepp's theoretical performance looked good to me, so I designed and built an EDZ antenna for the 12-meter band. **Fig 10-13** shows its configuration. I decided to cut mine for 24.950 MHz. Each EDZ element is 25 feet, 3 inches long, and consists of #14 stranded copper wire. The antenna elements are center-fed by a short matching section made of a 5-foot, 5-inch length of 450-Ω open-wire line. Connection to 52-Ω coaxial feed line is made by means of a 1:1 balun

EXTENDED DOUBLE-ZEPP CALCULATIONS

John Reh's article, "An Extended Double Zepp Antenna for 12 Meters," is interesting from both a technical and constructional point of view; I found the 3-dB gain figure attractive. But I wanted to build the antenna for 20 meters instead of 12 meters. Using John's article and performing some research in the *ARRL Handbook*, I reworked the calculations and came up with the following formulas. I thought others who wanted to build EDZs for other frequencies might find this information useful.

- A constant (984) is used to determine the electrical length of a wire in feet: W(ft) = 984/f, where f is the desired operating frequency in MHz.
- The overall length of each leg is calculated by

$$L = W \times 0.64 \qquad \text{(Eq 1)}$$

- The 450-ohm open wire matching line for a single EDZ is calculated by

$$M(sgl) = 52/360 \times 0.95 \times W \qquad \text{(Eq 2)}$$

The 450-ohm line is made of #18 wire spaced 1-inch center to center. The line has a velocity factor of 0.95. For phased EDZs, the following calculations apply:

- The length of the 11-degree matching line is calculated by

$$M(pha) = 11/360 \times W \times 0.95 \qquad \text{(Eq 3)}$$

- The length of the 4-degree matching stub is calculated by

$$S(pha) = 4/360 \times W \times 0.95 \qquad \text{(Eq 4)}$$

- Spacing for phased EDZs is W/8.

The input impedance of the dipole (142 – *j* 555) was calculated for #14 wire. The *ARRL Handbook* defines the characteristic impedance of #12 - 14 wire as 500 - 600 ohms at a height of 10 to 30 feet. If you use other wire sizes for the dipole itself, the matching section length may require changing, so start with a longer matching section and trim it as required.

For a 20-meter EDZ, the numbers worked out this way: The antenna has an overall length of 88 feet and a 9.53-ft matching section. A 10-meter phased EDZ looks quite easy to build, and should exhibit a gain of 8 dB over a dipole. I'm not sure if this design approach will work for 2-meter band antennas, but the dimensions look quite manageable.—*Bob Mandeville, N1EDM*

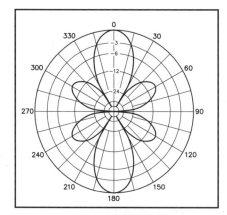

Fig 10-12—Horizontal directivity pattern for an extended double Zepp antenna in free space. Relative to a half-wave dipole, it exhibits a gain of approximately 3 dB. The antenna elements lie along the 90°-270° line.

transformer. My EDZ is strung between two trees, 35 feet above ground.

Matching Section

You may consider this "reinventing the wheel," but I used a series section transformer. The open-wire-line matching section is 52 electrical degrees long (0.145 λ). The matching section transforms the EDZ's input impedance to about 55 Ω, as measured with a noise bridge. The matching-section dimension

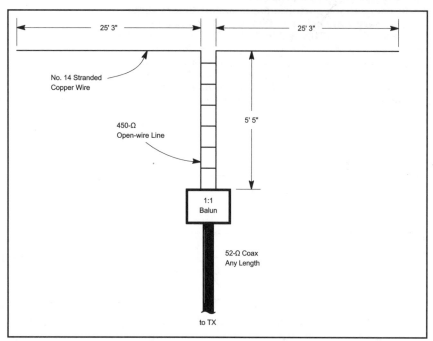

Fig 10-13—The extended double Zepp at K7KGP, cut for 24.950 MHz. The 450-Ω matching section transforms the EDZ's calculated input impedance (142 –*j* 555 Ω) to 55 Ω (measured) for connection to 52-Ω coaxial cable by means of a 1:1 balun. The electrical length of the matching section is 52°; the linear dimension shown in the drawing assumes 450-Ω line with a velocity factor of 0.95.

given in Fig 10-13 assumes a velocity factor of 0.95 for the 450-Ω line.

Trimming the matching section to size is the only adjustment necessary

with the EDZ. Make the transformer a little long to begin with, and shorten it an inch or two at a time to bring the system into resonance. (You can check

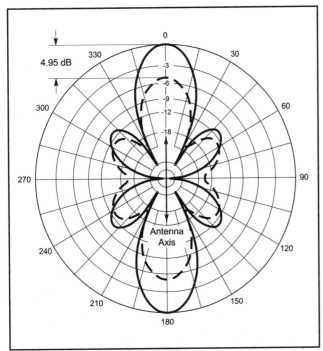

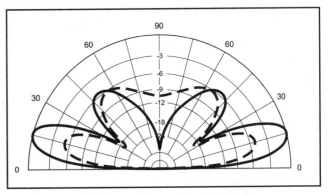

Fig 10-15—Comparison of the calculated vertical directivity patterns of one EDZ (dashed line), and two EDZs spaced at 1/8 λ and fed 180° out of phase (solid line).

Fig 10-14—Comparison of calculated horizontal directivity patterns of one extended double Zepp (dashed line) and two EDZs spaced at 1/8 λ and fed 180° out of phase (solid line). The antennas lie along the 90° –270° line, and the antennas are mounted 35 feet above average earth. The phased EDZs exhibit nearly 5-dB gain over a single EDZ. This is 7 to 8 dB gain over a half-wave dipole. Beamwidth of the two-EDZ array is 30°. The antenna axis is the same for the single EDZ and both EDZs in the phased array. The two-EDZ configuration characterized here is an end-fire array because maximum radiation occurs along its axis.

resonance with a noise bridge or by monitoring the SWR.) Do not change the length of the elements—the EDZ's gain and directivity depend on its elements being 0.64 λ long.

Phasing Two EDZs for More Gain and Directivity

Properly phased, two extended double Zepp antennas can give improved gain and directivity over a single EDZ. **Fig 10-14** compares the calculated horizontal directivity patterns of a single EDZ and an array consisting of two EDZs spaced at 1/8 λ and fed 180° out of phase. **Fig 10-15** compares the vertical radiation patterns of the single and phased EDZs.

Fig 10-16 shows the dimensions of a practical two-EDZ configuration. With proper adjustment, it exhibits an SWR of 1.3:1 across the 24-MHz band. In the array I built, lightweight broom handles serve as spreaders between the element ends; the center spreader is a wooden slat. I used nylon rope to haul the array up between two trees. This antenna system works well, and the contacts I have had with it have been entirely satisfactory.

The matching method shown in Fig 10-16 is somewhat clumsy because the combined length of the phasing lines is greater than the spacing between the EDZs. The feed method shown in

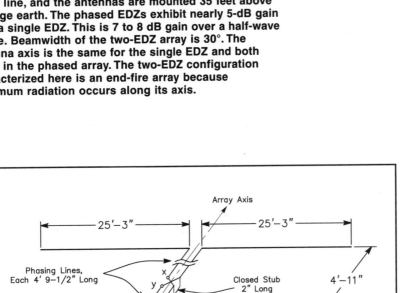

Fig 10-16—One method of phasing two EDZs for greater gain and directivity. The array is bidirectional, with maximum radiation occurring along the array axis. The impedance across points X and Y is 50 Ω, balanced; with a 1 :1 balun at XY, the array can be fed by means of 52-Ω coaxial cable. The stub, 1.5° long, cancels a capacitive reactance of approximately 13.5 Ω at the feed point. This array works well, but its matching system is clumsy because the combined length of the phasing lines is greater than the spacing of the two EDZs. Fig 10-17 shows an alternate feed method.

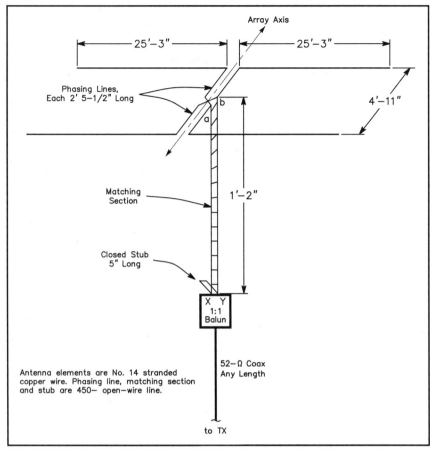

Fig 10-17—Alternate method of phasing two EDZs. In this arrangement, the length of each phasing line is half the EDZ spacing. Calculated impedance across points a and b is 15 – *j* 112 Ω. The matching section—11° in length— transforms this to a calculated impedance of approximately 55 – *j* 32 Ω (balanced) across points x and y. The stub, 4° long, cancels the capacitive reactance (32 Ω). A 1:1 balun transformer allows the array to be fed by means of a 52-Ω coaxial cable. See text.

Fig 10-17 should be easier to build because the combined length of the phasing lines equals the spacing between the EDZs. I've not tried this matching method, but I'm confident that my calculated dimensions are close to what will actually be encountered.

Conclusion

If the extended double Zepp has caught your attention, but 12 meters hasn't, you can scale the linear dimensions given here for other bands of interest (see sidebar). Once your EDZ is up and working, I think you'll agree that the performance of the "old-fashioned" extended double Zepp isn't old-fashioned at all!

A Wideband 80-Meter Dipole

This project by Rudy Severns, N6LF, first appeared in July 1995 *QST*. Severns deals with a common problem—how to cover both ends of the 80-meter band with a single antenna. His solution is worth your consideration.

The 500-kHz width of the 80-meter band makes it by far the widest HF amateur band on a percentage basis—13% of the center frequency. Over the years, a legion of articles have described antennas that have purported to provide an SWR of less than 2:1 over the whole band. Some did, and some didn't. With my two transceivers—a Drake TR-7 and Yaesu FT-757GX— even a 2:1 SWR isn't low enough because the rigs automatically begin to reduce output power before a 2:1 SWR

is reached. I suspect this is not an uncommon occurrence with other rigs (not equipped with built-in automatic antenna tuners) as well.

What's really needed is an antenna that provides an SWR below 1.6 or 1.7:1 over the entire band. It'd be really convenient to jump from one end of the band to the other without having to think about retuning the antenna tuner or rig, or buying an automatic antenna tuner. Such a requirement makes antenna design tough!

The following is a description of an antenna that meets the need. This one has been built and it works great with no noticeable SWR degradation caused by rain, snow, wind or other weather elements. Surprisingly, it's a simple wire antenna that's only as long as a standard dipole.

Earlier Antennas

My idea has its roots in two well-known antennas: the open-sleeve dipole and the folded dipole. With an open-sleeve dipole, additional conductors are added in close proximity to but not connected to a common single-wire dipole, as shown in **Fig 10-18**. In addition to the fundamental resonance of the simple dipole, the added conductors create new resonances. This effect can be used to multiband or broadband an antenna— and it's an idea that's been around since WW II.

A folded dipole's bandwidth is greater than a single-wire dipole made of the same wire size. Although the bandwidth attainable with a folded dipole is better, by itself, it's still not good enough for our needs. **Fig 10-19** shows the typical SWR plot for a folded dipole, using 12-inch element spacing, #14 wire and centered on 3.750 MHz. This antenna's 2:1 SWR bandwidth is approximately 375 kHz. You can improve things a bit by using greater element spacing, but then the weight and length of the spacers gets to be a hassle and you still won't have sufficient bandwidth.

Antenna Height

One common problem with any 80-meter antenna is installing it high enough to do some good. Because the current maximum is at the center of the dipole, it's important to keep that part of the antenna as high as possible. For most installations, 70 feet is pretty high, but at 80 meters, 70 feet is only one quarter of a wavelength.

A dipole's radiation angle is largely determined by the height of its center. If the antenna is strung between two supports, there's bound to be some sag, height is lost and the radiation angle raised. Weights of any sort—baluns, long lengths of coax, matching networks, etc, particularly near the antenna's center—contribute to sag. The resultant high-angle radiation is great for local QSOs, but bad news for DXing.

If I can't provide support for the antenna center, I prefer to use lightweight transmitting twinlead (weighing

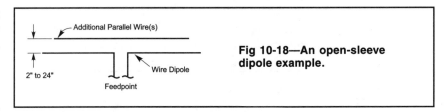

Fig 10-18—An open-sleeve dipole example.

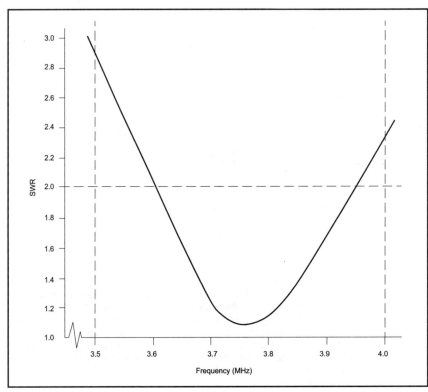

Fig 10-19—Typical SWR for a folded dipole resonant at 3.75 MHz.

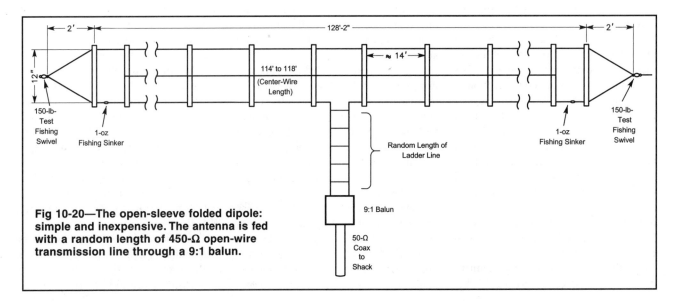

Fig 10-20—The open-sleeve folded dipole: simple and inexpensive. The antenna is fed with a random length of 450-Ω open-wire transmission line through a 9:1 balun.

in at 2.4 lb/100 ft versus the 9.4 lb/100 ft of RG-8 coax), with the balun at ground level. The 450-Ω ladder line is quite efficient, relatively light and costs about 16 cents a foot, much less than coax.

The feed-point impedance of a folded dipole is about 300 Ω. Although 300-Ω ladder line is available, making the transition from 300 Ω to 50 Ω requires a 6:1 balun. Such baluns can be bought or made, but 4:1 or 9:1 baluns are much more common.

A Broadband 80-Meter Antenna

The antenna I came up with is shown in **Fig 10-20**. It's simply an open-sleeve version of the folded dipole. The resonator wire added midway between the two folded-dipole elements is supported by the spacers already used for the folded dipole. That's all there is to it: a single wire down the middle of a folded dipole! One interesting result of adding the wire is that not only is the antenna very broadband, but by juggling the spacing and wire lengths a bit, Zr is very close to 450 Ω which fits in nicely with available transmission lines and a 9:1 balun. The transmission line operates with a very low SWR and can be of virtually any length.

A graph of the measured SWR for two lengths of the center wire (L_C) is shown in **Fig 10-21**. The measurements were made with considerable care, using Bird wattmeters. For $L_C = 118$ feet, the highest SWR is 1.5:1, and is less than that over most of the band. For $L_C = 114$ feet, the worst-case SWR is 1.8:1, but the overall 2:1 bandwidth is extended to 800 kHz. This would be advantageous to MARS operators operating just above the upper band edge. Experimenting further, I shortened L_C to 112 feet, which pushed the 2:1 bandwidth up to nearly 1 MHz (3.3 to 4.25 MHz). For most hams, that may not be of great importance, but it's something to keep in mind.

Fig 10-20 shows the number and separation of the wire spacers. It's important to keep the spacers as light (and inexpensive!) as possible. The two spacers on each end have to be fairly stiff, so I used sections cut from solid fiberglass electric-fence wands. These wands which measure $^3/_8$-inch in diameter and are 4 feet long, are available from farming supply stores and Sears.

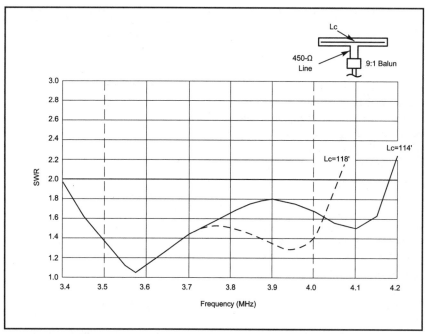

Fig 10-21—SWR curve of the open-sleeve dipole of Fig 10-27, showing curves for different lengths of the center wire (L_C).

The rest of the spreaders are made from half sections of $^1/_2$-inch CPVC plastic pipe. They're about half the weight of the fiberglass wand spreaders. I could have used full sections of the CPVC pipe for the end spreaders but, for the same weight, they would have had more wind loading.

Summary

Modeling this antenna, which is essentially a transmission line, doesn't work very well on *MININEC*-based programs. *NEC* programs such as *NecWires* are needed, and even then, you have to use 50 to 100 segments per λ/2 for the final design. Using *NecWires*, the total computed loss was only 0.07 dB (1.6%) for #14 wire and 0.09 dB (2%) for #16. Combined with the very low loss of the open-wire transmission line, if a low-loss 9:1 balun is used, the overall efficiency will be quite good.

At best, these antennas will be close to the ground in terms of wavelengths. The ground effects are important and will affect the impedances and final dimensions. This antenna was modeled at a height of 70 feet over poor ground (ε = 13, σ = 2 mS), which corresponds (more or less) to my location

and support height. I only had to adjust the center wire a bit to get the predicted performance. At another location or antenna height, the final performance and dimensions may be different.

A folded dipole loves to rotate when being hoisted and it twists when the wind blows, which really upsets the SWR if the parallel wires short together. In Fig 10-21, I've included a couple of details that help reduce this problem. The ends of the dipole are not symmetrical. To aid in avoiding antenna twist, 1-oz fishing sinkers are added to the bottom wire on each end. I also use two heavy-duty (150-pound-capacity) fishing-line swivels at the antenna support points.

Performance isn't the only criterion for a good antenna. For most hams, cost is always a consideration. This design uses 380 feet of wire (a total cost of $34 at 9 cents per foot) and about a buck's worth of $^1/_2$-inch CPVC pipe. The CPVC can also be used for the center and end insulators. The 450-Ω open-wire transmission line costs 14 to 16 cents per foot, so add another $15 to the total. So, for $50, you've got everything but the balun and the lead-in coax. You've also got a darn good antenna.

An 80-Meter Broadband Dipole with 50-Ohm Feed

Frank Witt, AI1H, developed, built and published the story of his answer to the problem of covering the 80-meter band with a single antenna. His article, entitled "The Coaxial Resonator Match and the Broadband Dipole" appeared in April 1989 *QST*. Here are excerpts from that article:

Out of the search for a simple dipole with acceptable SWR over the entire 80-meter band has come a matching technique with broadbanding properties and potential for many applications. This antenna and matching technique are extensions of earlier work by the author. In the sections that follow, the complete description of an 80-meter broadband dipole is provided, including performance data and construction details.

An 80-Meter Broadband Dipole

Fig 10-22 shows the detailed dimensions of the 80-meter coaxial-resonator-match broadband dipole. Notice that the total length of the coax is an electrical quarter wavelength, has a short at one end, an open at the other

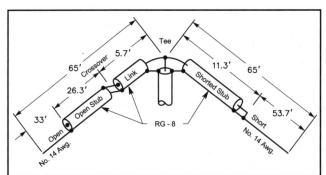

Fig 10-22—Coaxial-resonator-match broadband dipole for 80 meters. The coax segment lengths total ¼ wavelength. The overall antenna length is the same as that of a conventional inverted-V dipole.

end, a strategically placed crossover and is fed at a T junction. (The crossover is made by connecting the shield of one coax segment to the center conductor of the adjacent segment and by connecting the remaining center conductor and shield in a similar way.) At AI1H, the antenna is constructed as an inverted-V dipole with a 110° included angle and an apex at 60 feet. The measured SWR v frequency is shown in **Fig 10-23**. Also in Fig 10-23 is the SWR characteristic for an uncompensated inverted-V dipole made from the same materials and po-

sitioned exactly as was the broadband version. SWR measurements were made with a Daiwa Model CN 520 cross-needle SWR/power meter. Corrections were made for the cable loss between the antenna and the meter.

The antenna, made from RG-8 coaxial cable and #14 AWG wire, is fed with 50-Ω coax. The coaxial cable should be cut so the stub lengths of Fig 10-29 are within ½ inch of the specified values. PVC plastic pipe couplings and SO-239 UHF chassis connectors can be used to make the T and cross-

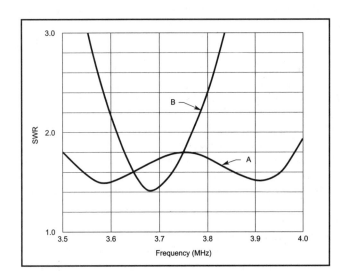

Fig 10-23—Curve A, the measured performance of the antenna of Fig 10-22. Also shown for comparison is the measured SWR of the same dipole without compensation, curve B.

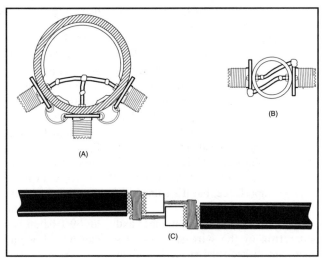

Fig 10-24—T and crossover construction. At A, a 2-inch PVC pipe coupling can be used for the T, and at B, a 1-inch coupling for the crossover. These sizes are the nominal inside diameters of PVC pipe that fits these couplings. The T could be standard UHF hardware (an M-358 T and a PL-258 coupler). An alternative construction for the crossover is shown at C, where a direct solder connection is made.

over connections, as shown in **Fig 10-24** at A and B. Alternatively, a standard UHF T connector and coupler can be used for the T, and the crossover can be a soldered connection (Fig 10-24C). I used RG-8 coax because of its ready availability, physical strength, power handling capability and moderate loss. An RG-58 model was also designed and built, and it performed well electrically. I don't recommend the RG-58 version, however, because it is too fragile. For example, the coaxial cable stretches enough from its own weight to affect the tuning. Also, RG-58 will have substantially lower power-handling capability than RG-8.

Cut the wire ends of the dipole about three feet longer than the lengths given in Fig 10-22. If there is a tilt in the SWR v frequency curve when the antenna is first built (a lopsided "W" shape), it can be flattened to look like the shape of curve A in Fig 10-23 by increasing or decreasing the wire length. Each end should be lengthened or shortened by the same amount. Try 6-inch changes at each end with each adjustment. Increasing the dipole length will lower the SWR at the low end of the band; decreasing the dipole length will lower the SWR at the high end of the band.

A word of caution: If the chosen coaxial cable is not RG-8 or equivalent, the dimensions will have to be modified. For example, RG-8X has a different insulation material than RG-8, and its use would dictate different segment lengths. The following cable types have about the same characteristic impedance loss and velocity factor as RG-8 and could be substituted: RG-8A, RG-10, RG-10A, RG-213 and RG-215.

Important point: The calculated coaxial segment lengths were based on the assumption that the Q and radiation resistance at resonance of the uncompensated dipole were 11.5 and 70 Ω), respectively. If the Q and radiation resistance differ markedly from these numbers because of different ground characteristics, antenna height, surrounding objects and so on, then different segment lengths would be required. In fact, if the dipole Q is too high, broadbanding is possible, but an SWR under 2:1 over the whole band cannot be achieved.

What is the performance of this broadband antenna relative to that of a conventional inverted-V dipole? Aside from the slight loss (about 1 dB at band edges, less elsewhere) because of the non-ideal matching network, the broadband version behaves essentially the same as a dipole cut for the frequency of interest. That is, the radiation patterns for the two cases are virtually the same. In reality, the dipole itself is not "broadband," but the coaxial resonator match provides a broadband match between the transmission line and the dipole antenna. This match is a remarkably simple way to broaden the SWR response of a dipole.

Fat Dipoles

Because this topic is an important one, here's yet another way to construct a broadband 80-meter dipole. Robert C. Wilson wrote the following for *The ARRL Antenna Compendium, Vol 2*.

Antennas without problems make radio communications enjoyable. I design overseas radio stations for a living, so I'd rather not have to fight my own ham station when just relaxing and rag chewing. Fat dipoles do the things I want. They match the coax line well over a wide band. and they launch the signal remarkably well.

Theory

Making a dipole conductor thicker than normal with respect to wavelength will increase the bandwidth and modify the working impedance of the antenna. The trick is to make a dipole "fat" in such a way that it may be easily constructed from cheap materials, be highly efficient and at the same time arrange things so that it will match the transmission line from the lower band edge to the upper band edge.

I started with the assumption that my band of interest would be the 80/75-meter band. From end to end, this requires a 13% bandwidth to the 2:1 SWR points for my broadband-solid-state final. I also assumed that this antenna was going to be at a nominal height of 30 feet or 0.11 wavelength above ground. The calculations indicated that a dipole built of four quarter-wavelength #14 wires (0.064 inch) with a spacing of 0.0114 wavelength would produce the necessary results. The correct length would have to be 0.45 wavelength to match a 50-ohm line.

Length = 442.5/f feet

Width = 11.25/f feet

Height = 112.5/f feet

where f = center frequency in MHz

Construction

Very few problems will be encountered in building this simple fat dipole if you follow the drawing (**Fig 10-25**). First you will need five good insulators. I prefer egg type insulators but there is no critical problem here. One insulator is for the center of the dipole and the others are for the four ends. You will need four 3-foot-long broomsticks or 1-inch wood or plastic rods with good weatherproofing. I painted mine with auto undercoating but outdoor paint or varnish should also work. Copperweld wire is very desirable because it won't stretch and change the tuning of your antenna. This type of wire is available through advertisements in *QST*. The same source may also be able to supply the essential wide-band balun transformer and coax. Either the RG-58 or RG-8 types of coax cable are satisfactory but the latter requires more support because of its greater weight.

Measure your wire carefully and leave enough extra so that the insulators can be attached. The final length will need to be the calculated value, from insulator wire end to insulator wire end. After building the four-wire section, attach dowel rods as shown to act as spreaders. Fasten each rod in place with pieces of wire threaded through the holes and then wrapped around the antenna wire. Wrap these spreader wires tight enough so that the rods will not slip out

Table 10-2
Dimensions and Bandwidths on Various Bands

Frequency MHz	Length, ft	Spacing (A), ft	Bandwidth, MHz
1.9	233	5.9	0.252
3.75	118	3	0.5
7.15	62	1.6	0.951
14.175	31.2	0.8	1.885
21.225	20.85	0.53	2.823
28.860	15.34	0.39	3.837

of place. Snip off projecting wire ends wherever they occur to prevent RF corona power loss. Then, using either wire or rope, make a bridle to hold the ends of the antenna.

Last, solder the balanced end of the balun transformer to the dipole. Each wire from the balun should go to the pair of wires on the same side of the dipole. The solder job should be of the best quality and permanent because it is hard to repair later. The coax needs to be connected to the unbalanced side of the balun. If you use large-diameter coax (³/₈ inch) then think about ways to support the weight. Perhaps a piece of nylon rope from the dipole center insulator to the coax will help take the load, but I'll leave the details of the problem up to you. After this final construction step, haul the antenna up in the trees, using care that no twists are allowed.

Operation

For once I had a 75-meter antenna that worked better than predicted. The SWR was 1.6:1 or better from 3.5 to 4.0 MHz. Better yet, reports received were excellent with my old 100-watt solid-state transceiver. Moving up and down the band gave no loading problems from the broadband final. The fat dipole is just what I needed for a good, relaxing rag chew after a hard day with the 500-kW rig at the office.

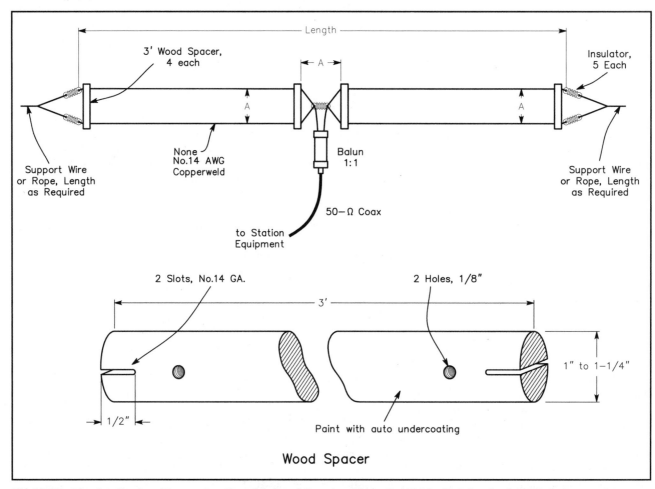

Fig 10-25—The fat dipole with construction details of the spreaders. See Table 10-2 for the length and spreader dimensions (A).

11 More Facts About Feed Lines

Selecting and Using Open-Wire Balanced Lines

By Dean Straw, N6BV

Earlier, I covered the subject of coaxial-cable transmission lines in Chapter 3. In this chapter I'll discuss *open-wire balanced lines*, which are also known as *parallel-wire lines* or sometimes simply as *open-wire lines*. A theoretically perfect open-wire line would consist of two closely spaced parallel wires separated by nothing but a vacuum. In actual practice, such a line would have some mechanical problems (to put it mildly!) so real-world open-wire line uses some sort of insulators to act as spacers between the two wires.

Fig 11-1 is a photograph showing three typical types of open-wire transmission line. The line at the top, with almost-clear plastic insulation, is 300-Ω "twin lead" used for TV reception. Hams don't use this type of line too commonly because it isn't rated for handling much transmitting power and is easily affected by dirt and pollution when used with high-SWR, non-resonant antennas. Still, twin lead is lightweight and inexpensive, two attributes that appeal to people who love to backpack their QRP rigs into the wilderness.

The darker-colored transmission line in the middle of Fig 11-1 is a heavier-duty version of 300-Ω line, called "transmitting twin lead." The insulation in this line is plastic with air injected into it to create a sort of foamed insulation. While popular overseas, especially in Britain, 300-Ω transmitting twin lead is not used by many US hams.

The last variety shown in Fig 11-1 is popularly called "window line," since the plastic between the two conductors has windows cut into it. Cutting windows serves two purposes:

- They reduce the weight of the line.
- They reduce the amount of surface area that could pick up dirt and contaminants, which degrade the characteristics of the insulation.

In the very early days of ham radio, hams used to construct their own open-wire transmission lines. They used wood dowels about 5 inches long, with notches cut at the ends to secure the two wires. In order to weatherproof them, hams used to boil these homebrew insulators in paraffin wax. Frankly, this always sounded like a lot of hard and messy work to me! I have visions of the wax melting in the hot sun, much like the wings of the mythological Icarus, as he tried to fly too close to the sun.

Anyhow, open-wire lines are enjoying something of a revival, after being considered "old-fashioned" for about 50 years since low-loss, high-quality coaxes became readily available after World War II. Even with relatively high levels of SWR encountered on some multiband antennas, open-wire lines are far less lossy than coaxial cables. Further, open-wire lines are comparatively inexpensive compared to coax.

High-power window line costs roughly $0.25 per foot in long rolls, while high-quality RG-213 sells for almost twice as much. At 1000 MHz, RG-213 is rated at about 8 dB/100 feet of matched-line loss, while window line is rated at about 1 dB/100 feet. When hams want multiband performance from a single antenna (like the 135-foot long HF dipole K8CH described in Chapter

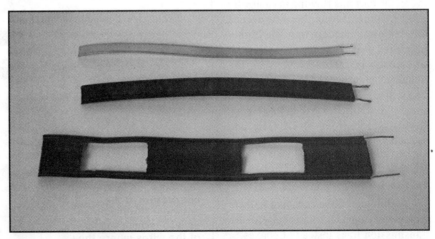

Fig 11-1—Photo showing three common types of open-wire lines: At the top, TV receiving type 300-Ω "twin lead," heavier duty transmitting type twin lead, and 450-Ω "window" ladder line.

10), which has high SWR on some ham bands, they need to use a very low-loss feed line or else suffer significant losses in the line itself.

MAIN CHARACTERISTICS OF OPEN-WIRE LINE

Like their coaxial-cable brethren, open-wire lines exhibit the same essential characteristics:

- Characteristic impedance, Z_0: Generally in the range from about 100 to 600 Ω. A nominal Z_0 of 450 Ω is the most popular nowadays.
- Velocity Factor: Generally in the range 80% to 92%.
- Matched-Line Loss: Lower than coax at the same frequency.

See **Table 11-1** for a summary listing of popular open-wire transmission lines. Just for reference, a high-quality RG-213 type of coax exhibits a matched-line loss of 2.1 dB/100 feet at 100 MHz.

Unlike their coaxial-cable brothers, parallel-wire transmission lines don't have a shield to prevent radiation from the line (or onto it). If the spacing between the two wires in an open-wire line is very small in terms of wavelength, the phase difference between the two currents flowing in the wires will be 180°, and if the amplitude of the currents is the same, the net result is that the fields from the two wires cancel out.

For a fixed distance between the wires (say, 1 inch for 450-Ω window line) the spacing in terms of wavelengths goes up as the frequency is raised. Thus the phase difference between the currents flowing in each wire will be different from the 180° needed for complete cancellation for higher frequencies. For this reason open-wire line loses its effectiveness as the frequency goes into the low UHF range. You will rarely find open-wire line used above the 450 MHz band, while coax is still going strong at 1.2 GHz and beyond.

DRAWBACKS OF OPEN-WIRE LINES

While they have advantages, there are other drawbacks to using open-wire transmission lines instead of coaxes:

- Open-wire lines require a balun to transition from balanced to unbalanced to work with modern-day transceivers, which have coaxial-cable outputs. See Chapters 2 and 3 for more about baluns.
- You must keep open-wire lines away from nearby metallic objects that might unbalance them.
- Sharp bends should be avoided (for both coax and open-wire lines!).
- Open-wire lines are poor choices for rotating antennas, such as Yagis or quads, because open-wire lines can't be secured to the rotating metal mast that turns such antennas.
- Open-wire lines require an antenna tuner of some sort to provide the 50 Ω needed by modern transceivers.
- When used in high-SWR situations (such as multiband dipoles), dirt or contamination from air pollution can change the tuning because the Z_0 changes if the dielectric changes.
- Open-wire lines, especially at center-fed dipoles, need some form of mechanical strain relief because they are more fragile than coax cable.

These are not huge objections, not by any means—they are mainly precautions. When high-power shortwave stations such as the VOA (Voice of America) absolutely need to run very long transmission lines to their antenna arrays in distant fields, they almost universally use open-wire lines. Of course, they install and maintain these lines very carefully.

USING OPEN-WIRE LINES, SOME TIPS

Keeping Open-Wire Line Away From Other Conductors

A good rule-of-thumb is to space the line away from nearby conductors (such as coaxes or a metal tower) by a factor of three times the wire spacing. For example, 450-Ω window line has

Table 11-1
Common Types of Open-Wire Transmission Line

Type	Z_0 Ω	Velocity Factor, %	Wire Gauge	Power Handling	Matched-Line Loss, 100 MHz
TV Twin Lead	300	80	#22	Low	1.4 dB/100'
Twin Lead	300	80	#20	Med	1.1 dB/100'
Generic Window	405	91	#18	High	0.3 dB/100'
High-Power Window	450	91	#16	High	0.3 dB/100'
Open-Wire	600	92	#12	High	0.2 dB/100'

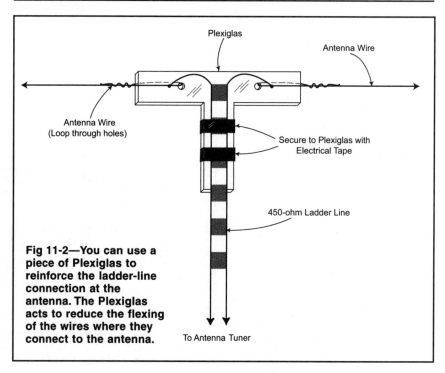

Fig 11-2—You can use a piece of Plexiglas to reinforce the ladder-line connection at the antenna. The Plexiglas acts to reduce the flexing of the wires where they connect to the antenna.

about 1-inch spacing between the wires. The line should be kept at least 3 inches away from nearby conductors, using standoff insulators. Some hams use insulators designed for electric-fence installations.

Strain Relief

When an open-wire transmission line is used to feed a center-fed dipole, it must support its own weight. This means that you should use some form of mechanical strain relief—not doing so will almost surely result in broken wires, not to mention an unsightly pile of open-wire line on the ground under the antenna! **Fig 11-2** shows a method employed by Steve Ford, WB8IMY, to provide mechanical strain relief using electrical tape to secure the ladder line to a piece of Plexiglas.

Michael Pellock, NA6J, described a clever and inexpensive method for providing strain relief in his article "Unique Ladder-Line to Wire-Antenna Feedpoint Termination" in *The ARRL Antenna Compendium, Vol 5.* Here's what he said.

For years I've built antennas using ladder-line and for years I've been frustrated to find my ladder line lying broken and tangled under the antenna after a major windstorm. Some of the mechanical solutions I've tried over the years have been either time consuming to fabricate, overly costly, or both.

I finally came up with a method that is very simple and very inexpensive. It uses a piece of Romex insulation to support the ladder line at the feed point and 12 inches below, yielding a strong mechanical connection. I suspect that you can find the parts in your junk box. (If not, you might be able to persuade an electrician to give them to you for free!)

The feed-point termination starts out with a 17-inch long piece of 10-2G Romex electrical house wire. This contains two #10 insulated wires, with an uninsulated ground wire. You will actually use only the outside-insulated sheath. Do not try to use smaller size Romex, such as 14-2G or 12-2G— the insulation used on these Romex wires is not strong enough to stand up under adverse weather conditions. Pull out all three wires from the Romex by clamping each wire in a vise and pulling

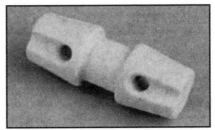

Fig 11-3—Photo of modified plastic insulator. The ribs in the center were removed with a coping saw and a flat file to create a groove approximately ⁵⁄₈ inch wide and ¹⁄₈ inch deep.

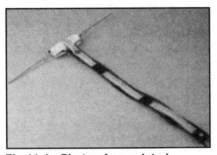

Fig 11-4—Photo of completed assembly, showing Romex insulation threaded through windows in ladder line and secured by a loop around the modified plastic insulator. The #6 machine screws toward the top and bottom of the Romex hold it to the ladder line for a strong mechanical connection.

it out of the insulated sheath.

Next, cut out one plastic section from the end of the "window" ladder line, leaving about three inches of insulated wire for attachment to the antenna. Using a leather punch or an

awl, punch a hole to clear a #6 screw in the center of the first "window" section below the top three inches of insulated wire. Punch another hole in the sixth window section, approximately 10³⁄₄ inches below the first hole.

Remove the center ribs from the plastic insulator using a coping saw. Smooth the cut-away section using a flat or square ¹⁄₂-inch file. See **Fig 11-3**, a photo of the modified insulator. Now, insert the two ladder-line wires through the holes in the ends of the modified insulator and pull them up tight. These wires will be attached later to the antenna wires.

See **Fig 11-4**, which shows the completed assembly. Wrap one end of the 17-inch piece of Romex insulation around the center of the insulator. Punch out a hole to clear a #6 machine screw using the leather punch, lining it up using the hole previously punched in the ladder-line insulation.

Fasten together this portion of the assembly with a 6-32 × ¹⁄₂-inch pan-head machine screw. Use flat fiber washers against the Romex on both sides. (If a round-head screw is used rather than a pan-head screw, install an additional ¹⁄₄-inch OD flat metal washer between the head of the round-head screw and the fiber washer.)

Weave the Romex insulation through the ladder line as illustrated and punch a #6-size hole in the Romex insulation, lining it up using the second hole punched in the ladder line insulation. Fasten this part together

Fig 11-5—K8CH's entry panel, with provision for four coaxes, a lightning-protection ground wire, and feed-through insulators for an open-wire feed line.

using another 6-32 machine screw and associated hardware. I dabbed both screw ends (threaded part) with Elmer's weather-tight wood glue to prevent the nuts from loosening.

Finally, attach the antenna wires to the plastic insulator and the ladder-line wires, making sure you solder the connections properly. This completes the assembly, which should be able to stand up under any kind of weather because the Romex insulation is very tough.

Twisting in the Wind...

Even with a good mechanical means of strain relief up at the feed point, it's also a good idea to twist window-type ladder line several turns per foot. This tends to minimize the wind-surface area and prevents excessive flexing that can lead to breakage.

Getting Open-Wire Line Into the House

See Chapter 3, especially Chuck Hutchinson's sidebar *Coax Entry Panel*, which also includes provision for getting an open-wire line into the house using two feed-through insulators through a Plexiglas panel. **Fig 11-5** is a photograph of his completed panel.

12 A Potpourri of Antenna Ideas

This chapter comprises a savory and eclectic collection of antenna projects and ideas that are presented here to stimulate your thinking and to provide you with a variety of alternative antennas. Projects range from simple to fairly complex, but they're all fun. Perhaps you'll find just what you're looking for in this chapter.

One Stealthy Wire

By Steve Ford, WB8IMY, October 1998 QST.

I can never leave well enough alone. There used to be a perfectly good HF trap dipole antenna in my backyard. With its whiter-than-white PVC-encased traps dangling in the sunshine, it was a work of art. Best of all, the antenna radiated a halfway decent signal on 40, 20 and 15 meters.

But on a quiet Saturday morning I found myself staring glumly at my beautiful skywire. I drummed my fingertips on the windowsill, wrestling with a vague sense of discontent. With propagation conditions rapidly improving, I wanted access to every HF band—the whole enchilada. Being on 40, 20 and 15 didn't cut it anymore.

In classic Hollywood fashion, two miniature figures suddenly appeared on my shoulders. One was decidedly angelic. A single glance at her wholesome countenance would spike your blood sugar. The other visitor was a demonic caricature that I recall seeing on a jar of "Burned Beyond Recognition" salsa.

"Your antenna has been a loyal friend," the angel cooed. "You wouldn't dare abandon it now. Besides, you have better things to do—like fixing that leaky kitchen faucet."

"Don't listen to her!" the goblin snapped. "What's more important to you, ham radio or a few errant drops of water? Think about it. Why settle for three lousy bands when you can have all nine?"

"I have to be careful," I sniffed. "I

Fig 12-1—My ICOM AH-4 remote automatic antenna tuner secured to the rear wall of my tool shed. The insulator at the end of the sloping wire is visible as well.

don't have much room and I promised my wife that I wouldn't string up something she considered 'obnoxious'."

"I have the perfect solution," he whispered, "and all it takes is one stealthy wire."

"No!" the Lilliputian angel cried. "Don't do it!"

The little devil raised his index finger and grinned. "One wire. Just one wire."

"Who were you talking to?" my wife asked.

"No one," I replied as the figures vanished in puffs of pink smoke. "I was on my way outside to do some antenna work."

She rolled her eyes. "What now?"

" A different approach," I replied as I flipped open my toolbox. "It's an end-fed sloping wire."

"And what is this fed thing going to look like?"

"End-fed wire" I corrected cheerfully. "You'll hardly see it. It will merely glitter like the silvery wisp of a spider's web laced with morning dew."

"What?"

"Trust me. Have I ever lied to you about my antenna projects?"

"Well, there was the time you . . ." but I was already out the door.

To Infinity, and Beyond!

With the proper counterpoise or ground system, a single wire can make a fine radiator. Ask anyone who owns any number of end-fed antenna schemes. I crafted my end-fed radiator from 80 feet of stranded copper. Why 80 feet? I wanted a wire that would not be a $\frac{1}{2}$ wavelength at any of my target bands (80 though 10 meters, or multiples thereof). By avoiding $\frac{1}{2}$-wavelengths I could keep the impedance at the feed point to a manageable level—at least to a value that I could easily "transform" to 50 Ω with my crude matching network (more about this later).

An 80-foot wire can go zipping off in just about any direction, including straight up. If you have some really tall trees in your yard, more power to you. In my case, however, the tallest support is a 50-foot maple with poor self-esteem that will probably make a suicidal plunge into my family room during the next hurricane. Our tool shed makes a nice location for the feed point and matching network, but it is at least 70 feet from the base of the tree. So, I decided to slope the wire from the shed into the highest point of the melancholy maple (see **Fig 12-2**).

I struck a firm, commanding pose as I launched a weighted length of fishing line into the tree with my Kmart slingshot. Slingshots being the precision instruments that they are, it required several tries to place the line exactly where I wanted it. Observing this bizarre exercise was the high point of my daughter's morning. Before each attempt I would shout the Buzz Lightyear line from the movie *Toy Story*, "To infinity, and beyond!" It's kind of like yelling "fore!" on a golf course, but with a more startling effect. Try it at the country club sometime.

With the line finally in the tree, I attached the insulators and slowly hauled 80 feet of wire skyward while singing "Old Man River" at the top of my lungs. With the radiator in place, it was time to do something about the ground system.

Radials? I Don't Need No Stinkin' Radials!

When I was a brand-spanking new Novice in the winter of 1971, I erected my first antenna—a $\frac{1}{4}$-wavelength vertical for 15 meters—immediately behind the apartment building where I lived. The meager instruction sheet supplied with the antenna warned that a good ground system was necessary for proper operation. No problem. I hammered a 6-foot copper rod into the semifrozen earth and called it a day. My antenna system was complete.

I marveled at the fabulous SWR. It was almost 1:1 across the band! This miraculous SWR bandwidth should have touched off a crescendo of alarm bells in my head. Instead, I gleefully began calling CQ . . . and calling . . . and calling . . . and calling. No one answered. Not a peep.

It wasn't until I described my antenna system to an old-timer at the next club meeting that the problem became obvious. When I outlined my ground system he suddenly excused himself. I heard what sounded like distant, hysterical laughter, but I wasn't really sure. When he returned—gasping and holding one hand across his abdomen—he produced a piece of paper and diagramed a real ground system.

"These are radials," he said with a smile. "They're wires that you connect to the shield of your coaxial cable at the base of your antenna. They form the ground system that your antenna works against. Don't worry about how long they are. Just put down as many as you can. Bury them in the ground or lay them on top of the soil, it doesn't matter. Connect the radials together at that ground rod of yours. That's about all it's good for!"

Of course, the old-timer was right. I put down four long radials and, lo and behold, I started getting answers to my calls! My antenna system had been transformed from an air-cooled dummy load to something that really radiated.

Twenty-seven years have passed and the lesson is still firmly planted in my memory. I commandeered my wife's garden edging tool—the ideal instrument for laying down radial wires—and went to work. An hour later I had four radials, the longest of which was about 60 feet, keeping company with the grubs below our lawn. All that remained was the matching network.

Matchmaker, Matchmaker

My first matching network was about as crude as they get (see **Fig 12-3**). It was little more than a fat coil. Being an incorrigible packrat, I happened to have just the right item in stock: a $2\frac{1}{2}$-inch diameter coil made from 28 turns of #14 wire spaced about $\frac{1}{4}$ inch between each turn. You'll still find these types of coils for sale at hamfest fleamarkets and at surplus dealers. Of course, you can make your own.

The top of my coil was soldered to a short piece of wire, which was in turn soldered to the lower end of the antenna. The bottom of the coil was attached to another short wire that connected to my radial system, along with the braid of my coaxial cable. I soldered

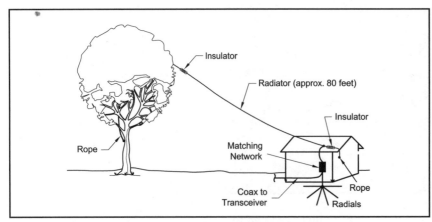

Fig 12-2—This is my backyard end-fed scheme. The matching network and the lower end of the antenna are virtually out of sight behind a tool shed. The radiator slopes up into the limbs of a spreading maple tree.

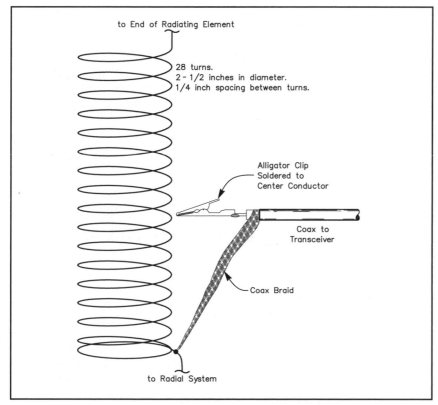

to End of Radiating Element

28 turns.
2-1/2 inches in diameter.
1/4 inch spacing between turns.

Alligator Clip
Soldered to
Center Conductor

Coax to
Transceiver

Coax Braid

to Radial System

Fig 12-3—My initial attempt at a matching network involved little more that the coil you see here. Later I opted for the remote-control approach.

a tiny alligator clip to the center conductor of my coax and proceeded to find the locations on the coil that resulted in the lowest SWR on each of my favorite band segments.

This stage of the project involved a certain amount of child labor. I sat my daughter in front of my transceiver with a large bag of M & Ms (her favorites) and showed her how to watch the reflected-power needle on my wattmeter. I set the rig to low output, sent a quick ID and left the CW key within her grasp. Between mouthfuls of candy, we finally finished the job.

"Let 'er rip, honey!"

"The needle is going reeeeally high, Daddy!"

I would mutter under my breath and select another coil tap. "Try it again, hon."

"Now the needle is barely moving!"

Bingo!

It Worked!

The end-fed wire worked like gang busters. I spent the rest of the afternoon gathering signal reports, most of which far exceeded my expectations. As far as I could tell, the antenna was performing as well as my dipole, but on many more bands. The best "report" came from my wife. I found her standing in the driveway eyeballing the wire as it snaked upward into the leaves.

"This is pretty good," she said at last. "I can just barely see the wire."

"Yes," I replied happily," and now I can get on every band from 80 through 10 meters. I can probably get the thing to work on 160, too."

"Yeah. Well, whatever."

The Lazy Way Out

My end-fed "sloper" seemed to perform well, but I still wasn't entirely satisfied. I disliked having to run outside and change coil taps whenever I changed bands. Tap changing was particularly hazardous at night. If you've ever stepped on an upturned rake and taken the handle full in the face, you know what I mean. Once I ran outside at midnight, only to have my wife duti-

fully lock the door behind me. The result looked like the end of the Flintstones cartoons where the credits are rolling and Fred is frantically beating on the door and shouting "Wilma!"

There had to be a better way—and there was.

Consider the common antenna tuner. Remove the frills and features and what do you have? It's an adjustable impedance-matching device. Now consider the tapped coil at the end of my antenna. Is it not also an adjustable impedance-matching device?

Most hams place their antenna tuners in their shacks for convenience sake, but there is no reason why a tuner can't be located directly at the feed point of an antenna. As long as you can protect the tuner from the weather and operate it by remote control, why not?

The beast I needed, therefore, was a remote-controlled automatic antenna tuner. Fortunately, we're blessed with remote-controlled autotuners in abundance. SGC Inc makes several nice units designed for outdoor use, and LDG Electronics manufactures a relatively inexpensive autotuner that is capable of remote control (although you'd have to supply the weatherproof enclosure). SGC and LDG advertise often in *QST*. Most transceiver manufacturers have turned out their own remote autotuners as well. As the owner of an ICOM IC-706, I settled on ICOM's new model AH-4.

The coil went back in my junkbox and the AH-4 found a home on the shed wall. The tuner works beautifully, loading up the antenna on 80 through 6 meters within two seconds or less. Whenever I change bands I merely press the TUNE button on the front of my rig. That beats a rake handle in the face any day.

I put my installation to the test on Field Day and was gratified by the results. I dabbled at the IARU HF World Championships last July and was impressed again. I even managed to work into eastern Europe on 80 meter phone—not bad for an antenna that's only about 1/3 wavelength at that frequency!

If you lack the space for a long wire antenna, or if you're "aesthetically challenged" as I am, an end-fed wire is something to consider. An autotuner makes it a remarkably convenient all-band antenna, but if you are only interested in a couple of bands, save your money and use the coil instead.

End-fed wires are ideal for apartment and condo dwellers, too. Toss one end into the nearest tree (check for power lines first!), then bring the other end through the window and attach it to the "long wire" post of an antenna tuner. Instead of a radial system you can get by with single counterpoise wires cut to $1/4$-wavelength for each desired band. You can use ultra-thin wire for the counterpoises, attaching them to the antenna tuner ground lug and snaking them along the baseboards. No one will ever notice. Just watch out for high RF voltages at the ends of the counterpoises. Even at low power levels they can give you (or a curious pet) an unpleasant bite. The RF works wonders on cockroaches, though.

The Care and Feeding of a Condo Antenna Farm

Al Alvareztorres, AA1DO, of the ARRL HQ staff in the introduction to this article said, "A little diplomacy and a good measure of 'stealth technology,' go a long way." That pretty well sums up the theme of what he wrote for April 2001 *QST*. Here's what Al had to say.

In the mid-1980s my wife and I bought a townhouse condominium. We knew from the very beginning that the association rules forbade outside antennas. You couldn't even attach a temporary antenna to your balcony.

I installed a mobile HF station in the car while thinking of the possibilities of a station at home—something that might push the envelope of the association rules while staying well within the spirit of those rules. I was fortunate that the front of our four-townhouse building faced away from the rest of the complex, making it somewhat easy to keep things from general view. The real trick would be putting up some antennas in that space that worked. See **Fig 12-4**.

My first attempt at a condo antenna farm was a partial failure. I had an old 20-foot Gotham bottom-loaded vertical antenna (remember the Gothams?) with taps on the loading coil for several bands. In a feeble attempt to hide the antenna, I planted it in the ground about two feet from the building between our balcony and the one next door. The performance was just this side of abysmal. I also installed a 2-meter Cushcraft Ringo Ranger antenna on the balcony railing and sprayed it with flat black paint—my first stealth antenna.

Fig 12-4—You have to look closely to see the antennas in this view of my condo—and that's the idea!

The antenna was fine for local VHF work, but my HF fun was still taking place in the car.

The Stealth Wire

Some time later a fellow at our local club suggested I put up a random-wire antenna made from very thin wire. Since I was working at a company that made transformers at the time, it was simple to get the "spool ends." These could have over 200 feet of wire left on them!

I settled on #24 enameled wire for strength vs stealth. Running a short length of coax out the window, I attached the antenna wire to the center conductor. Being careful to reconnoiter the area for hidden power lines or other hazards, I snaked the wire up the side of my building to the third floor, but I wasn't done yet. I had plenty of wire remaining—more than enough to jump the gap to a distant tree.

I used a white shirt-button insulator to make the transition between the end of the antenna wire and a length of monofilament fishing line. The other end of the fishing line was tied to a wrench, which I tossed over the limbs of the target tree. Pulling slowly, I raised the remaining antenna wire to a horizontal position between my condo and the tree, then tied off the fishing line on a nail in the tree trunk.

This antenna worked—sort of. It blessed me with RF in my shack, but quite a few signals in the bargain. I had to repair it often, but at least I was making contacts. I ceremoniously "installed" the ancient Gotham on the scrap pile in the garage.

The Arrival of the Condo Police

A couple of years later a new board member was elected. He was an elderly gentleman who seemed to occupy his time by roaming the complex in search of association rule violations. Soon the residents were peppered with missives from The Association warning of infractions. Bicycles were not to be stored in the balconies, pool towels were not to be draped on the balcony railings, no bird feeders were allowed, etc. Finally, it was my turn—my antennas had to be removed immediately. After about seven years of Amateur Radio bliss, I had been "discovered."

Ironically, the president of the board lived across the way in plain view of the long wire and had never noticed it. Other than our eagle-eyed enforcer, no one had ever noticed it except my immediate neighbors (the antenna passed several feet in front of their bedroom window).

Pleading my Case

I requested to attend the following board meeting and my request was granted. A couple of weeks later, my wife Donna, AA1DQ, and I came home from work, prepared to face the judges. Since we both had office jobs, we were wearing business suits as we walked across the parking lot to the president's unit for the meeting. (Don't knock the suits. Impressions count!)

As an armchair legal maven, I isolated two association rules that I felt would present the thorniest obstacles to our success (the emphasis is mine):

"2. Owners shall not use . . . their premises in any manner that would be **disturbing** or be a **nuisance** to other Owners or in such a way as to be **injurious to the reputation of the property**.

"8. Unit owners shall not cause or permit anything to be displayed on the outside . . . of walls of the building, and no sign, **awning, canopy**, shutter, **radio or television antenna shall be affixed to or placed upon the exterior walls . . . or any part thereof** . . ."

Everyone at the meeting was very polite, in fact friendly, when they pointed out that we were in violation of the rules—no antennas were allowed and there was to be nothing attached to the balconies. I agreed, keeping the atmosphere of friendliness (I felt this was of utmost importance if we were going to win). However, I pointed out that it was obvious that the purpose of the association rules is to preserve the appearance of the areas and protect the value of the properties. I emphasized the spirit of the rules. They agreed, and I think this gave me the upper hand.

I started by telling them that the Federal Communications Commission licensed both Donna and me to operate our equipment, and that we had taken qualification tests. Also, by mandate, in time of emergency my equipment was at the disposal of the complex if needed. I told them that I had performed experiments with my immediate neighbors and was causing no interference.

These comments raised a buzz of conversation. One board member said, "Oh, we didn't realize that you had passed FCC exams, and that you had already conducted interference tests. Very impressive." The first obstacle (rule #2) was out of the way.

I continued by reminding the board that we were owners and not renters, and therefore extremely interested in maintaining the value of the properties. I then turned to a nearby sliding glass door and gestured to a unit across the parking lot. I drew their attention to the fact that the screen on my neighbor's kitchen window was in disrepair and had been so for at least a year. Was this not an eyesore? Our unit, in contrast, was immaculate. And could my antenna (speaking of the long-wire) be an eyesore when it had taken so many years to be even noticed? The dipole is almost invisible to the majority of the complex. Were we not living up to the spirit of the rules?

In addition, I mentioned that most of our neighbors had sun umbrellas attached to their balcony railings. If we were to enforce rule #8 equitably, couldn't we insist that our neighbors remove their umbrellas? Of course not. The logic of this argument also caused a buzz among the members. They discussed my appeal among themselves for a few moments.

The president moved that the rules be changed. All but one board member agreed—the condo policeman, of course. He made a strong "slippery slope" argument that officially allowing one type of antenna in the rules would soon result in a forest of CB ground planes, DBS satellite dishes and more. The board president suggested a compromise: the rules would not be changed, but in the case of my antennas the board would "look the other way."

I had lost the war, but I had won the battle, and an armistice was agreed upon—one that holds to this day.

Compromise and civility were the keys to my "victory." I never made demands. I never asserted my "rights." If they had demanded that I remove my antennas, they would have come down and I would have continued operating mobile and portable. I sincerely admitted I was in the wrong. My case was that I was doing no harm—and, in fact, might do some good. If you go into these situations with a belligerent state of mind, the battle is probably lost before you begin.

The Off-Center-Fed Longwire

With the Commissar off my case, it was time to turn my attention back to improving my HF antenna. My newfound confidence urged me to start looking for a replacement. With that trusty tree over 200 feet away, off to one side, and a line of trees about 60 feet away running parallel to the building, the lay of the land just begged for a better multiband antenna. But it would be almost impossible to put up a standard, flattop, center-fed dipole on any band.

I found a candidate in *W1FB's Antenna Notebook* (see Fig 12-5). It was an off-center-fed long wire, which I cut to a full wavelength on the CW portion of the 80-meter band. The total length is about 274 feet. The antenna is fed $1/4$ wavelength (on 80-meters) from one end (at about the 68-foot point). Perfect! I could run the long leg to the far tree and the short leg to a tree across the front lawn. According to the article, this configuration used coax to feed it, so I followed suit.

I figured that if I was going to "push the envelope" I might as well go first class, so I used Copperweld antenna wire, purchased proper insulators and black Dacron rope (the rope would be camouflaged within the tree limbs anyway). The antenna has a somewhat awkward appearance: although the long leg is almost parallel to the ground, there is a slight rise in elevation. It is attached to the building at about 30 feet, and to the far tree at a height of 40 or 50 feet. The short leg goes off at about 45° away from the building and also about 45° down to a small tree.

The antenna worked well on several but not all bands from 160 to 15 meters. After using this antenna for two or three years, I decided to switch the feed line from coax to 450-Ω ladderline. The antenna now tunes on all bands from 160 to 10 meters and has worked all continents and all areas of

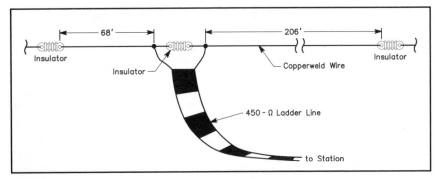

Fig 12-5—AA1DO's version of the off-center-fed long-wire antenna.

Fig 12-8—My improvised "window treatment" passes several coaxial feed lines and my ground wire.

Fig 12-6—My latest VHF antenna additions: an AEA 6-meter Halo with a 2-m/70-cm antenna above it. Note that everything except the Halo is painted black to blend in with the balcony railing.

Fig 12-7—The 450-Ω ladder line finds its way into the condo through two banana jacks and plugs.

the US using 100 W. I operate almost exclusively on CW to maintain a low profile, and only use the 500-W amplifier occasionally, late at night, to break a pileup.

Since the antenna is a somewhat drooping horizontal V, I was able to counterweight it in the center using a plastic pulley to protect it from occasional high winds and snow loading. Dacron rope is used to connect to a chain that holds three old window sash weights that I got from a friend when he remodeled his old house.

A few more VHF antennas have been added to the original 2-meter Ringo: an AEA 6-meter Halo with a 2-

m/70-cm antenna above it, and a 220 MHz Ringo. See **Fig 12-6**. The coax feed lines from the VHF antennas are tie-wrapped together and form a drip loop, as does the ladder-line from the dipole. The ladder-line is twisted about every 18 inches to present a smaller profile to the wind.

Feeding the Feed Lines

The feed lines enter the family room via a sliding window. I cut a board to size and installed coaxial feed-throughs. The board was sealed against the weather with silicone windshield sealer (bathtub sealer will do, also). Where the two windows no longer meet in the center, I placed a Styrofoam strip between the metal frame of the inner window and the glass of the outer win-

dow. A strip of wood jammed between the open window and the frame locks it securely. The ladder-line passes into the condo using heavy-duty banana plugs and sockets found at a local stereo store. See **Fig 12-7** and **Fig 12-8**.

Of course, all the equipment in the station is grounded together. I used the shield from discarded RG-8 to make straps. These are then soldered to busses made from the same material along the back of the shelves. The straps were then soldered to grounding wire, which exits the window to three ground rods placed about one foot apart.

You *Can* do Amateur Radio from a Condo

Hamming from a condo or apartment is not only possible, it's enjoyable! A little common sense and courtesy toward your neighbors is essential. For instance, I usually stay off the air during prime TV viewing hours, or during major TV events. I maintain my antennas frequently, to keep them as unobtrusive as possible. Co-existence is the key word. I don't publicize that I'm a ham, but I don't hide it either.

Occasionally there are comments from inquisitive neighbors. Once, when asked what the long wire was for, I off-handedly replied, "It's a short-wave antenna." The curiosity usually stops right there.

Cheap-and Dirty Multiband Antenna

This project comes to us from Jeff Brone, WB2JNA, and was published in *The ARRL Antenna Compendium, Vol 6.*

Here's an antenna that will work on multiple bands, costs about $10 to make (including the feed line) and takes about an hour to put together. It's great for apartment dwellers, and can also be used in a permanent installation.

Being an apartment dweller, and an incredible cheapskate, I resisted buying a multiband limited-space antenna. I knew such antennas had to be compromise propositions, and I figured that I might be able to make something that would work fairly effectively on my own.

I ran across a great article by Robert H. Johns, W3JIP, in the August 1998 issue of *QST*. He detailed an end-loaded antenna (with a coil) balanced by a counterpoise. The design was a classic and I modified it to fit my limited technical and building aptitude. The result is an antenna that's so simple and easy to make, you'll hardly believe it works as well as it does.

Here's what you'll need:
- 32 feet of #14 to #18 copper wire (20 feet of it should be bare in order for winding the loading coil)
- Two "dog-bone" end insulators
- An empty two-liter soda bottle
- Two alligator clips
- 32 feet of insulated wire, such as #16 or #18 speaker wire for the counterpoise
- Coax to connect your rig to the antenna.

See **Fig 12-9** in the following explanation. Measure and cut off about 13 feet of wire. This will give you enough for a span of about 12 feet after you have secured each end of the wire to its insulator. Secure some more wire to the end of the left-hand insulator shown in Fig 12-9 and push it through the top opening of a two-liter plastic soda bottle. Push the wire through a hole you punch in the bottom of the bottle. (You can also use a short piece of wire as a "snake" through the bottle, starting at the fat end (the left-hand side in Fig 12-9), and then use the snake to pull a rope through the bottle to the second insulator.

Now, solder the end of a 20-foot length of bare wire to the 12-foot wire. Thread the bare wire into the neck of the bottle and through a small hole you poke a few inches down from the neck. Wrap about 17 to 20 turns of the wire around the bottle to make your loading coil. Try to space the turns more or less evenly so that there is enough room for an alligator clip to fit without shorting to adjacent turns.

Use duct tape, coil dope, silicone sealant or whatever you like to hold the turns in place. Depending on how stiff the wire is, this will be, believe it or not,

the hardest part of the whole project. Hang the antenna wherever it's convenient, but make sure you can easily get to the coil.

Take a length of coax and solder an alligator clip to the center wire. Solder a piece of wire to the braid to be used as a counterpoise. The length of the counterpoise wire will depend on the lowest band you intend to use, so let's try 32 feet for 40 meters, the lowest band on which this particular design will work. Connect the center conductor's alligator clip to the coil, about 13 turns from the main radiating wire. Run the 32 feet of counterpoise along the floor of your apartment, on the ground or wherever you can. Keep the end away from areas where kids or pets might be able to touch it, because there is a surprising amount of RF at the end, even for QRP operation.

Connect the other end of the coax to your rig and transmit into the antenna. Try different turns of the coil with the alligator clip and experiment with the location and length (you may end up trimming some) of the counterpoise for the best SWR. That's it; you're ready for a QSO!

To use the antenna on 20 meters, connect the alligator clip about 2 to 3 turns from the front of the coil. You may want to cut the counterpoise about 16 feet in length and attach an alligator clip to its end for attaching the other 16 feet when you want to work 40 meters.

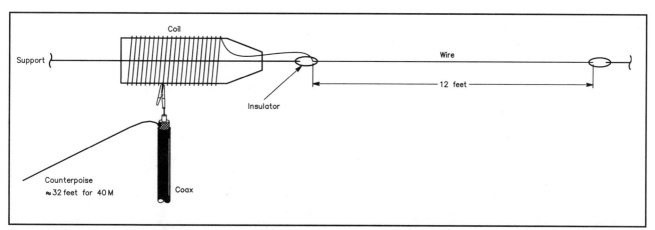

Fig 12-9—Layout of WB2JNA's simple and compact multiband antenna. The coil is wound on a plastic soda bottle and the main radiator is only 12 feet long. The coax feed line uses an alligator clip for determining the appropriate tap on the loading coil, with a quarter-wave counterpoise wire from the coax shield.

Sometimes, you may also just be able to wrap the unneeded length of the counterpoise into a small coil to make it shorter, depending on the length and shortening involved.

The antenna also should work on 30 meters, though I haven't tried it there yet. As an alternative, if you shorten the 12-foot wire element to about 8 feet, you should be able to use this antenna on 20, 17, 15 and 10 meters. I found the 12-foot wire is a bit too long for 15 meters.

Of course, use an appropriate length of counterpoise wire (about a quarter wavelength or a bit less) for any band you try. You might also try soldering two counterpoise wires in parallel at the coax shield. One would be 32 feet long for 40 meters and 16 feet long for 20 meters, for example. (To determine the length in feet for a quarter wavelength, divide 234 by the desired frequency in MHz.) You may also find that if you move too far within a band, you might have to readjust the coil tap.

I use my antenna indoors (at QRP, of course, for safety) and have worked Europeans on 20 meters and 40 meter CW, and many places east of the Mississippi on 40 meters. I just hang it up in my apartment and run the counterpoise on the floor. If you can manage to put the main radiating element outside, it should work even better.

The best part about this antenna is that it takes up very little open space. The counterpoise can be laid out almost anywhere and the wire and coil only take up about 13 feet in length. I find it amazing that more hams don't try an antenna like this. Many get discouraged when they don't have room to put up a conventional dipole or a Yagi. If you like to do a lot with a little, I think you may be pleasantly surprised by this project!

The Loop Skywire

There has been significant interest in this antenna since Dave Fischer, WØMHS, described it in his 1985 *QST* article. It has also undergone refinement. Here's what the 19th Edition of *The ARRL Antenna Book* has to say about it.

Are you looking for a multiband HF antenna that is easy to construct, costs nearly nothing and yet works well? You might want to try this one. The Loop Skywire antenna is a full-sized horizontal loop. Early proponents suggested that the antenna could be fed with coaxial cable with little concern for losses, but later analysis proved that this was a bit of wishful thinking—the relatively low values for SWR across multiple bands indicate that cable losses were part and parcel of performance. The best way to feed this versatile antenna is with open-wire ladder line, with an antenna tuner in the shack to present the transmitter with a low value of SWR.

The Design

The Loop Skywire is shown in **Fig 12-10**. The antenna has one wavelength of wire in its perimeter at the design or fundamental frequency. If you choose to calculate L total in feet, the following equation should be used:

$$L_{total} = 1005 / f$$

where f equals the frequency in MHz.

Given any length of wire, the maximum possible area the antenna can enclose is with the wire in the shape of a circle. Since it takes an infinite number of supports to hang a circular loop, the square loop (four supports) is the most practical. Further reducing the area enclosed by the wire loop (fewer supports) brings the antenna closer to the properties of the folded dipole, and both harmonic-impedance and feed-line voltage problems can result. Loop geometries other than a square are thus possible, but remember the two fundamental requirements for the Loop Skywire—its horizontal position and maximum enclosed area.

There is another great advantage to this antenna system. It can be operated as a vertical antenna with top-hat loading on other bands as well. This is accomplished by simply keeping the feed line run from the antenna to the

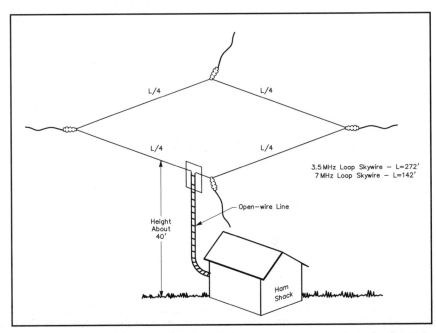

Fig 12-10—A complete view of the Loop Skywire. The square loop is erected horizontal to the earth.

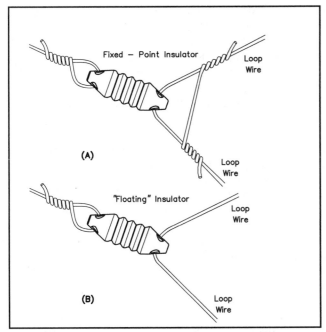

Fig 12-11—Two methods of installing the insulators at the loop corners.

shack as vertical as possible and clear of objects. Both feed-line conductors are then tied together, and the antenna is fed against a good ground.

Construction

Antenna construction is simple. Although the loop can be made for any band or frequency of operation, the following two Loop Skywires are good performers. The 10-MHz band can also be operated on both.

3.5-MHz Loop Skywire
 (3.5-28 MHz loop and 1.8-MHz vertical)
 Total loop perimeter: 272 feet
 Square side length: 68 feet
7-MHz Loop Skywire
 (7-28 MHz loop and 3.5-MHz vertical)
 Total loop perimeter: 142 feet
 Square side length: 35.5 feet

The actual total length can vary from the above by a few feet, as the length is not at all critical. Do not worry about tuning and pruning the loop to resonance. No signal difference will be detected on the other end when that method is used.

Fig 12-12—At A, azimuth-plane response of 142-foot long, 7-MHz Loop Skywire, 40 feet in the air at 7.2 MHz, compared with ¹/₂-λ dipole 30 feet in the air. At B, response of same Loop Skywire at 14.2 MHz, compared with ¹/₂-λ 14.2-MHz dipole 30 feet in the air. Now the loop has some advantage in certain directions. At C, response of the same Loop Skywire at 21.2 MHz compared to a 21.2-MHz dipole at 30 feet. Here, the Loop Skywire has more gain in almost all directions than the simple dipole. All azimuth-plane patterns were made at 10° elevation.

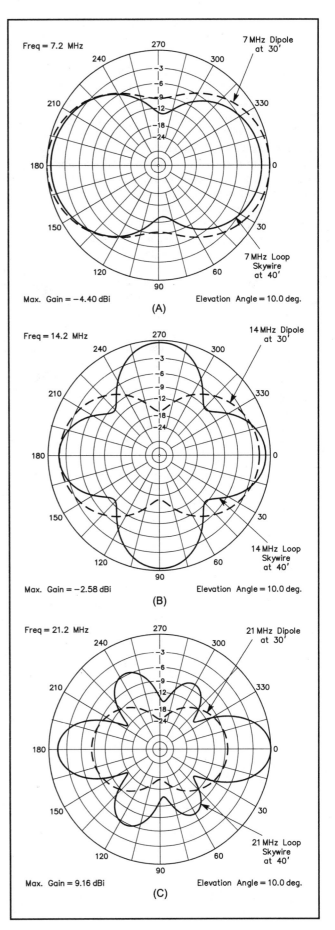

Bare #14 copper wire is used in the loop. **Fig 12-11** shows the placement of the insulators at the loop corners. Two common methods are used to attach the insulators. Either lock or tie the insulator in place with a loop wire tie, as shown in Fig 12-11A, or leave the insulator free to "float" or slide along the wire, Fig 12-11B. Most loop users float at least two insulators. This allows pulling the slack out of the loop once it is in the air, and it eliminates the need to have all the supports exactly placed for proper tension in each leg. Floating two opposite corners is recommended.

Fig 12-12A shows the azimuth-plane performance on 7.2 MHz of a 142-foot long, 7-MHz Loop Skywire, 40 feet high at an elevation angle of 10°, compared to a regular flattop $1/2$-λ dipole at a height of 30 feet. The loop comes into its own at higher frequencies. Fig 12-12B shows the response at 14.2 MHz, compared again to a $1/2$-λ 14.2-MHz dipole at a height of 30 feet. Now the loop has several lobes that are stronger than the dipole. Fig 12-12C shows the response at 21.2 MHz, compared to a dipole. Now the loop has superior gain compared to the $1/2$-λ dipole at almost any azimuth. In its favored direction on 21.2 MHz, the loop is 8 dB stronger than the dipole.

The feed point can be positioned anywhere along the loop that you wish. However, most users feed the Skywire at a corner. **Fig 12-13** depicts a method of doing this, using a piece of Plexiglas to provide insulation as well as strain relief for the open-wire ladder line. It is advantageous to keep the feed point mechanicals away from the corner support. Feeding a foot or so from one corner allows the feed line to exit more freely. This method keeps the feed line free from the loop support.

Generally a minimum of four supports is required. If trees are used for supports, then at least two of the ropes or guys used to support the insulators should be counterweighted and allowed to move freely. The feed-line corner is almost always tied down, however. Very little tension is needed to support the loop (far less than that for a dipole). Thus, counterweights are light. Several such loops have been constructed with bungee cords tied to three of the four insulators. This eliminates the need for counter-weighting.

Recommended height for the antenna is 40 feet or more. The higher the better, especially if you wish to use the loop in the vertical mode. However, successful local and DX operation has been reported in several cases with the antenna as low as 20 feet. **Fig 12-14** shows the feed arrangement for using the Loop Skywire as a top-loaded vertical fed against ground on the lower bands.

Because the loop is high in the air and has considerable electrical exposure to the elements, proper methods should be employed to eliminate the chance of induced or direct lightning hazard to the shack and operator. Some users simply completely disconnect the antenna from the antenna tuner and rig and shack during periods of possible lightning activity.

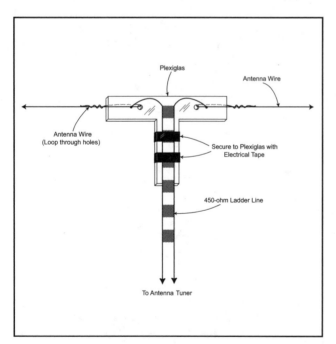

Fig 12-13—Most users feed the Skywire at a corner. A high-impedance weather-resistant insulator should be used for the feedpoint insulator.

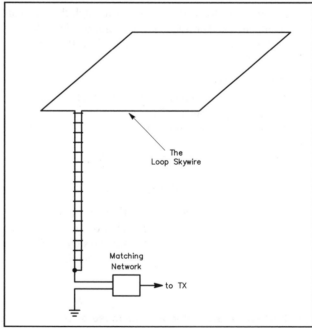

Fig 12-14—The feed arrangement for operating the 7-MHz Loop Skywire as a vertical antenna.

The Hentenna—
The Japanese "Miracle" Wire Antenna

This antenna, popular in Japan, was first introduced to US hams in a 1982 issue of *QST*. It was more recently brought up-to-date by Shirow Kinoshita, JF6DEA/KE1EO in *The ARRL Antenna Compendium, Vol 5.* Here's what JF6DEA said.

Perhaps some of you may have heard the name *Hentenna* during QSOs with Japanese operators. The Hentenna is a wire antenna that is very easy to make. Since it first appeared in the Japanese ham literature, the Hentenna has become popular on the HF as well as the VHF/UHF bands.

In Japanese, the word "Hen" means fantastic or miraculous. This is the origin of the name Hentenna, recognized as a "fantastic antenna" by many Japanese amateurs because of its many useful properties.

History

In July 1972, Mr Someya, JE1DEU, the youngest member of the Sagami Club, located near Tokyo, suggested a prototype of this antenna. This was constructed using two quad loops fed in phase. He was just a junior high school student at the time. After that, Mr Tadashi Okubo, JH1FCZ, and a number of other amateurs (JA1RKK, JA1TUT, JH1ECW, JH1HPH, JH1XUQ and JR1SOP) experimented to establish the basic form of the Hentenna. They were encouraged by their measurements, especially since they found the new antenna compared with the gain of a conventional two-element quad. The biggest problem they faced at first was achieving a low SWR.

Five Useful Properties of the Hentenna

The general shape of the Hentenna is shown in **Fig 12-15**. It is a rectangular loop—λ/6 wide by λ/2 tall. The Hentenna is fed with 50-Ω coaxial cable at the center of a horizontal wire spaced about λ/6 from the bottom.

The azimuth pattern for a horizontally polarized Hentenna is shown in **Fig 12-16**. The beam pattern is a figure eight, perpendicular to the

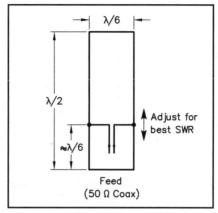

Fig 12-15—The basic shape of Hentenna, λ/2 high and λ/6 wide. This form of the antenna is horizontally polarized. Exact feed tap points are adjusted experimentally for best SWR.

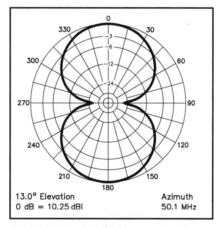

Fig 12-16—Azimuth pattern for 6-meter Hentenna mounted 20 feet above average ground.

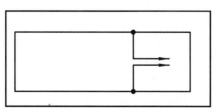

Fig 12-17—Vertically polarized Hentenna, turned on its side.

loop's plane. The basic Hentenna is horizontally polarized. This is the first useful property of the Hentenna—if you should want vertical polarization, the antenna can be rotated 90°, as shown in **Fig 12-17**.

A second useful property of the Hentenna is that the physical dimensions are not particularly critical. The permitted range of overall loop length is about ±10%. By mistake, one 50-MHz antenna was constructed with 3.5-meter long sides, about 117% of the nominal λ/2 length desired on 6 meters. Nonetheless, even this antenna worked fine, with an SWR of 1.2:1.

A third useful property of the Hentenna is the relative ease by which it may be tuned, which is by sliding the driven-element wire up and down along the vertical element and then soldering it where the SWR is lowest.

A fourth useful property of the Hentenna is that it has gain roughly equal to a two-element Yagi [or a short-boom three-element tribander. —*Ed.*] Yet it is a lot smaller than a full-size two-element Yagi! JH1FCZ measured a gain of 8 dBd in November 1972. Professor Mushiake at Tohoku University computed the free-space gain at 5 dBi, as announced in the Journal of the Institute of Electronics, Information and Engineers in Japan. [No doubt, JH1FCZ measured gain over ground. This would include ground-reflection gain of about 5 dB. Free-space modeling of the Hentenna using *NEC-2* shows a gain of just over 5.1 dBi, just a little less than the gain of a typical full-size two-element Yagi. A gain of 5.1 dBi in free space would result in just over 10.1 dBi of gain—or 8 dBd referenced to a dipole in free space—when the Hentenna is placed over ground with a dielectric constant of 13 and a conductivity of 5 mS/m.—*Ed.*]

A derivative of the basic Hentenna form results in the so-called Half Hentenna shown in **Fig 12-18**, also called the Fork Hentenna. The Hentenna can even be made circular, as shown in **Fig 12-19**. Here, it is useful as a vertically polarized antenna. The round ver-

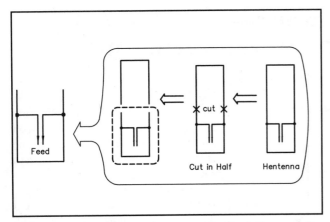

Fig 12-18—Evolution of Hentenna into "Fork Hentenna" or "Half Hentenna."

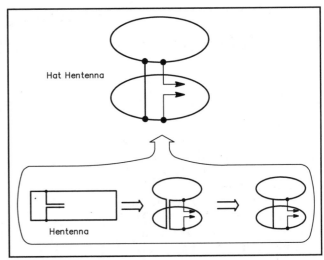

Fig 12-19—Evolution of Hentenna into circular form—the "Hat Hentenna."

sion of the Hentenna is called the Hat Hentenna, because it is similar in shape to a derby hat.

Loop Width and Feed-Point Impedance

The loop width of a typical rectangular Hentenna is $\lambda/6$. If you make the width narrower, then the feed-point impedance goes lower. If the width is made wider, the impedance becomes higher. (See **Fig 12-20**.) A wider loop has a larger SWR bandwidth, implying a lower-Q antenna. When you make a Hentenna, you can adjust the impedance any way you like, so you can make a special Hentenna having the same impedance of your coax or transmitter.

An Example: How to Make a 50-MHz Hentenna

On the 6-meterband in Japan, we usually use horizontal polarization, so the Hentenna is most often constructed in the "tall" configuration. See **Fig 12-21**. The parts list for this antenna is shown below.

a) Two aluminum spreader tubes, 10 to 12 mm OD ($^3/_8$ to $^1/_2$ inch OD), $\lambda/6 = 1$ m (3 feet, 3 inches) long
b) Two insulated copper wires, $\lambda/2 = 3$ m (9 feet, 9 inches) long
c) #14 or #12 copper wire a little longer than $\lambda/6 = 1$ m (3 feet, 3 inches)
d) Two plates with U-bolts to fix the aluminum pipes (a) to the mast
e) A mast, of adequate size to support the antenna

Flatten both ends of the aluminum spreader pipes with a hammer and drill holes to secure lugs crimped onto the vertical copper wires. The two horizontal spreaders attach to the mast $\lambda/2$ apart. You don't need to electrically isolate the spreaders from the mast, unless you want vertical polarization, in which case the Hentenna is turned on its side.

Next, take care to strip off part of the insulation near the lower aluminum spreader. Connect the driven wire to the vertical wires temporarily, perhaps using alligator clips. Adjust the Hentenna by moving the driven-element wire up and down along the vertical elements while measuring SWR. When you find the point with the lowest SWR, solder the connections. Be sure to use conducting paste between the screws and the terminal lugs on the copper wires, and to seal all joints with electrical tape.

Another Example, JA6YBR 6-M Beacon Hentenna

JA6YBR is the station of the Miyazaki University Radio Club, located in Miyazaki, in the Southwest of Japan. Miyazaki is well known as a place which typhoons often visit from the summer through autumn. The beacon antenna needed to have the following properties:

a) horizontal polarization
b) omnidirectional coverage
c) a small wind-surface area

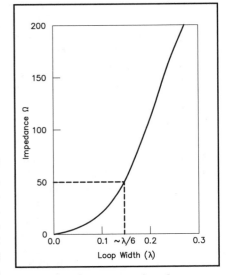

Fig 12-20—Graph showing the relationship between feedpoint impedance and loop width in λ. The impedance is 50 Ω at a width of about $\lambda/6$.

d) as much gain as possible

The original antenna, installed in 1985, had been a stacked "Squaro," but the gain was inadequate. They next tried a turnstile dipole. They found this to have too large a wind-surface area, considering the typhoon problem. In May 1990, JA6YBR installed a two-loop turnstile Hentenna. See photo in **Fig 12-22**. It has been a good performer, damaged only once during 1993's memorable typhoon.

Throughout Cycle 22, JA6YBR's signal was reported throughout the Pacific, South America and Africa.

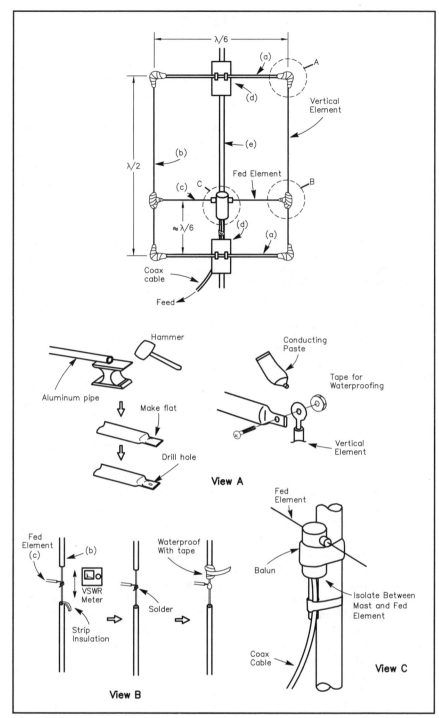

Fig 12-21—Construction details for 50-MHz Hentenna. See parts list in text of the article.

Fig 12-22—Photograph of JA6YBR omnidirectional turnstile Hentenna. This antenna has survived numerous typhoons common to the region around Miyazaki.

JA6YBR's 6-meter signal was even received on the US West Coast via multi-hop sporadic E in July 1995. The turnstile Hentenna presently in use at JA6YBR was made by Mr Masayoshi Eguchi, JI6KGZ. A photo of this antenna was published in "The World Above 50 MHz" column in the July 1995 issue of *QST*.

[Note that the gain of the omnidirectional version of the Hentenna will be down about 3 dB compared to the conventional bi-directional version.—*Ed.*]

Hentennas for 75-Meter DX!

The Hentenna can be used on any frequency you like. In Japan, JA1JRK and JM1BPP have used the Hentenna for 75-meter DX and they have had good results. The Hentenna is better than a full-sized dipole, with higher gain and a smaller wind surface area. The Hentenna is a wonderful antenna, small in size and easy to make. Many JA operators have used it as their prime antenna on 6 meters or for field operation.

Bidirectional Antennas

My friend Chip Margelli, K7JA, published this article in June 1998 *QST*. The theme has a distinctive Field Day flavor, but the stew of ideas that Chip presents can just as easily be used in your home station installation. As you read this, you should be able to gather some insight as to why Chip is such a successful competitor, not only in Field Day, but also in all sorts of contests.

Everyone who has operated Field Day has experienced times when it feels like you've "worked 'em all," and that there are no new stations to contact. You call CQ repeatedly with no replies. Is the problem related to a lack of activity? Or have you really equipped your station with the right antenna(s)?

This article provides planning and construction information for a time-honored class of antennas which can "spray" your signal in more than one direction, while still providing competition-grade gain. As an additional benefit, several of the antennas described provide deep side nulls, which can be useful in minimizing inter-station interference in multi-transmitter Field Day operations.

Population Density and Antenna Patterns

It is well known that the eastern states and Canadian provinces contain the most widespread area of high population density in North America. Yet California has more than twice as many amateur licensees than any other state (over 100,000!). Significant amateur concentrations are also found in northern Oregon, Washington, and British Columbia.

But if you're in the midwestern part of the continent, what sort of antenna did you use, say, on 10 meters last year? A three-element Yagi? And which direction did you point it during Sunday morning's sporadic-E opening? Probably toward South Carolina, with its 8500 friendly licensees, at the expense of all the potential QSOs toward the west. What you need for maximum scoring success in any contest or Field Day effort is the widest exposure possible to the most amateur population with the loudest possible signal. And

Fig 12-23—Falmouth Amateur Radio Association (MA) Field Day site, K1RK, June 2001. HF yagi antennas (TH-5 tribanders, one for SSB and one for CW; 2-el 40 yagi on CW) are fixed slightly south of due west for maximum coverage.

unless you're operating from a space capsule, this probably means that you'll need to spray your RF energy in more than one direction at a time.

The problem isn't just one of signal strength in the rear direction. Activity patterns on the bands are also important. One might conclude that, if you're S9 in the front direction with a beam that has 24 dB of front-to-back ratio, your signal off the rear will be S5, still enough to make a contact. On Field Day, though, clubs and groups operating in classes like 1A (single transmitter) have to make hard decisions about the band on which they operate at any given time. If the operators of a California club only hear S5 signals from the Midwest on 10 meters, but S9 signals on 20, chances are that they'll stay on 20. If the poor W6 *does* go to 10, it doesn't take too many times calling a station in Arkansas with no response (because the W5 is working S9+ *East Coast* stations) to cause the 6-land operator to QSY back to 20!

Opportunities for the utilization of bidirectional antennas are not limited to the highest bands, either. On 20 meters, for example, a station in the middle part of the East Coast (say, North Carolina) might want a three-element Yagi for

working to the west, but a bidirectional antenna for simultaneously working stations in New England and Florida on those big Sunday morning E-layer openings which always seem to occur on Field Day. A dual antenna system such as this, with quick-switch capability, will be a formidable weapon in the competitive aspect of Field Day, while demonstrating the benefits of multiple antennas for emergency communication planning.

Antenna Design Examples for Increased Coverage

One of *my* favorite Field Day antennas is the "Bisquare." An easy-to-build variant of the "Lazy-H" antenna, it can be built out of wire and, for frequencies above 21 MHz, be erected on a lightweight mast of about 40 feet in height. The Bisquare is easily tuned by a wide-range balanced-feed antenna tuner; for both efficiency and sentimental reasons, I use the old Johnson "Matchbox" tuner for this purpose.

Despite its appearance (see **Fig 12-24** and **Fig 12-25**), the Bisquare is not a "loop" antenna, as it is *open* at the top. It produces a horizontally polarized signal, which at moderately low heights emits broad signal lobes that can illuminate a wide geographical area. **Fig 12-26A** shows the azimuth (horizontal view) pattern for a 28-MHz Bisquare with its apex at a height of 30 feet, while Fig 12-19B shows the elevation (side view of main lobe) pattern. For comparison, **Fig 12-27A** and B show the corresponding patterns for that most typical of all Field Day antennas, the three-element Yagi. In analyzing these patterns, we need to look at two important factors:

1) How does our signal compare in strength to our reference antenna (the above-mentioned three-element Yagi) in its favored direction?

2) What additional coverage area, if any, do we pick up with the (bidirectional) Bisquare compared to the (unidirectional) Yagi?

Comparison of Figs 12-26 and 12-27 shows that the three-element Yagi has a peak gain (over "real" ground) of

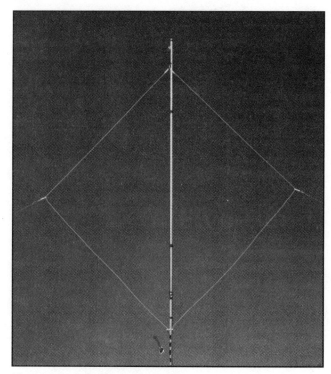

Fig 12-24—A Bisquare antenna.

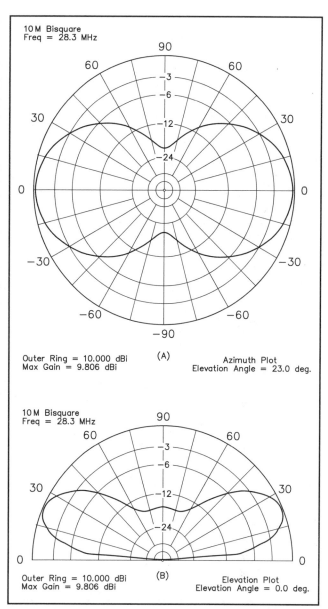

Outer Ring = 10.000 dBi
Max Gain = 9.806 dBi

(A)

Azimuth Plot
Elevation Angle = 23.0 deg.

Outer Ring = 10.000 dBi
Max Gain = 9.806 dBi

(B)

Elevation Plot
Elevation Angle = 0.0 deg.

Fig 12-26—(A) The 28-MHz Bisquare azimuth pattern; apex at 30 feet. (B) Bisquare elevation pattern; apex at 30 feet.

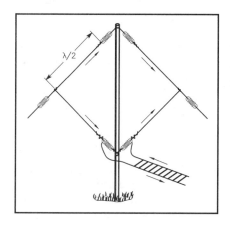

Fig 12-25—Basic layout of a Bisquare antenna. Note that the top corner of the antenna is open-circuited.

13.0 dBi, while the Bisquare is somewhat lower at 9.8 dBi (the *apex* of the Bisquare and the *boom* of the Yagi are both assumed to be at a height of 30 feet, or about 0.87 λ). The front/back ratio (F/B) of the Yagi, however, being 27.6 dB, means that the Bisquare has a gain *advantage* of 24.4 dB in the rearward direction of the Yagi. If we assume that the Yagi is producing an S9 signal somewhere in its peak forward direction, this means that the Bisquare's signal will "only" be S8.5 (assuming 6

dB per S unit). Moreover, the 27.6 dB F/B of the Yagi means that the Yagi's signal at 180° away from its peak will be about S4.5, *while the Bisquare's will still be S8.5!* Small rear lobes of the Yagi not in the 180° position mean that, in some directions, the difference will not be quite so dramatic; on the other hand, even deeper nulls in the Yagi's pattern mean that the difference may be *greater* on some headings. Note also the rather large high-angle lobe from the Yagi in Fig 12-27B. Since this angle

often cannot be refracted via the ionosphere on 28 MHz, this signal power may disappear into outer space as wasted energy.

What does all this data mean for a Field Day group in Oklahoma City? With a three-element Yagi on 28 MHz at a height of 30 feet, they might illuminate an E-layer path which includes the population centers in the W3, W4, and W9 call areas without falling outside the −3 dB (½ S-unit) boundary in the azimuth pattern. But with the Bisquare, the

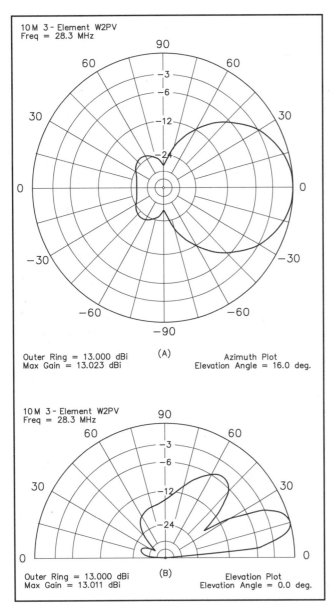

10 M 3 - Element W2PV
Freq = 28.3 MHz

Outer Ring = 13.000 dBi
Max Gain = 13.023 dBi

(A)

Azimuth Plot
Elevation Angle = 16.0 deg.

10 M 3 - Element W2PV
Freq = 28.3 MHz

Outer Ring = 13.000 dBi
Max Gain = 13.011 dBi

(B)

Elevation Plot
Elevation Angle = 0.0 deg.

Figure 12-27—
(A) Three-
element Yagi
28-MHz azimuth
pattern; boom
at 30 feet. (B)
Three-element
Yagi elevation
pattern; note
the high-angle
lobe.

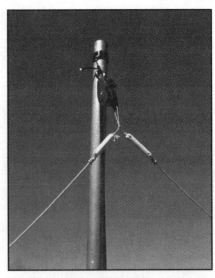

Fig 12-28—Typical rigging of the top
corner of the Bisquare antenna. The
top of the Bisquare must be open-
circuited.

−3 dB azimuth points now include W1, W2, W3, W4, W8, and W9 in the easterly direction, *plus* W6 and southern W7 to the west. The added westerly contribution of 150,000+ amateurs (in Arizona, California, Nevada, Oregon and Utah) means the opportunity for many more QSOs in the log.

To provide coverage of the Chicago, Minneapolis/St. Paul, Toronto, and other due-north metropolitan areas, a northward-pointing Yagi could be mounted on its own mast at about 26 to 30 feet, or two Bisquares may be suspended from a single mast, and fed independently; there will be minimal interaction between the two arrays. A simple coaxial switch will allow quick direction change.

Building a 10-Meter Bisquare

Unlike most parasitic antenna arrays (such as the Yagi or quad), the dimensions of the Bisquare are entirely noncritical. The Bisquare consists of two one-wavelength wires, formed into a diamond, and fed at the bottom. From the formula $L = 984 \div F$ (MHz), we find that a length of 34 feet 9 inches produces the proper length at 28.316 MHz—perfect for Field Day operation! Cut two such wires, leaving an additional 4 inches on each end for looping through the top and bottom

insulators. Find the center point of each wire, and install an insulator at that point. Now install insulators at the "top" end of each wire (see **Fig 12-28** for details on a simple method of insulator installation), and at the bottom end. A small Dacron-cord loop may be tied to the top insulator pair, and Dacron cords may be tied to the center insulators so that they may ultimately be pulled outward to form the final (square) shape.

Install a pulley on top of your mast, and tilt the mast to the vertical position. Once the guy ropes (nonconductive material is essential!) are secure, pull up the two wires to the maximum height. Now it's time to attach the feed line. The feed line is of the open-wire type. Commonly available "ladder line" will also work just fine in this application. The open-wire feed line is soldered to the bottom ends of the two wires, and is allowed to hang downward so as to reach the antenna tuner. In this application, we do not worry about the high SWR that may be present on the feed line, as the extremely low loss of the open-wire line means that the *additional* loss due to SWR will be negligible (for an extensive discussion of this subject, see Chapter 24 of *The ARRL Antenna Book*, 1997 edition). Once the feed line is attached, you may pull outward on the lines attached to the center insulators.

When tuning up an antenna of this type at the Western Amateur Radio Association's N6ME Field Day site, I use an "Antenna Analyzer" manufactured by MFJ Enterprises which allows me to adjust the Johnson Matchbox for a perfect match in less than 30 seconds *without* the need for a generator to power a transceiver (similar products are also manufactured by Advanced Electronic Applications and Autek). When adjustments have been completed, the antenna tuner is wrapped inside a plastic garbage sack to protect it from the weather (it *always* rains on Field Day!), and I'm on the air!

The Bisquare is not the only bidirectional antenna type that may be useful for Field Day applications. Let us now explore some other antenna types, each of which has its own advantages and disadvantages.

The Kraus (W8JK) Flat-Top Array

This simple bidirectional array was invented by Dr. John Kraus, W8JK, and is described extensively in his book *Antennas*; it also is documented in most all amateur texts, including *The ARRL Antenna Book* (Chapter 8 of the 18th edition). The Kraus Array consists of two closely spaced dipoles fed out-of-phase via a crossed phasing line. Open-wire line is then used to feed the array, as with the Bisquare. **Fig 12-29A** shows the basic layout of a typical Kraus Array.

This versatile antenna may be built with half-wavelength elements (known as a Single-Section 8JK), one-wavelength elements (Two-Section 8JK), or even longer elements. However, going beyond the two-section model will narrow the beamwidth excessively, confounding our mission to "spray" our signal over a greater area. Depending on your location, you probably will need to use the single-section Kraus Array to achieve the necessary beamwidth; even so, this antenna at a height of 30 feet produces a peak 28 MHz gain of 10.8 dBi, which is about 1 dB greater than that produced by the Bisquare (with its apex at the same 30-foot height as the 8JK).

A major advantage of the Kraus Array is that it is a horizontal-plane antenna; it therefore requires less mast height to achieve the same takeoff angle as the Bisquare. Another advantage is the excellent null at 90° off of each main lobe (**Fig 12-30**). If this null is directed at the station (on the opposite mode) on the same band at your Field Day site, overload problems may be significantly reduced. A disadvantage of the Kraus Array is that it requires two supports, unlike the Bisquare; a Kraus Array may easily be suspended between two masts or trees, however, and the dimensions on 14 MHz, 21 MHz, or 28 MHz are quite reasonable (even a 40-meter version is not out of the question; two standard-length dipoles spaced about 18 feet will do the trick).

The Kraus Array tends to be a fairly high-Q antenna, which means you may need to restrict your operating frequencies (unless you can reach the controls of your antenna tuner). The single-section version

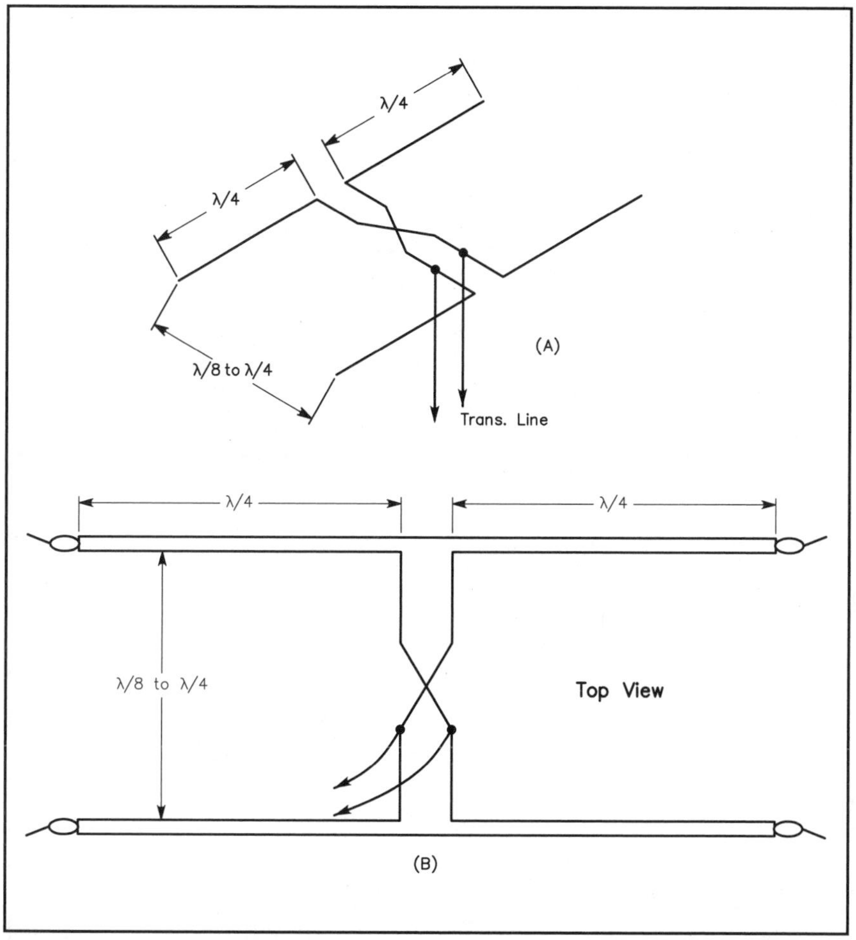

Fig 12-29—(A) The single-section Kraus Array. (B) A single-section Kraus Array constructed with folded dipole elements will provide greater bandwidth without retuning.

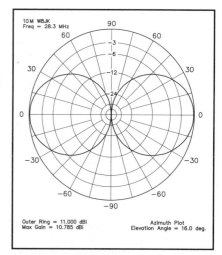

Fig 12-30—The azimuth pattern of a 28-MHz single-section Kraus Array at a height of 30 feet.

may benefit from the use of "Folded Dipole" elements, which raise the impedance and broaden the response. A typical example of this type of construction is shown in Fig 12-29B.

Stacked Dipoles

Two half-wavelength dipoles may be stacked and phased, as shown in **Fig 12-31**, to produce a very effective bidirectional beam. A vertical spacing of one-half wavelength allows the array to be fed in the center (with no transposition of the phasing line, as shown in Fig 12-31, or at the bottom, with the two dipoles being phased by a crossed piece of open-wire line. At half-wavelength spacing, this array produces a bidirectional gain of 9.5 dBi. With the top element at a height of 30 feet, the bottom element of a 28 MHz array will be at about 12 feet, and this antenna's main lobe will only be down about three-tenths of a dB compared to the Bisquare.

A particular advantage of this type of array is the very broad horizontal lobe, since the vertical stacking produces the gain of this antenna. This means that you can illuminate a huge geographical area within the (80-degree-wide) -3 dB points (see **Fig 12-32**). Another advantage stems from the very low RF voltages present at the centers of the dipoles; simple split-dipole elements may therefore be used.

If you have some aluminum tubing available, and can construct a suitable center mount for a dipole element, this is a terrific antenna that is easy to erect. It may also be made using wire, utilizing ceramic end/center insulators, if you have two masts available. Although the gain increases slightly if the spacing is increased to $^5/_8 \lambda$ the gain advantage is less than 1 dB, making pointless any additional effort at providing this wider spacing.

The Lazy-H

Similar in appearance to the "stacked dipole" array, the Lazy-H is an array of *four* half-wavelength elements, stacked two-over-two to achieve gain via collinear *and* vertical stacking (see **Fig 12-33**). Although the gain of the Lazy-H is about 2 dB greater than that of the stacked dipole array, the Lazy-H is of reasonable dimensions for Field

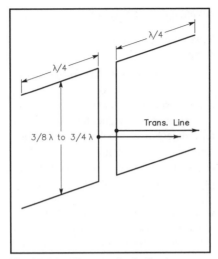

Fig 12-31—The stacked-dipole array.

Day erection on the 28 MHz band (total "wingspread" of about 35 feet) if suspended between two masts. If tall trees are available, a Lazy-H for 14 MHz or 21 MHz can easily be erected. When half-wave spacing is used, the Lazy-H may be fed at the bottom, with a transposed feed line connecting the top and bottom sections to establish the required in-phase currents.

The gain of the Lazy-H is approximately 1.6 dB greater than that of the Bisquare, and the horizontal pattern is about 10° narrower. Because these two antennas fundamentally are quite similar (the Bisquare being a Folded Lazy-H), the choice of which antenna to use may boil down to a constructional

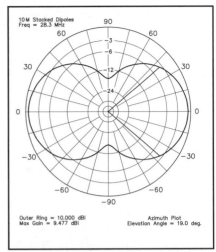

Fig 12-32—Azimuth pattern of a 28-MHz stacked-dipole array with the top element at a height of 30 feet. Note the broad azimuth coverage area.

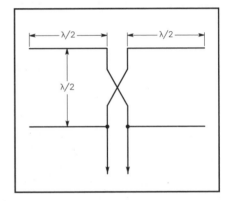

Fig 12-33—The Lazy-H antenna. Note that the elements are twice as long as the elements of the stacked-dipole array in Fig 12-31.

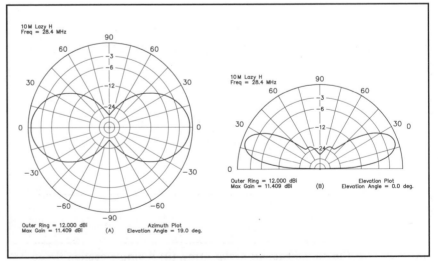

Fig 12-34—(A) The azimuth pattern of a 28 MHz Lazy-H Array with the top element at a height of 30 feet. (B) The elevation pattern of the Lazy-H.

issue. **Fig 12-34A** shows the azimuth pattern of the Lazy-H for 28 MHz (top at 30 feet), while Fig 12-34B shows the elevation pattern. Note the very clean elevation pattern, with no power wasted in high-angle lobes. This is really a great antenna, if you have the supports to get it up.

How Do They Work?

I have used a number of these antennas with good success over the years. On 15 meters from the N6ME FD site, for example, W7 and VE7 stations that were inaudible on a four-element Yagi aimed to the east were a solid S6 on a simple Bisquare positioned to favor the north-south paths. On 10 meters, a similar antenna has occasionally provided *stronger* E-layer signals than a (higher) Yagi pointed the same direction, due to a null in the Yagi's elevation pattern at a critical angle.

While testing a "stacked dipole" antenna at my home in the preparation of this article, I was listening one afternoon to 10 meters toward the East Coast on my six-element monoband Yagi at 70 feet. See **Fig 12-35**. I heard traces of a weak signal that I could not identify in the local noise; rotating the Yagi back and forth about 45° did not peak the signal. Switching to the stacked dipole array, which was broadside to the eastern USA and mid-Pacific regions, I discovered that the signal was from V73AT in the Marshall Islands, at a solid

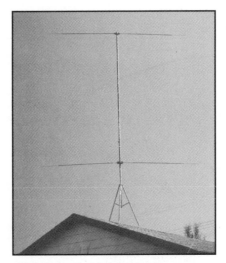

Fig 12-35—A stacked-dipole array perched atop a roof tripod.

S7! Although the V73 peaked at between S8 and S9 when the long, high Yagi was pointed at him, one can easily see how a simple bidirectional antenna can really open the door to many contacts that might otherwise be missed!

Summary

Many centrally located Field Day groups make the mistake of considering only a (unidirectional) Yagi-type beam antenna. To change directions, either an electro-mechanical rotator must be installed (something else which can break down!), or someone must run outside and turn the antenna manually.

With summer sporadic-E propagation changing so quickly, it frequently is impossible to catch every opening. And from a location in the midsection of North America, there is a *very* good chance that you will experience simultaneous propagation to the East and West Coasts, a situation that demands a bidirectional antenna capability.

The antennas described previously are simple to construct, cost very little, and require minimal takedown time (a *very* desirable feature on Sunday afternoon!). Because they are "force-fed" via an antenna tuner, adjustment time is measured in seconds; how many of us have wasted *hours* fiddling with a Yagi's gamma match as the sun goes down Friday night before FD? Two bidirectional antennas, erected at right angles, can provide coverage of most of the continent's population centers, with *instant* direction switching. All this at a sacrifice of *perhaps* one-half of an S unit compared to a Yagi's peak gain, while you pick up a *gain* of *several S units* compared to the Yagi's rearward direction. Moreover, in the true spirit of Field Day, the building of high-performance bidirectional wire arrays teaches one the tricks of the trade in setting up an emergency station quickly.

I hope that you will build and enjoy one or more of these antennas in conjunction with your club's Field Day event. You'll be pleasantly surprised at the results!

Having a Field Day with the Moxon Rectangle

Let's carry the Field Day theme forward another step. Here is a gain antenna that L. B. Cebik, W4RNL, described in the June 2000 issue of *QST*.

Field Day antenna installations tend to pass through phases. Phase 1 is the starter for any group: Get some antennas—usually dipoles and inverted Vs—into the air and see how well they perform. Phase 2 rests on an evaluation of the initial results. It generally consists of mechanical improvements to place the same or similar antennas higher using stronger materials. It also includes making better use of potential antenna supports at the site.

Real antenna design work usually begins with Phase 3. Based on the improved results with Phase 2 changes, the group begins to think about where they want the signals to go and how to get them there. At this stage, the group takes its first steps toward designing wire beams for the HF bands. (In Phase 4, we find the use of portable crank-up towers, rotators and multi-band arrays. I'll not delve into Phase 4 in this article.)

Wire beams and arrays have one significant limitation: We can't rotate them. Therefore, we must resort to carefully planned aiming during installation. Still, we can only cover so much of the

area across the country with the beamwidth available from gain arrays. Dreamers will always wonder if they could have garnered a few more contacts lost to the deep front-to-side ratio offered by most two-element Yagi designs.

So let's explore an alternative to the two-element wire Yagi, one that is only about 70% as wide, side to side, and which offers some other benefits as well: the wire Moxon Rectangle.

The Moxon Rectangle

In its most fully developed monoband form, a Moxon Rectangle outline looks like the sketch in **Fig 12-36**. A is the side-to-side length of the parallel driver and reflector wires. B is the length of the driver tails, while D is the length of the reflector tails. C is the distance between the tips of the two sets of tails. If any dimension of the Moxon Rectangle is critical, it is C. E, the total front-to-back length of the array, is simply the sum of B, C, and D.

The history of the Moxon Rectangle is itself fascinating. Basically, it derives from early experiments with a square shape by Fred Caton, VK2ABQ, although the very first experiments were performed in the 1930s. Les Moxon, G6XN, outlined in his classic *HF Antennas for All Locations*, a rectangular variant in which he remotely tuned the driver and the reflector. Curious about the basic properties of the rectangle, I modeled and built variations of the design for about eight years, using wire and aluminum tubing.

The Moxon Rectangle has three properties that recommend it for Field Day use:

- It is not as wide as an equivalent wire Yagi, because the two elements fold toward each other.
- It offers—with the right dimensions—a 50-Ω feed-point impedance so no matching system is required (although use of a choke to suppress common-mode currents is always desirable).
- It presents a very useful Field Day pattern, with good gain and a very high F/B.

Fig 12-37 overlays the pattern for a typical two-element Yagi (reflector-driver design) and the Moxon Rectangle. The pattern may appear odd since it uses a linear decibel scale (rather than the usual log decibel scale) to enhance the detail at the pattern center. Although the Yagi has slightly more gain, the Moxon's deficit won't be noticeable in operation. Most apparent is the F/B advantage that accrues to the Moxon. In practical terms, the Moxon effectively squelches QRM to the rear. Of equal importance is the broader beamwidth of the Moxon. The azimuth pattern does not show deep nulls off the ends of the beam elements. Instead, the deep nulls are about 15 to 20° farther back. Signals off the beam sides are

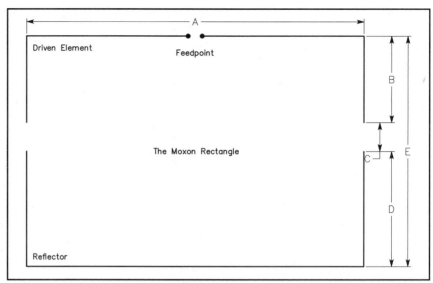

Fig 12-36—Outline of a Moxon Rectangle with various dimensions labeled. See the text for an explanation of the labels.

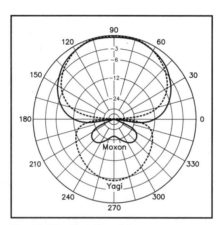

Fig 12-37—Relative free-space azimuth patterns at 14.175 MHz for a wire Yagi (driver and reflector) and a wire Moxon Rectangle. These patterns use a linear decibel scale to enhance detail at the pattern center (rather than the more usual log-decibel scale). Compare the pattern scale to that used in Fig 12-40.

stronger than those of a Yagi, even though the rear quadrants themselves are that much quieter than the Yagi. (At low heights, from ³/₈ λ to 1 λ, the Moxon's side gain ranges from 2 to 6 dB greater than that of a similarly positioned two-element Yagi.) As a result, the Moxon provides useful signal strength from one side to the other—as if it had good peripheral vision.

A Moxon Rectangle aimed in the general direction of the greatest number of potential Field Day contacts will

generally gather signals from a broader sector of the horizon than most other antennas—with the bonus of good QRM suppression from the rear. Stations located near one of the US borders may discover that a basic, fixed Moxon Rectangle is all they need. For those stations located inland and needing coverage in all directions, I'll have a solution a bit later. But first, let's design a Moxon Rectangle.

Designing a Moxon Rectangle

The objective in designing a Moxon Rectangle is to produce a set of dimensions for the wire diameter used that yields maximum F/B, maximum gain and a 50-Ω feed-point impedance at the design frequency. For this exercise, I chose #14 bare copper wire, perhaps the most popular Field Day antenna material. I also aligned the maximum F/B and 50-Ω resonant feed-point frequencies. Of course, gain varies across the band as it does with any two-element parasitic array.

With these design criteria, **Table 12-1** provides the dimensions of Moxon Rectangles for 80, 75, 40, 20, 15 and 10 meters—all potential Field Day bands of operation. The design frequencies are listed with the band of operation. Because the 40 and 10-meter bands are wide relative to the wire size used, I moved their design frequencies below the mid-band point in order to obtain low-end

Table 12-1
Dimensions of Wire Moxon Rectangles for 80-10 Meters
All dimensions refer to designations in Fig 12-36. Dimensions are in feet and apply to #14 AWG bare-wire antennas.

Band	Frequency (MHz)	A	B	C	D	E
80	3.6	99.98	15.47	2.16	18.33	36.96
75	3.9	92.28	14.28	2.00	16.92	33.20
40	7.09*	50.69	7.82	1.15	9.35	18.32
20	14.175	25.30	3.87	0.62	4.70	9.19
15	21.225	16.88	2.56	0.44	3.14	6.14
10	28.3*	12.65	1.90	0.35	2.36	4.61

*Because of bandwidth versus wire-size considerations, 40- and 10-meter design frequencies are below the mid-band points to obtain less than 2:1 50-Ω SWR over as much of the band as possible. See the text for alternative strategies.

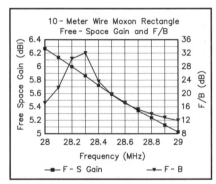

Fig 12-38—The pattern of free-space gain and 180° F/B across 10 meters for a #14 AWG wire Moxon Rectangle.

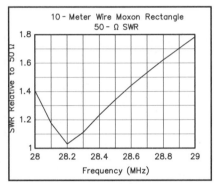

Fig 12-39—50-Ω SWR pattern across 10 meters for the #14 AWG wire Moxon Rectangle in Fig 12-38.

coverage at an SWR under 2:1.

The Moxon Rectangle functions by virtue of the mutual coupling between parallel element segments and the coupling between the facing element tips. Hence, the gap between element tips (dimension C in Fig 12-36) is the most critical dimension. Measure the gap accurately and ensure that the spacing does not change over time. The other dimensions follow from setting the gap in order to obtain the desired performance characteristics.

Fig 12-38 shows the gain and F/B curves for a 10-meter version of the #14 wire Moxon Rectangle designed for 28.3 MHz. I chose 10 meters because even the first megahertz represents a very wide band. Note that the gain curve is nearly linear across the band. However, the F/B peaks near the design frequency and tapers off—more rapidly below the design frequency than above

it. **Fig 12-39** shows a similar curve for the 50-Ω SWR, with the rate of increase more rapid below the design frequency than above it.

There is no absolute need to align the maximum F/B frequency with the resonant 50-Ω feed point. We can move one or both of them by small adjustments in the antenna dimensions. To sample the rates of change in performance parameters relative to small changes in dimensions, I altered some dimensions of a 20-meter version of the antenna by one inch. (One inch at 20 meters is, of course, approximately equivalent to changes of four inches on 80, two inches on 40, and a half-inch on 10 meters.) In all cases, the gap (dimension C) is held constant.

• Decreasing or increasing the side-to-side dimension (A in Fig 12-36) raises or lowers the maximum F/B and the resonant feed-point

frequencies by about 40 kHz. For small changes in dimension A, the resonant feed-point impedance does not change.

• Increasing or decreasing only the length of the driver tails (dimension B) by one inch lowers or raises the resonant frequency of the driver by about 70 kHz. The new resonant feed-point impedance will be a few ohms lower (for an increase in driver length) than before the change. The frequency of maximum F/B will not change significantly.

• Increasing or decreasing only the length of the reflector tails (dimension D) by one inch lowers or raises the peak F/B frequency by about 70 kHz. The driver's resonant frequency will not significantly change, but the impedance will be higher (for an increase in reflector length) than before the change.

With these guidelines, you can tailor a basic Moxon Rectangle design to suit what you decide is best for your operation.

One of the realities of Field Day is that you will not operate your antenna in free space. Actual antenna heights over real ground may range from ¼ λ to over 1 λ depending on the band and the available supports. To sample the operation of the Moxon Rectangle at various heights, I modeled a 10-meter version of the antenna at various heights, listed in **Table 12-2** in terms of fractions of a wavelength. The performance of versions for other bands will not materially differ for equivalent heights.

Note that as the antenna height increases, the take-off angle (or the elevation angle of maximum radiation) decreases, as do the vertical and horizontal beamwidths between half-power points. These properties are in line with those of any horizontally polarized array. Hence, the gain increases slightly with antenna height increases. **Fig 12-40** overlays the azimuth patterns for all of the heights in the table to demonstrate the small differences among them. Moreover, the feed-point impedance of the antenna undergoes only small changes with changes in heights. Indeed, the excellent F/B performance at the low height of

Table 12-2
Relative Performance of a Wire Moxon Rectangle at Different Heights Above Ground

Height (λ)	TO angle (Degrees)	Gain (dBi)	F/B (dB)	VBW (Degrees)	HBW (Degrees)	Feed Point Z (jX Ohms)
Free-space	—	5.9	37.1	—	78	53 + j 2
0.375	34	9.5	30.1	44	86	53 + j 8
0.5	26	10.5	21.3	32	82	59 + j 3
0.75	18	11.0	23.5	20	79	50 + j 1
1.0	14	11.3	30.4	5	79	56 + j 3

The modeled antenna is a 10-meter #14 AWG wire Moxon Rectangle at 28.5 MHz. Take-off (TO) angle refers to the elevation angle of maximum radiation. The 180° F/B is used in this table. Vertical bandwidth (VBW) and horizontal bandwidth (HBW) refer to the beamwidth between points at which power is down −3 dB relative to the maximum power. The feed-point impedance (Z) is given in conventional resistance/reactance terms. See Fig12-40 for comparative azimuth patterns.

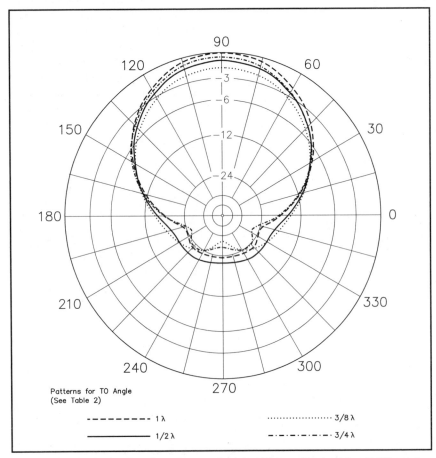

Patterns for TO Angle (See Table 2)

- - - - - - - - - 1 λ
———————— 1/2 λ
·················· 3/8 λ
-·-·-·-·-·-· 3/4 λ

Fig 12-40—Typical azimuth patterns of a wire Moxon Rectangle at different heights (in wavelengths) above ground. Each azimuth pattern is taken at the elevation angle of maximum radiation (take-off angle).

³/₈ λ holds promise for 40-meter and lower-frequency installations. The upshot of this exercise is that a Moxon Rectangle falls in the class of "well-behaved" antennas, requiring no finicky field adjustments once the basic design is set and tested.

Of course, you should always pretest your Field Day antennas using circumstances as close as possible to those you will encounter at the actual site. Testing over a prairie and operating in a forest can produce surprises (and problems) for almost any antenna. However, the semi-closed design configuration of the Moxon Rectangle tends to yield fewer interactions with surrounding structures than antennas with linear elements, an added advantage for Field Day operations.

A Direction-Switching Moxon Rectangle

If you live somewhere within the vast central region of the country, you may be interested in signals from both sides of the Moxon Rectangle. The antenna can accommodate you with fair ease. Following the design lead of Carrol Allen, AA2NN, we can design the Moxon Rectangle for direction-switching use. **Fig 12-41** shows the outline. Essentially, we create two resonant drivers using the same dimensions as for the basic antenna. Then we load the one we select as the reflector so that it becomes electrically long enough to perform as a reflector. Our loading technique employs a length of shorted 50-Ω cable. By bringing equal length stubs to a central point, we can switch them. The one we short becomes part of the reflector. The other one is connected to the main feed line and simply becomes part of the overall system feed line.

One switching caution: Use a double-pole double-throw switch so that you switch the center conductor and the braid of the coax lines used as stubs. When in use as a shorted stub, the line should not be electrically connected to the main feed line at all. A plastic box used to insulate the coax fittings from each other makes a good Field Day switch mount.

Table 12-3 lists the suggested dimensions for Field Day directional switching Moxon Rectangles for 80 through 10 meters. Because two drivers are used, with their shorter tails, the overall front-to-back dimension (E) of each antenna is smaller than that of its one-way versions. The shorter front-to-back dimension lowers the feed-point impedance by 5 to 7 Ω into the mid-40-Ω range; still a very good match for a coax feed line.

Table 12-3 also lists two stub lengths. The shorter one is the basic length of a shorted 50-Ω stub to achieve the required reflector loading. All of the designs required just about 65 Ω inductive reactance to electrically lengthen the reflector so that the

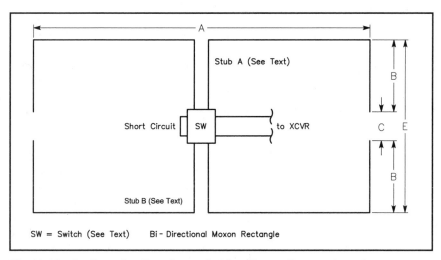

Fig 12-41—Outline of a direction-switching Moxon Rectangle, using transmission-line stub loading to electrically lengthen the reflector. See the text for details of the switching arrangement.

Table 12-3
Dimensions of Direction-Switching Wire Moxon Rectangles for 80-10 Meters
All dimensions refer to designations in Fig 12-36. Dimensions are in feet and apply to #14 AWG bare-wire antennas.

Band	Frequency (MHz)	A	B	C	E	Simple	Stub +1/2 λ
80	3.6	99.98	15.47	2.16	33.10	39.78	176.39
75	3.9	92.28	14.28	2.00	30.56	36.72	162.82
40	7.09	50.69	7.82	1.15	16.79	20.20	89.56
20	14.175	25.30	3.87	0.62	8.36	10.10	44.80
15	21.225	16.88	2.56	0.44	5.56	6.75	29.92
10	28.3	12.65	1.90	0.35	4.15	5.06	22.44

Stub lengths are based on an inductively reactive load of 65 Ω. for the reflector element at the design frequency. Listed stub lengths are for 50 Ω. cable with a 1.0 velocity factor. Multiply listed lengths by the actual velocity factor of the line to obtain the final length.

maximum F/B frequency aligns with the driver resonant point. Hence, the basic stub length for the shorted stub is about 52.4° Because you have a choice of cables with solid and foam dielectrics, you must multiply the listed length by the *actual velocity factor* of your stub cable. In general, solid-dielectric 50-Ω cables have velocity factors of 0.66 to 0.67, while foam cables tend toward a velocity factor of about 0.78. However, I have found significant departures from the listed values, so measuring the velocity factor of your line is a good practice. Otherwise, expect to cut and try lengths until you hit the right one.

Because the shorter length of the stub for some bands may leave them hanging high in the air, I have also listed the lengths of stubs that add a ¹/₂ λ of

line to them. The loading effect will be the same as for the shorter stub, but the lines may now reach a more convenient level for switching, especially in field conditions. It is wise to keep the lines suspended in the air, with the switch box hanging from a tree limb or tied to a post or stump. Again, multiply the listed values of longer lines by the velocity factor of the line you are actually using. Finally, be aware that coax stubs are not lossless and thus may slightly alter the performance of the array relative to the perfect lines used in models. In most cases, the differences will not be noticeable in practice.

The principles of reflector loading apply not only to Moxon Rectangles, but as well to wire Yagis, deltas, quads and a host of other two-element parasitic

arrays. With good preplanning, they yield antennas simple enough to be manageable in the field. At the same time, you gain the benefits of a directional pattern that may nearly double your score. In non-scoring terms, a directional-switching array means more effective communication under almost all conditions.

Field Construction of a Moxon Rectangle

Despite their simplicity and low cost, wire beams can be ungainly. Hence, you should survey the Field Day site in advance—and if possible, practice raising and lowering the antennas. For the Moxon Rectangle, look for or plan for suitable supports to stretch the antenna at its corners. Of course, the higher the support, the better. Because the Moxon Rectangle is only about 70% the side-to-side width of a comparable two-element Yagi, its space requirements are relatively modest, allowing the site designer somewhat greater flexibility.

Fig 12-42 outlines two types of systems for supporting the Moxon Rectangle. Consider them to be only the barest starting points for a real system. The four-post system at the left is suitable for any band. The posts can be trees, guyed masts, or building corners. The rope terminating at the post can be tied off there, if the ring point is accessible. Or, run the rope over a limb or through an eyebolt so that the corner can be easily raised and lowered.

The ring at the end of the corner rope through which the wire passes is used to reduce mutual abrasion of the wire and rope and can be a simple loop in the rope or even a plastic bottleneck. Because the shape of the Moxon Rectangle is important, the corner bends should be locked. A short piece of wire that runs from main wire to tail, but which goes around the corner ring, can effectively keep the corner in place. A permanent installation might call for soldering the ends of the locking wire to the antenna elements, but a short-term field installation can usually do well with just a few twists of the locking wire on the element.

The two-post construction method is more apt to the upper HF bands. It uses a long pole, PVC tube, or similar

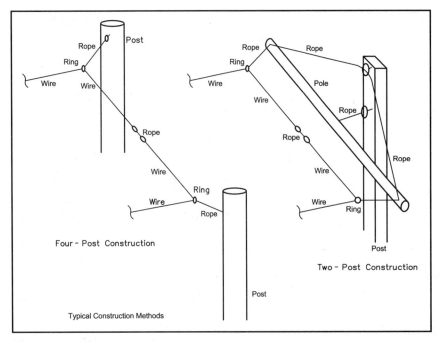

Fig 12-42—Four-pole and two-pole mounting arrangements for a wire Moxon Rectangle, shown only in barest outlines.

nonmetallic structure to anchor the corner ropes. The corner rope can be terminated at the pole or passed through it and run to the post. The sketch shows a two-anchor mounting for the pole. The upper support ropes align the pole horizontally. Thus, the rope should be locked to the ring or other support to keep everything horizontal. Alternatively, you can brace the pole directly to the support post, tree, or mast so that it remains horizontal. The remaining attachment mechanisms are the same as for the four-post method of support.

The rope that separates the driver and reflector tails should not stretch. Its job is to maintain the tail gap spacing as securely as possible. In addition, since the degree of coupling between tails is a function of the wire diameter, the wire fold-back used to make an attachment loop in the element tails should be as tight and flat as possible without weakening the antenna wire. For added strain relief and dimensional precision for upper HF versions of the Moxon Rectangle, it is possible to place the non-metallic pole at or inside the perimeter of the antenna. With some judicious use of electrical tape where the elements end along the pole, you can omit the tail-to-tail rope altogether. For a larger, lower, HF-band version of the antenna, you can use a rope that runs from each front ring to the corresponding rear ring and tape the driver and reflector tails wires to it.

For field use, lightweight coax (ie, RG-8X for 50-Ω applications) helps reduce the stress on the driven element(s) at the feed point. However, where

conditions permit, supporting the element centers is advisable. In fact, slightly Ving the elements will normally produce no adverse effects in performance. However, if you contemplate a shallow inverted-V form of the antenna, pretest the assembly to assure that everything will work as planned.

Field Day antenna construction is a primary exercise in adapting easily obtainable materials to particular site configurations. Hence, it is not possible to provide universal guidance for every situation. However, these notes should get you started. Survey your local Home Depot and other such outlets for fixtures and nonmetallic connectors that might prove useful for a Field Day antenna. You may find them anywhere in the store. The plumbing and electrical departments are good starting places to find adaptable PVC fittings.

The Moxon Rectangle offers good potential for Phase 3 antenna improvements in Field Day installations. It is certainly not the only good antenna for this important exercise. The final decision you make in selecting an antenna should be the result of extended planning activities that review: (A) What is possible at the site; (B) what is possible with the available construction crew and (C) which antennas when properly oriented will improve communications the most from a given site. What you learn about various antennas that may be candidates for the next Field Day will serve you well in the long run—both at home and in the field.

Of course, the Moxon Rectangle—when it has done its Field Day service—need not be retired to storage awaiting next year's duty: It can serve very well in many home-station installations. The size and the signal pattern may be perfectly suited to the needs of at least some operators.

An Aluminum Moxon Rectangle for 10 Meters

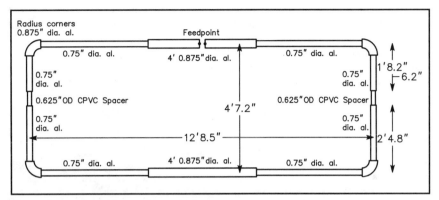

Fig 12-43—General outline of the 10-meter aluminum Moxon rectangle, showing tubing dimensions. See text for hardware and mounting details.

Closely related to the previous project, this one also come from L. B. Cebik, W4RNL, and was published in *The ARRL Antenna Compendium, Vol 6.*

I occasionally receive inquiries from folks who cannot quite support the width of a 10-meter Yagi of two or three elements because obstructions restrict them to less than the 16.5 feet needed. Is there an antenna with decent performance that will fit in a space about 13 feet wide? If it can be home-built to save money and to require no complex tuning or matching system, so much the better.

In fact, there is an antenna that fits this description almost perfectly. Imagine an antenna with the gain (over real ground) of a two-element Yagi (> 11 dBi), nearly the front-to-back ratio of a three-element Yagi (> 20 dB from 28.3 to 28.5 MHz), and an SWR below 2:1 from one end of the band to the other. Also imagine that the antenna has better than 15 dB F/B all the way down to 28 MHz, and retains about 12 dB F/B at 29.7 MHz.

Imagine also that the antenna can be directly connected to 50-Ω coax (even though I always recommend a 1:1 choke or bead balun). Now imagine that you can make it yourself from hardware store materials, that it will weigh about 10 pounds including the boom (under 5 pounds without the boom), and that you can make it in your garage with no special tools. Finally, imagine that when it is done, you will still have change from a $50 bill.

Imagine no more. The antenna is the Moxon rectangle. Les Moxon, G6XN, derived the original design from VK2ABQ squares. He tunes both elements of his wire version to form a two-way, fixed-mounted beam. However, we can optimize the dimensions to form an aluminum beam that is easy to rotate.

Fig 12-43 shows a sketch, with dimensions, of my latest version. It uses hardware-store 7/8 and 3/4-inch diameter aluminum tubing to form the main elements, with 3/4-inch tubing for the side elements. The corners can use radius-bent tubing or be squared by making corner supports from L-stock. Cut the straight tubing at 45° end angles and use 1/16-inch

Fig 12-44—A close-up of the corner assembly. The 7/8-inch diameter corner piece makes a good fit over the 3/4-inch diameter straight pieces and requires only a single fastener at each end (with a light coat of "Penetrox A" at the joint).

thick L-stock to fashion upper and lower supports. One to two-inch lengths of support each way around the corner, using stainless-steel sheet-metal screws or pop rivets, solidify the corners with minimal weight. I also tried 1/2-inch conduit Ls but had to ream out the ends to accept the 3/4 inch tubing.

The corners I use are 7/8-inch aluminum radius-bent sections sent to me by Tom Schiller, N6BT (of Force 12), to speed up the experimentation. You can bend your own by filling the aluminum tube with sand (or cat litter) and bending it around a 6-inch or larger wheel or pulley. Work slowly. Keep the

sand well packed in the tube to prevent kinking.

The combination of 7/8-inch and 3/4-inch aluminum tubing lets you telescope the ends into the center for a precise fit or a center frequency adjustment. A similar advantage accrues from using l-inch and 7/8-inch hardware-store aluminum tubing. **Fig 12-44** is a close-up photograph of a corner assembly.

The side-to-side length is the key to centering the SWR curve for lowest reading at 28.4 to 28.5 MHz. The center frequency changes about 150 kHz for every inch of length adjustment. Hence, using the U-shaped outer ends as trombone slides will let you center the antenna anywhere in the 10-meter band. If you use slightly larger stock, say l-inch and 7/8-inch tubing; performance will change very little. With 7/8-inch tubing for the outer main elements and the sides, you can weld or otherwise fasten (with Penetrox or another conductive paste) 3/4-inch copper plumbing pipe Ls at the corners.

Since the end spacing and alignment is somewhat critical to the antenna's full performance, you can slide a piece of CPVC or similar lightweight, durable tubing either inside the ends or over the ends and fasten them in place with sheet-metal screws. The rigid spacer also limits the twisting force placed on the corners. Sheet-metal screws also connect the 3/4-inch and 7/8-inch tubing together. Be sure that all hardware is stainless steel. Pop rivets will also do well, if you use sufficiently sturdy ones.

The feed-point assembly is shown in **Fig 12-45**. I used a very simple system. I cut one side of the driven element tubing 1 inch short at the feed point. I then cut a 2-inch section of ¹/₁₆-inch thick L stock, and cut a ⁵/₈-inch diameter hole at one end. A chassis-mount female coax connector (with a lock washer) fits into the hole, with the plug side pointed at the mast. Stainless-steel sheet metal screws attach the longer side of the L stock to the cut-off tube. A #14 copper wire (tinned the entire length) goes from the center pin to the other side of the feed point, where it is fastened to the tubing by a sheet-metal screw. Feel free to devise your own method of feed-point connections. After testing, but before committing the antenna to permanent installation, be sure to waterproof the rear of the coax connector as well as the coax plugs.

For element-to-boom plates, you can use any durable material. Spar varnished ³/₈-inch plywood or LE plastic make good plates. About 3 by 9 inch (or longer) plates give ample room to U-bolt the elements to the plate and have room for U-bolts that go over the mast.

My prototype uses ¹/₂-inch PVC electrical conduit U straps fastened in place with #8 stainless-steel hardware. Since ⁷/₈-inch tubing overstresses these straps, I placed an extra washer between

Fig 12-45—A close-up of the feedpoint assembly, with ³/₄-inch wide U-stock used for the coax receptacle. After initial tests the rear of the coax fitting, the bare wire-to-tube connection and the connector from the ferrite-bead choke balun were sealed with butylate. Experience with other outdoor uses suggests that the gray PVC half-clamps should be replaced every two to three years during routine maintenance.

the U strap and the plywood plate. The object is a firm grip, but not a broken strap. Two straps hold the reflector center tube in place; the driven element requires two on each side of the feed point.

As with all good antenna structures, let the elements hang under the boom. What boom? Well, you can use almost anything, from 1¹/₄-inch PVC (which I had on hand) to a good grade of aluminum tubing (thicker-wall than the usual 0.055-inch hardware store variety—or two pieces nested) to a 5-foot length of spar varnished 1¹/₄-inch-diameter closet rod. PVC is the heaviest, aluminum the lightest; but at 5 feet, the boom weight is not a significant issue. Make a boom-to-mast plate similar to the boom-to-element plates, only a bit more nearly square, and you are in business.

The antenna dimensions in the drawing are given to three decimal places, being direct translations of the computer model used to generate the antenna. Try to keep the dimensions within about ¹/₄ inch of the drawing, and you won't be able to tell any difference in performance. Squaring the corners or missing the dimensions by a half inch will shift the performance centers by

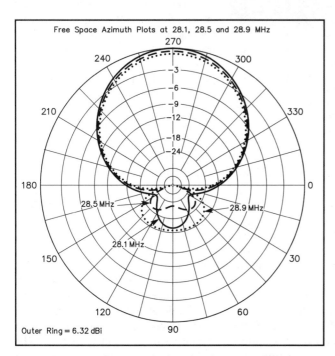

Fig 12-46—Free Space Azimuth Plots at 28.1, 28.5 and 28.9 MHz. (All computer plots were made with *NEC-4* using the *EZNEC Pro* software from Roy Lewallen, W7EL, PO Box 6658, Beaverton, OR 97007.)

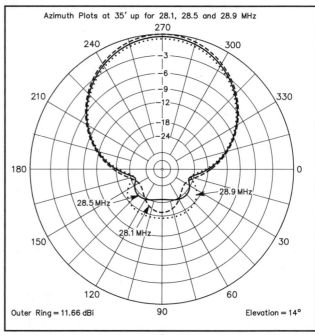

Fig 12-47—Azimuth plots at 28.1, 28.5 and 28.9 MHz at an elevation angle of 13° with the antenna at 35 feet.

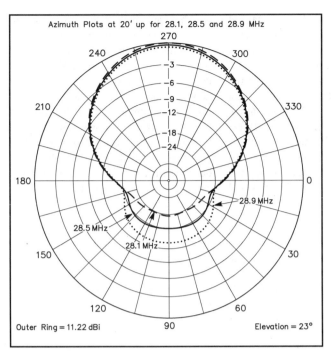

Fig 12-48—Azimuth plots at 28.1, 28.5, and 28.9 MHz at an elevation angle of 23° with the antenna at 20 feet.

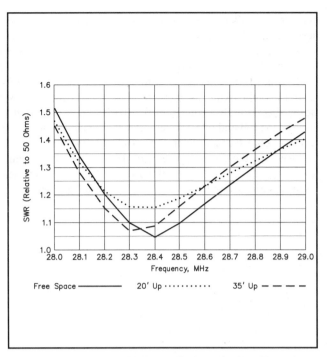

Fig 12-49—Computer SWR predictions for the Moxon rectangle between 28 and 29 MHz.

about 100 kHz at most. In most cases, you will not be aware of any difference at all. To assure that the assembly is neatly squared and close to the prescribed dimensions, you can draw the outer dimensions and centerline on the shop/garage/basement floor with a marker pen and then assemble the pieces within those boundaries. As shop experts always say, measure twice, cut and assemble once.

Note that the antenna is about 12 feet, 8 inches wide and less than 5 feet front-to-back, for a turning radius of about 6 feet, 8 inches. Strapped up on the side of the house, the antenna is unlikely to overhang the property line. The antenna is light enough for hand rotation, but an old TV rotator might come in handy. Because of the antenna's characteristics, you may not need to rotate it much.

The free-space azimuth patterns, shown in **Fig 12-46** for 28.1, 28.5, and 28.9 MHz, show the possibilities for the Moxon rectangle. Note the very broad forward lobe, almost a cardioid, giving reception and transmission as wide as your peripheral vision. Behind you is silence—or at least a significant amount of silencing. The performance charac-

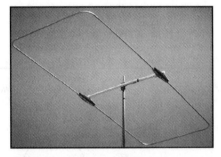

Fig 12-50—The completed 10-meter aluminum Moxon rectangle on its test mast. Despite some stiff breezes, the physically closed assembly has remained very stable.

teristics promise to hold up well across the most active part of 10 meters.

But what about performance at real heights above real ground? At 35 feet, about one wavelength, the antenna provides most of its free-space performance across the band, as shown in **Fig 12-47**. At greater heights, the performance moves closer to free space. The elevation angle at 35 feet for maximum gain is 13° to 14°, similar to that of a dipole or Yagi.

Even at 20 feet up, a typical portable antenna height at 10 meters, the antenna continues to display excellent

front-to-back characteristics with the gain of a typical driven element-reflector two-element Yagi (which does not have good front-to-back characteristics at this height—perhaps 9 or 10 dB). See **Fig 12-48**. The elevation angle of maximum radiation is about 23° at the $^5/_8$-wavelength height.

As shown in the computer projections of **Fig 12-49**, the Moxon rectangle is quite stable with respect to feed-point characteristics as the antenna is raised and lowered, The curves actually flatten somewhat over real ground. Therefore, setting up the antenna for operation is simple.

My initial procedure was to fasten the antenna, pointed straight up, to a 20-foot mast propped up by a sturdy tripod. The reflector was no more than 5 feet above ground. I then adjusted the side-to-side length to minimize SWR at 28.450 MHz, using the trombone-slide end sections. After fastening down the sections and raising the antenna, there was no detectable change in SWR performance from the adjustment position pointing at the sky.

Fig 12-50 is a photograph of my antenna mounted in place on its test mast. On-the-air tests with Moxon rectangles verify that the antenna shows less than 2:1 SWR across the entire 10-meter band when the design center frequency is about 28.5 MHz. The gain and front-to-back ratio continue to decrease as the frequency increases, but some directionality and gain persist even at the top end of 10 meters. Local contacts confirm that the front-to-back ratio within the first megahertz of 10 meters is far superior to that of a comparable driven element with reflector two-element Yagi. I cannot measure gain, but there is no detectable difference between the Moxon and a two-element Yagi at my station.

Contrary to claims made for the VK2ABQ squares, these antennas do not like to be nested for a multiband array. Stacking requires a minimum of 10 feet between 10 and 15-meter models. However, you might consider back-to-back 10 and 15-meter antennas. Computer studies suggest that a 13-foot boom would hold both antennas, reflector-to-reflector, with minimal interaction.

The Moxon rectangle will not overpower big competition. However, it does provide wideband gain with very good directional performance and a good match to common coax for the 10-meter operator with limited space and budget. Construction is straightforward using commonly available materials. These may be enough good features to earn the antenna a place at many stations.

A Two-Band Loop for 30 and 40 Meters

This antenna adds versatility to a basic 40-meter delta loop antenna. It was built and described by James Brenner, NT4B, in the Hints and Kinks column of March 1989 *QST*.

After trying to find a way to place a 30-meter delta loop inside an existing 40-meter loop, I remembered an article in *All About Cubical Quad Antennas*[1] describing a $1\frac{1}{2}$-λ, or "Mini X-Q," loop The gain of this antenna was said to be about 1 dB more than a 1-λ loop. I installed a large, ceramic SPST knife switch in the center of the delta loop's bottom leg (see **Fig 12-51**). With this switch open, the full-wave, 40-meter loop becomes a $1\frac{1}{2}$-λ, 30-meter loop! I found the resonant frequency of this arrangement to be 10.5 MHz. By adding 18-inch wires to the loop at both sides of the switch, I obtained resonance at 10.125 MHz.

Since the bottom of the loop is only 12 feet above ground, it's a relatively simple matter to reach the band switch from ground level.

(Caution. High RF voltage appears at the switch when the antenna is used for transmitting on 30 meters.) Incidentally, the loop also works well on 15 m (SWR under 2.1 across the band) when set for 40 meters, and I have used the 30-meter configuration successfully on 80 meters with the help of an antenna tuner.

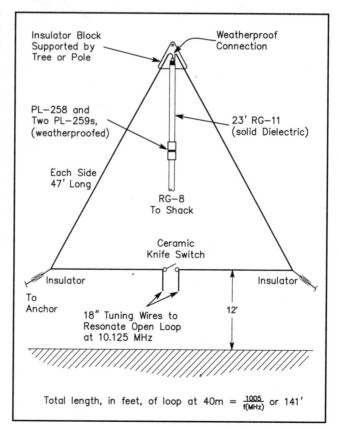

Fig 12-51—Jim Brenner's 30 and 40-meter loop. Note the 18-inch tuning wires used to lower the antenna's 30-meter resonance from 10.5 to 10.125 MHz. The antenna is top-fed via a $\frac{1}{4}$-λ 40-meter matching section See text.

Insulator Block Supported by Tree or Pole

Weatherproof Connection

PL-258 and Two PL-259s, (weatherproofed)

23' RG-11 (solid Dielectric)

Each Side 47' Long

RG-8 To Shack

Ceramic Knife Switch

Insulator

To Anchor

18" Tuning Wires to Resonate Open Loop at 10.125 MHz

Insulator

12'

Total length, in feet, of loop at 40m = $\frac{1005}{f(MHz)}$ or 141'

[1]W Orr and S Cowan, All About Cubical Quad Antennas (Wilton, CT. Radio Publications, 1970)

KØEOU's Truly Broadband Antenna for 80/75 Meters

If you are fortunate enough to have a tower, this may be the antenna you'd want to install to cover the 80/75-meter band. The major appeal of this design is that it covers the entire band from 3.5 to 4.0 MHz—not just a narrow sliver. It is also fairly compact and I can attest from personal experience (more on that later) that it works well for DX contacts. Brian L. Wermager, KØEOU, developed and built this antenna and here's how he described it in April 1986 *QST*:

With declining sunspots and poor conditions on the higher HF bands, 80 meters has suddenly become very popular. But, unfortunately, many hams are not able to use this band to its full potential. It offers every kind of ham activity from CW to phone, from nets and ragchewing to great DXing, but many hams are too limited by the frequency range of their antennas to enjoy this band completely.

Antenna-matching networks are one answer, but they spoil the advantage of the no-tune feature of modern transceivers. Matching networks also are often less effective than many hams think; they introduce losses. The losses can be significant at some settings which provide a match. With these things in mind, I decided to try some ideas that might give me a more broadbanded antenna. The prime requirement was that it be fed with common 50-ohm coaxial cable, with no traps, coils or capacitors.

First, I tried a quarter-wave sloper. This antenna worked very well, with a bandwidth of 300 kHz between the 2:1 SWR points. It still, however, limited me from operating CW DX at the bottom of the band and the phone nets at the top of the band. There had to be a better antenna.

Antennas can be broadbanded by using large-diameter elements. With this in mind, I began experimenting with two-wire slopers, attached to a common feed point, but with the wire ends fanned out from each other. (See **Fig 12-52**.) This seemed to help, but not as much as I had hoped. It did, however, shorten the length required for the sloper. For those with a short tower, this idea could make

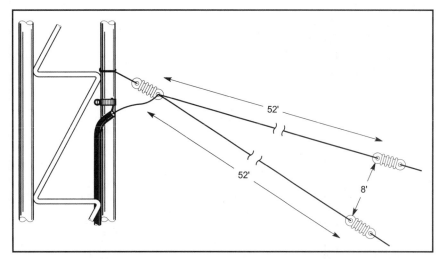

Fig 12-52—Arrangement of the original KØEOU experiment. The coaxial cable shield is connected to the tower, with both wires of the two-wire element connected to the center conductor. The wires are spread approximately 8 feet at the ends and are each approximately 52 feet long.

an 80 or 160-meter sloper possible when a single-wire sloper would be too long.

The Fickle Finger of Fate Strikes!

While I was trying one of these two-wire antennas at a low height on my tower, the SWR was less than 2:1 from 3.5 to 4.0 MHz! After several attempts to get it to work the same way at the top of the tower, I discovered that these results could be attained only when my old quarter-wave sloper was at the top of the tower and grounded to the tower. (See **Fig 12-53**.) The two antenna elements were obviously interacting with each other. Broadening the bandwidth tremendously. Further pruning of the lengths of both the sloper and the two-wire element resulted in the amazing SWR curves shown in **Fig 12-54**.

What's Going On?

I will leave the question of why it works to the experts. (See the sidebar to this article.—*Ed.*) Like a true ham, I subscribe to the old saying, "If it works, leave it up and don't mess with it." My guess, however, is that it is something like one-half of a two-element log periodic seeking its mirror image in thee grounded tower. The top element is

tuned for the lower portion of the band and the two-wire element for the upper portion. In fact, there is a little SWR "bump" in the middle of the band that seems to give further evidence of this.

How Well Does It Work?

Although I have no way of scientifically plotting the antenna pattern, it does seem to be vertically polarized. Good DX performance from the antenna seems to verify this. Because many contacts have been made in all directions, the antenna probably has a fairly omnidirectional pattern. On-the-air comparisons with a quarter-wave sloper across town show that the antenna performs at least as well as the sloper. It also seems to have a little less noise on receive than the sloper.

Getting One Up for Yourself

If you have a tower over 40 feet high, you should be in business. The element dimensions will vary according to the height of your tower. My friend Kelly Davis, KD7XY, constructed one of these antennas on his 50-foot tower so we could see how the dimensions would change. Measurements of his antenna are shown in **Fig 12-55**.

It is interesting to note that the

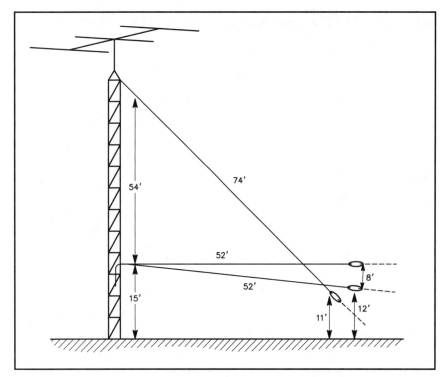

Fig 12-53—The antenna as constructed at KØEOU. The tower is 70 feet high. The feed point is as described in Fig 12-52 and is 15 feet above ground level on the tower. The sloper element is 74 feet long, is connected to the tower at the top end and slopes to a point 11 feet above ground level at the end.

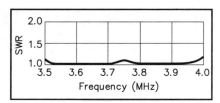

Fig 12-54—SWR measurements for the antenna at KØEOU. The highest SWR measurement between 3.5 and 4.0 MHz is 1.2:1.

height of the feed point on the tower does not appear to be critical at all. The angle of the wires in the two-wire element does not seem to be critical either. The sloper element, however, should come down between the two wires of the lower element. The sloper angle is about 45 degrees. As you attempt to get the lowest possible SWR from the antenna, remember that the angle of the sloper to the tower and its distance from the ground at the end will have an effect on the bandwidth. Because these antennas can be pruned from the ground, the trial-and-error method is easy. When pruning the antenna, remember that the two elements are cut for different frequencies. Changing the length of the top element changes the performance at the lower part of the band. Changing the lengths of the two-wire elements changes the performance at the top part of the band. Don't give up until your antenna SWR is, at the very most, 1.5:1 from band edge to band edge.

Use good insulators at the ends of each of the three wires. I used nylon fishing line at first, but one foggy, wet night the wire in the top element burned through in three places. It surprised me that there could be such high currents in a part of the antenna not even connected to the feed line, but I should have known better. Remember also that other objects around the antenna, such as other antennas or guy lines, could adversely affect antenna performance. Keep the antenna as much in the clear as possible.

Some Untried Ideas

I hope others will try some modifications to this antenna. For example, there should be no reason why

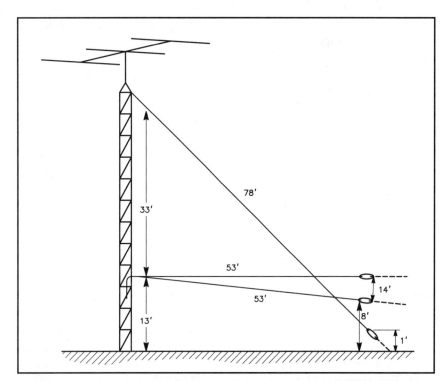

Fig 12-55—The antenna installation at KD7XY. The tower is 50 feet high. The sloper element is attached at 46 feet, is 78 feet long, and is only 1 foot above ground level at the end. The two-wire element is 53 feet long and is attached to the tower at 13 feet above ground level. Like KØEOU's antenna, it is virtually "flat" across the band; highest measured SWR is 1.4:1.

THE MININEC ANALYSIS OF THE KØEOU THREE-ELEMENT HALF SLOPER

The Mini-Numerical Electronics Code (*MININEC*) analyzes thin-wire antennas, solving an integral equation representation of the electric fields using a method-of-moments technique. *MININEC* solves for the currents, impedance and patterns for antennas composed of wires in arbitrary orientations in free space and over perfectly conducting ground.

The impedance at the feed point calculates to be $79.4 + j\,1859.8$ ohms. This assumes a perfect ground beneath the structure and simply a 3-foot extension of the tower above the connection of the upper wire. In practice, the impedance will be affected by both the ground conductivity and the top-loading effect of a beam antenna atop the tower.

A fair amount of current flows in the top section above the upper wire connection point. Top loading will affect the phase of this current, which will be reflected as a change in impedance at the feed point. In other words, the calculated data is not absolute. Use it as an approximation only.

A relatively high current flows at the base of the tower to ground—more than in any other part of the system. This indicates that a good earth connection, and even a radial system, would offer highest efficiency.

The antenna patterns, **Figs 12-A**, **12-B** and **12-C**, are also approximations. Polarization is predominantly vertical—at low angles it may be considered to be almost completely vertical. Broadside to the direction of the wires, the polarization becomes horizontal at high radiation angles; ie, above 75 degrees. At 60-degrees elevation, the vertical component is almost 16 dB greater than the horizontal. The vertical component increases significantly at lower elevation angles, being in excess of 30 dB above the horizontal component at a 5-degree elevation. These figures all apply in a direction broadside to the wires. In the direction of the wires, both "front" and "back," the radiation is entirely vertically polarized.—*Gerald L. Hall, K1TD*

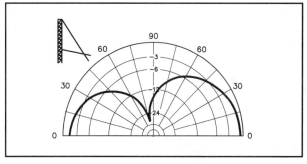

Fig 12B—Antenna elevation radiation pattern, in the direction of the wires, for the KØEOU antenna. Values are in dBi. Add 6.0 dB to the values shown.

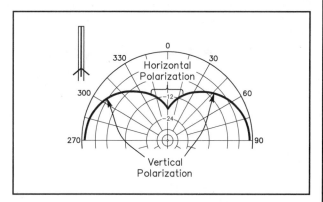

Fig 12C—Antenna elevation radiation pattern, in a direction broadside to the wires, for the KØEOU antenna. Values are in dBi. Add 6.0 dB to the values shown.

Azimuth Pattern

——————— At the Horizon
– – – – – – 30° up from the Horizon
·············· 60° up from the Horizon

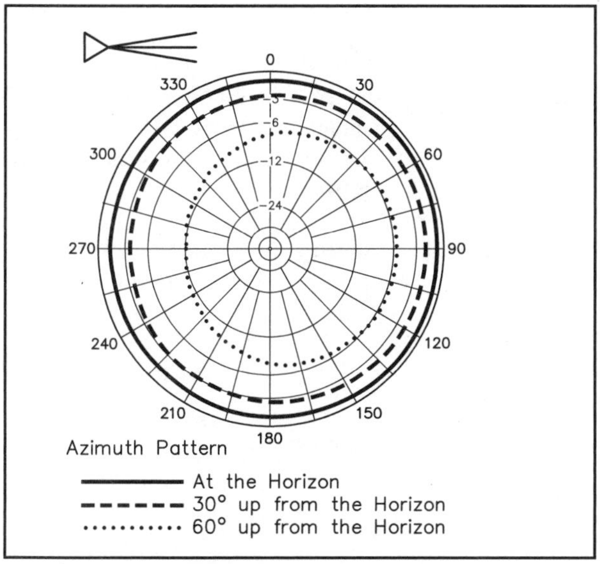

Fig 12A—Antenna azimuth radiation pattern for the KØEOU three-element half sloper antenna. Values are in dBi. Add 6.0 dB to the values shown.

a single wire for the bottom element won't work. My small city lot doesn't give me room to try a single wire, as it would surely need to be longer than the two-wire element. I would also like to see someone try cutting the top element for the high end of the band, and the bottom element for the low end. This could shorten the sloper element for someone with a shorter

tower and may even give the antenna some gain in the direction of the two-wire element. It might also be possible to construct an antenna for another band inside of this one (40 meters, for example). The same feed point could be used, but with another sloper element for the second band. Another possibility is to construct the antenna with two dipoles.

It is my guess (and only a guess), that it is the merging of the ends of the elements that causes the 50-ohm impedance of the antenna.

Winter gives us the best conditions on the 80/75-meterband. You can be ready to use the whole band with this simple-to-construct and very broadband antenna.

Improved Efficiency for the KØEOU Antenna

This follow-up to the previous article was written when I was living in Connecticut. After you read this, you should understand why I chose to include the KØEOU antenna in this chapter.

When Brian Wermager's article. "A Truly Broadband Antenna for 80/75 Meters," arrived at HQ, I wanted to see if the antenna worked as well as claimed before publishing the information in *QST*. I stopped tuning the antenna when the SWR was less than 1.6 across the entire band.

For working DX the antenna seemed to work as well as, or better than, a dipole at 50 feet. Casual contacts were not difficult to make, but in contests, it was a different matter. The results were satisfactory, but could "satisfactory" be changed to "outstanding"?

The key to improving the efficiency of this antenna is found in the sidebar accompanying the article. The

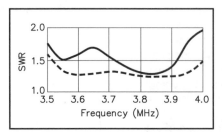

Fig 12-56—Graph showing SWR vs frequency for the KØEOU 80/75-meter antenna. The lower curve depicts results before adding ground radials; the upper curve was plotted after adding radials and retuning the antenna.

MININEC computer analysis done by Gerald Hall, K1TD, shows that: "A relatively high current flows at the base of the tower to ground—more than in any other part of the system. This indicates that a good earth connection, and even a radial system,

would offer highest efficiency."

A system of radial wires improves antenna efficiency by cutting ground resistance losses. The decreased resistance in ground losses will also narrow the antenna bandwidth. The question now becomes: Is the narrowing of the bandwidth too much? I decided to investigate that question next. With help from a brother-in-law, I installed 42 radials around, and bonded them to, the tower base. As expected, SWR increased across the entire band. After I retuned the antenna, the SWR was below 2:1 across the entire band (see **Fig 12-56**). As for results, DX stations are typically 2 to 6 S units stronger on the KØEOU antenna than on the dipole at 50 feet. Contest QSOs are now a reality. I am not the loudest East Coast station on the band, but I am very pleased with the performance of the broadband antenna. The dipole has been removed and stored!—*Chuck Hutchinson, K8CH*

13 VHF Beam Antennas

Yagis are kings of the hill on VHF/UHF.
Here are a number of 6-meter and 2-meter designs for you.

Along with the dipole and the quarter-wave vertical, radio amateurs throughout the world make extensive use of the Yagi array. This introductory section below on Yagis has been excerpted from *The ARRL Antenna Book,* 19th Edition.

The Yagi was invented in the 1920s by Hidetsugu Yagi and Shintaro Uda, two Japanese university professors. Uda did much of the developmental work, while Yagi introduced the array to the world outside Japan through his writings in English. Although the antenna should properly be called a Yagi-Uda array, it is commonly referred to simply as a *Yagi.*

The Yagi is a type of multielement array. At the minimum, it consists of a single driven element and a single parasitic element. These elements are placed parallel to each other, typically on a supporting boom. This arrangement is known as a 2-element Yagi. The parasitic element is termed a reflector when it is placed behind the driven element, opposite to the direction of maximum radiation, and is called a director when it is placed ahead of the driven element. See **Fig 13-1**. See the sidebar *Yagi Concepts and Definitions.*

In the VHF and UHF spectrum, Yagis with 30 or more elements are not rare. Large HF arrays may employ 10 or more elements. However, in this book we'll be looking at much smaller antennas.

The gain and directional pattern of a Yagi array is determined by spacing and tuning of its elements. Both length and diameter affect element tuning. The science and math behind this are complicated and so we'll not be getting into those details. Rather, we'll be looking at results.

For about 50 years amateurs and professionals created Yagi array designs largely by "cut and try" experimental techniques. In the early 1980s, Jim Lawson, W2PV, described in detail for the amateur audience the fundamental mathematics involved in modeling Yagis. The advent of powerful microcomputers and sophisticated computer antenna modeling software in the mid 1980s revolutionized the field of Yagi design for the radio amateur. In a matter of minutes, a computer can try 100,000 or more different combinations of element lengths and spacings to create a Yagi design tailored to meet a particular set of performance parameters. To explore this number of combinations experimentally, a human experimenter would take an unimaginable amount of time, and the process would no doubt suffer from considerable measurement errors. With the computer tools available today, an antenna can be designed, constructed and then put up in the air, with little or no tuning or pruning required.

Some Simple Beams You Can Build

This chapter starts with a new and previously unpublished design. In fact, there is a family of these new designs. During the planning process, we

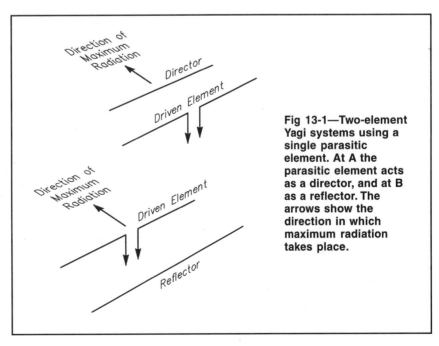

Fig 13-1—Two-element Yagi systems using a single parasitic element. At A the parasitic element acts as a director, and at B as a reflector. The arrows show the direction in which maximum radiation takes place.

YAGI CONCEPTS AND DEFINITIONS

Like most specialized hobbies, Amateur Radio throws a lot of jargon at the newcomer. Look carefully at **Fig 13-A**, which shows the parts for a typical Yagi installation. This is a 4-element beam antenna, placed on the top of a mast turned by a rotator. The rotator is nested inside a guyed tower. There's a lot more information about towers in Chapter 14 of this book, as well as in *The ARRL Antenna Book*.

In several earlier chapters, we discussed various measures of antenna performance. It is appropriate to discuss here performance in a little more detail. All antennas can be classified according to four characteristics:

- Polarization
- Feed-point impedance (which is related to losses)
- Radiation patterns
- Gain (which is related closely to radiation patterns and losses)

POLARIZATION

We've discussed polarization previously in Chapter 5, HF Verticals. There, we compared a vertically polarized antenna mounted over various types of ground with a horizontally polarized dipole. The ground-mounted vertical was superior at low elevation angles (those needed to work DX) unless the horizontal antenna was mounted high above the ground in terms of wavelength.

The polarization of an antenna is determined by the orientation of its electric field with respect to the earth. For most simple antennas, such as a dipole, if you mount it horizontally you have horizontal polarization. Mount a dipole vertically and you have vertical polarization.

FEED-POINT IMPEDANCE

This is pretty easy to understand—It's the impedance at the

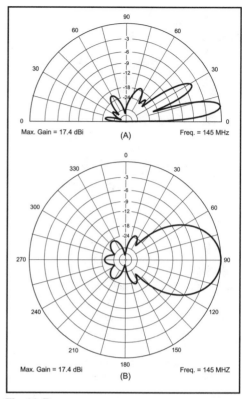

Max. Gain = 17.4 dBi   (A)   Freq. = 145 MHz

Max. Gain = 17.4 dBi   (B)   Freq. = 145 MHZ

Fig 13-B

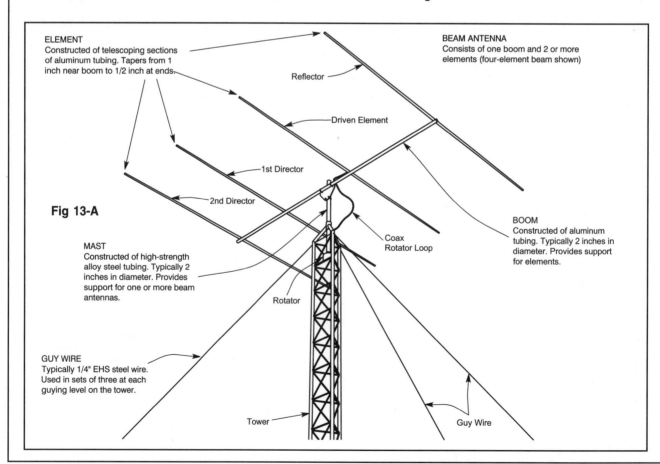

ELEMENT
Constructed of telescoping sections of aluminum tubing. Tapers from 1 inch near boom to 1/2 inch at ends.

BEAM ANTENNA
Consists of one boom and 2 or more elements (four-element beam shown)

Reflector

Driven Element

1st Director

2nd Director

Fig 13-A

Coax Rotator Loop

BOOM
Constructed of aluminum tubing. Typically 2 inches in diameter. Provides support for elements.

MAST
Constructed of high-strength alloy steel tubing. Typically 2 inches in diameter. Provides support for one or more beam antennas.

Rotator

GUY WIRE
Typically 1/4" EHS steel wire. Used in sets of three at each guying level on the tower.

Tower

Guy Wire

antenna's feed point. Complicating matters somewhat is that the feed-point impedance consists of several components: the *radiation resistance* of the antenna and the *losses*, not only in the antenna itself but also in the antenna's nearby environment. The losses in an antenna are made up of:

- Conductor I²R losses (often called "copper losses," even if the antenna is made of aluminum)
- Dielectric losses in any insulators used in antenna construction. Hopefully, your insulators are not so poor that they absorb RF power!
- Ground losses, a sort of catchall category.

Conductor and dielectric losses in the antenna itself are pretty easy to understand, but ground losses are a bit trickier, especially for verticals. I suggest you revisit the discussion in Chapter 5, HF Verticals. Ground-mounted verticals require many wire radials to lower ground losses, especially when the antenna is mounted over poorly conducting ground.

Even horizontal antennas can have surprisingly large ground losses when they are close to the ground, where the electric fields generated by the antenna can cause substantial currents to flow in the lossy ground. (This is sometimes called "warming up the worms.")

If you add up all the resistive components representing losses, you end up with a single equivalent loss resistance. When you subtract the equivalent loss resistance from the feed-point impedance, what you have left is the radiation resistance. The radiation resistance is the only component that actually does any useful work—it radiates your signal.

The feed-point impedance of an antenna is rarely exactly what we'd like it to be, usually 50 ohms to directly match a coax cable. Yagi designers tend to use either some form of gamma or hairpin match to match the antenna to the feed coax. What we hams measure down in the shack at the transmitter output is the SWR on the coax feeding the antenna. It is usually important that the SWR be as flat as possible across the whole amateur band we want to operate.

RADIATION PATTERNS

In numerous examples in the preceding chapters we've shown you elevation and azimuthal radiation patterns. These have mainly been polar plots, showing either a full 360° azimuthal view or a 180° elevation view. **Fig 13-B** shows both the azimuth and elevation patterns for an optimized 6-element 2-meter Yagi using an 8-foot boom, mounted 10 feet above ground. There have also been a few rectangular X-Y plots, when we wanted to show specific details in an expanded region, say from 0° to 30° in elevation, such as Fig 5-1 in Chapter 5.

You will run into two terms that attempt to succinctly describe an antenna's pattern without necessarily showing a graph: Front-to-Back ratio (F/B) and worst-case Front-to-Rear ratio (F/R). The term F/B refers to the response 180° behind the "nose" of the main lobe. In Fig 13-B, the F/B is about 26 dB. The term F/R refers to the worst-case lobe located anywhere from 90° to 270° behind the main lobe. For the Yagi in Fig 13-B, the F/R is about 25 dB at azimuths of 125° and 232°. The F/R is generally recognized as being a more suitable indicator of overall performance, since interfering signals are rarely located strictly 180° behind you.

The F/B or F/R will change over a range of frequencies, so it is a good idea to measure these properties across the entire range of frequencies of interest. Since snow or ice can

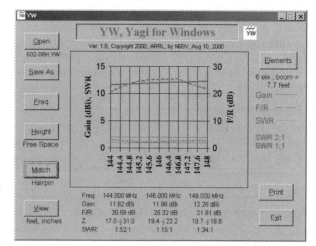

Fig 13-C

detune a beam when they form on the elements, designers of Yogis often "spread out" the frequency response in anticipation of such detuning effects.

GAIN

Closely related to the radiation patterns of an antenna is its *gain*. Think of gain this way: What you rob from Peter, you pay Paul. If you take away energy from one direction and focus it in another direction, you will have gain in that favored direction.

Look again at Fig 13-B. In the favored direction to the right of the plots, the Yagi focuses its energy into a sharp "nose," at the expense of energy going in other directions. It achieves a gain of 17.4 dBi, but that includes almost 5.6 dB of "ground-reflection gain" compared to a theoretical isotropic radiator—one that radiates equally well in all directions. You'll find that this Yagi has about 11.8 dBi gain in so-called "free space."

In the elevation pattern 10 feet above typical ground, the peak gain occurs at an elevation angle of 9°, with a second lobe at 29°. However, there is a deep null at 19° and very little energy in lobes higher than 29°.

Normally, the sharper the response in the azimuth plane, something we can gauge when we rotate the beam, the more gain a beam antenna has. Even when the pattern of an antenna suggests that our antenna has substantial gain, losses may negate the actual gain achieved. That's why antenna engineers are fond of pointing out that pattern *directivity* minus losses equals actual gain.

Like the feed-point impedance (and the resultant SWR) you should assess an antenna's gain across the whole frequency band of interest. In the case of a beam antenna like a Yagi, sometimes the pattern can actually reverse itself as you change frequency above or below the design frequency. At certain frequencies, this means that you could be pointing in the wrong direction from what you'd normally expect!

Fig 13-C shows a screen shot of the performance of a 6-element 2-meter beam from the ARRL program *YW* (included with *The ARRL Antenna Book*, 19th Edition). It shows the gain, F/R and SWR across the whole 2-meter band.—*Dean Straw, N6BV.*

decided that there was a need for new, short-boom VHF Yagi designs. Further, we wanted these to be based on lengths of aluminum tubing that would ship via UPS (United Parcel Service). We discovered that based on UPS shipping limitations, our limit would be 9 feet. However, to get a 9-foot length of aluminum tube, you'll have to buy a 12-footer and have the supplier cut it for you. You'll probably pay a little extra for shipping and handling. To simplify procurement matters for you, we have used 6 feet as the maximum tubing length wherever possible.

Two of these three Yagis are directly fed. That means no tuning network is needed. Let's look at them now.

N6BV 6-Element, 2-Meter Beam

This design is built on a 6-ft boom and covers the entire band from 144 to 148 MHZ with an SWR of 1.15:1 or better. This Yagi (see **Fig 13-2**) has 10.8 dBi free-space gain and can be fed directly with 50-Ω coax. An *optimum* two-meter Yagi on a 6-foot boom would normally use 5 elements. We've added a sixth element and made some minor modifications of element spacings and lengths to come up with the direct 50-Ω coax feed.

You can use 6063-T832 tubing with 0.058-inch wall thickness to construct the elements, which are 0.375 inch in diameter. The boom is a 6-foot length of 1.5-inch diameter aluminum tubing. Tubing is available from Texas Towers. Dimensions are given in **Table 13-1**. Do not substitute other sizes of tubing for the elements, because if you do you will not get the results you expect. The boom is not as critical, unless you mount uninsulated elements through the boom. More on that later.

You'll notice that element *half-lengths* are given in the table. That means the distance from the center to the element tip. The reflector is actually 40^1/$_2$ inches long from tip to tip. Each side of the driven element is 19^1/$_2$ inches long.

There are two reasons for giving element dimensions in half-lengths. The first is that it's a lot easier to deal with when more complicated elements than these are involved—ones that involve two or more different-diameter telescoping sections. The second reason is that these are the numbers used in some popular software packages. For example, *YW*, which is software that comes with *The ARRL Antenna Book*, 19th Edition, uses half-element dimensions. Also, while *EZNEC* does not use half-element dimensions directly, most antennas are laid out so that the antennas are centered on the X-axis,

which represents the boom. In this scheme, elements extend plus and minus of the boom (X-axis) in terms of their Y values.

In Table 13-1, I've also followed what has become a standard practice of giving boom positions as distance from the reflector, as is done in the most popular computer modeling programs. I also find it convenient to make the measurements along the boom from a single reference point.

Construction

As stated earlier, this design is a

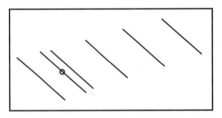

Fig 13-2—View of the six elements of the 2-meter beam. Neither the boom nor the mounting hardware is shown here. The element with the circle in the middle is the driven element.

Table 13-1
6-element, 2-meter All-Aluminum Yagi

All dimensions are in inches for elements insulated from the metallic boom.

	Element Boom Position	Half-Length
Reflector	0.000	20.250
Driven Element	10.744	19.500
Director 1	15.366	18.000
Director 2	32.275	17.750
Director 3	50.607	17.750
Director 4	69.000	16.500

direct 50-Ω feed. That means that no gamma or hairpin match is needed. To take advantage of this characteristic, mount the driven element on an insulated plate made of plexiglass, polycarbonate (such as Lexan) or other such material. Mount the plate on top of the boom—You need do that for only the driver, but feel free to use the same type of mounting for each element.

Feed your beam through a W2DU current balun, which you can build using six #43 beads slipped over the coax feed line. For RG-213, you can use either Amidon, Inc (**http://www. bytemark.com/amidon/**) part number FB-43-1020 or Palomar Engineers (**http://www.palomar-engineers.com/ Ferrite_Beads/ferrite_beads.html**) part number FB-102 or as their BA-8 kit (**http://www.palomar-engineers.com/ Balun_Kits/balun_kits.html**).

You can mount the other elements (reflector and directors) either on the boom or through it. For on-boom mounting, use a plate similar to the one that you use for the driven element. I prefer this method of mounting because it allows me to experiment with other element spacings. It's also easier to recycle the pieces when I want to try something new or different. Since the mounting plate positions the element above the metallic boom, it acts as though the elements were actually insulated electrically from the boom. Thus you can use the dimensions in Table 13-1 without modification.

Through-the-boom element mounting can be done two ways. You can insulate the elements from the boom, perhaps using nylon "shoulder washers," in which case you should use the dimensions in the table. However, you may find it mechanically difficult to use this technique.

Alternatively, you can mount the

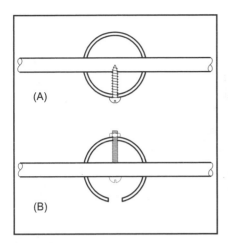

Fig 13-3—Two methods for securing elements that have been mounted through the boom. At A, a sheet metal screw keeps the element from shifting. At B, a #4 or #6 bolt and nut secure the element.

Fig 13-4—Photo of the PVC-boom Yagi in the horizontal position. See text.

elements through the boom without insulating them. A couple of ways of doing that are shown in **Fig 13-3**. In this case (and if you use the recommended 1.5-inch-diameter aluminum boom with no insulation between element and boom), lengthen each half-element length in the table by $^1/_{16}$ inch to compensate for the effect of the boom. (For a 2-inch boom, you'll need to add $^3/_{16}$ inch to each half.)

Other Possibilities

You might want to try using a PVC boom. I experimented with a 1-inch Schedule-40 PVC boom for a low-cost prototype version of this Yagi. I installed a PVC tee connector in the center of the boom. Because the PVC is a nonconductor, you can mount the elements through the boom using the dimensions in the table—No corrections are needed.

I secured the elements in place using the technique illustrated in Fig 13-3A. You'll note that the sheet metal screw that secures the element does not pierce the element. A slight pressure is enough to hold it securely.

Instead of cementing the boom sections to the tee, I used sheet metal screws to hold them in place. I did, however, cement the tee to the top of a length of 1-inch PVC tubing that serves as a mast. You can see a close up of the Yagi in the horizontal position in **Fig 13-4**.

To switch the antenna to vertical polarization, I loosen the screws that hold the boom in place. Next I twist the antenna 90° so the elements are vertical. A second set of holes in the boom sections then line up with the sheet metal screws. I tighten the screws, securing the beam in the vertical position.

For a sturdier setup, the 2-inch PVC conduit that was described in Chapter 4 should make an excellent boom for this antenna. For longer booms, or for lower frequencies, you may need to add a support truss for a PVC boom.

4-Element 6-Meter Beam

In keeping with the agreed-upon constraints, Dean came up with this design. The boom is 9-feet long and this Yagi has a gain of 8.36 dBi at 50.5 MHz. The F/R (worst-case front-to-rear ratio) peaks at 32 dB around 50.4 MHz and is better than 26 dB from 50 to 51 MHz. The SWR is 1.15:1 or better from 50.0 to 50.5 MHz, and it rises slowly to 1.68:1 at 51 MHz. What this all means is that this Yagi is a solid performer! See **Fig 13-5**.

Unlike the previous project, this is not a directly fed antenna. You'll

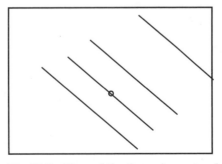

Fig 13-5—View of the four elements of the 6-meter beam. Neither the boom nor the mounting hardware is shown here.

have to use a matching section, but more on that later. Dimensions for this antenna are given in **Table 13-2**. As before, the table describes element half-lengths. In other words, the center of the element (Seg 1) is actually 72 inches (36 × 2) long. The dimensions in the table assume that a 4 × 4-inch aluminum plate is used to fasten the elements to the boom. Texas Towers carries the tubing and they also sell 4-inch-wide aluminum they will cut to length for you. Check with them for details.

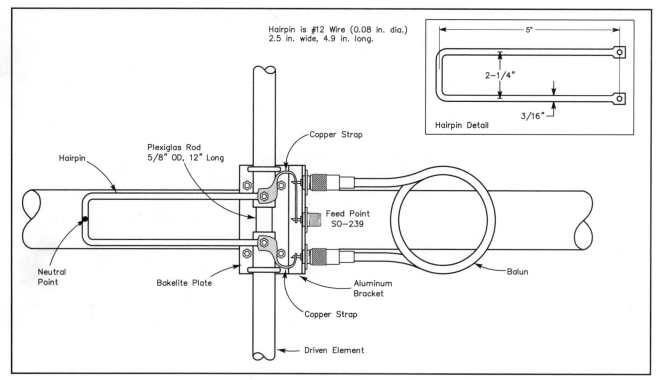

Fig 13-6—This shows how the driven element and feed system are attached to the boom. The phasing line is coiled and taped to the boom. The center of the hairpin loop may be connected to the boom electrically and mechanically if desired. Phasing-line lengths: For cable with 0.80 velocity factor—7 feet, 1 ³/₈ inches; For cable with 0.66 velocity factor—6 feet, 5¾ inches

Matching and Feeding

You'll need a 4:1 balun and a hairpin match to feed this Yagi. That may sound complicated, but it's not. The driven-element and feed-system details are shown in **Fig 13-6**. The driven element is mounted on an insulating plate. This can be a material such as Bakelite, plexiglass or Lexan. You can use a 12-inch length of 0.625-inch diameter fiberglass rod to reinforce the center of the driven element. Fiberglass rod is available from Max-Gain Systems, Inc.

An alternative mounting uses an aluminum plate. However, you'll need to insulate the driven element from that plate. I've used PVC pipe for that purpose, slipping it over the aluminum

Table 13-2
4-element, 6-meter Yagi

All dimensions are in inches for elements mounted with plates to the metallic boom.

	Boom Position	Seg 1	Seg 2
Diameter		0.750	0.625
Reflector	0.000	36.000	24.500
Driven Element	22.500	36.000	17.250
Director 1	47.000	36.000	18.250
Director 2	104.000	36.000	11.000

of the driven element. Be sure to slit the pipe so that it will close tightly on the element.

You can make the hairpin from #12 copper wire. With 2.5-inch spacing (width) the hairpin is 4.9 inches long.

The advantage to the hairpin match is that you can ground its center to the boom.

Would you still prefer a beam that is directly fed? If so, check out this next project.

5-Element 6-Meter beam

After designing the previous project, we still wanted a 6-meter beam with a direct feed. We reasoned that the hairpin and coaxial 1:4 balun of the 4-element model were complications. This project is what we came up with (see **Fig 13-7**).

The boom is 12-feet long and it has a gain of 9.77 dBi at 50.5 MHz. It has an F/R of about 24 dB. The SWR is about 1.5:1 from 50.0 to 50.8 and rises to 1.9 to 1 just above 51 MHz.

If you compare this 33% longer antenna to the previous (4-element version) you'll see that it has better gain, as you would expect. To achieve the direct-feed possibility, compromises had to be made and these resulted in a bit less F/R. However, all things considered, this is a fine antenna, and one

that is simple and that should result in a lot of fun for you.

Dimensions are given in **Table 13-3**. These assume that you are using 4 × 4-inch aluminum plates to mount the elements to the boom.

Construction Considerations

You can buy a 12-foot length of 1.5-inch diameter aluminum tubing for your boom, but it will not ship via UPS. You can make a stronger boom by using two 6-foot lengths of 1.5-inch and splice them together, telescoping them over a 6-foot length of 1.375-inch tubing. That gives you a double thickness in the center portion and adequate strength at the ends.

Reinforce and insulate the center of the driven element with a 12-inch

length of 0.625-inch diameter fiberglass rod. Center the feed point on the rod. You'll need to insulate the driven element from the mounting plate.

I recommend that you use six #43 ferrite beads as a balun. (For RG-213, you can use either Amidon, Inc (**http://www.bytemark.com/amidon/**) part number FB-43-1020 or Palomar Engineers (**http://www.palomar-engineers.com/Ferrite_Beads/ferrite_beads.html**) part number FB-102.) Slip the beads over the coax before you connect it to the beam. Tape the beads to protect them from the weather. Now you can connect the 50-ohm coaxial feed line directly to the driven element.

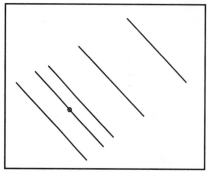

Fig 13-7—View of the five elements of the 6-meter beam. Neither the boom nor the mounting hardware is shown here.

Table 13-3

5-element, 6-meter Yagi; all dimensions are in inches

	Boom Position	Seg 1	Seg 2
Diameter		0.750	0.625
Reflector	0.000	36.000	24.500
Driven Element	23.500	36.000	22.500
Director 1	38.500	36.000	19.750
Director 2	78.625	36.000	18.750
Director 3	138.000	36.000	14.000

A 5-Element, 2-Meter Yagi for $20

This article by Ron Hege, K3PF, appeared in July 1999 *QST*. All photos are by the author.

In a matter of a few hours, you can easily build a broadband, 2-meter Yagi—complete with mounting hardware—for $20. The antenna offers a gain of about 10 dB, is lightweight, mechanically strong and rivals the performance of similar commercial antennas. See **Fig 13-8**.

The antenna's low cost is made possible by modifying a RadioShack FM broadcast receiving antenna (RS 15-2163). For $19.99, plus tax, you get a 70-inch-long by 1-inch-square boom, a set of six ³/₈-inch-diameter elements, antenna-mounting hardware and two

plastic end caps to seal the boom ends. In addition to RadioShack's antenna, you'll also need some nuts and bolts to remount elements, an 11-inch length of RG-8 (or similar) coax, an SO-239 connector and a 9 × 1-inch-long aluminum strip. This strip is cut into two pieces to fabricate a strap for the gamma match and a mount for the SO-239 connector. The thickness of the strip is not important as long as it can be bent easily and is strong enough to hold the SO-239 connector firmly in place. To close any unused holes and the tips of the elements, you'll need some non-corrosive sealant, such as RTV. Most amateurs I know have these items on hand. If you don't, you'll spend a few more dollars.

ELEMENT RELOCATION

Refer to the accompanying photo in Fig 13-8 and **Fig 13-9**. First, open all the antenna elements to their fully extended positions. Three of the elements are attached to plastic insulators and are tied together electrically with stiff, crossed, bare-aluminum wires. Each of these three elements looks like a dipole broken in the middle at the plastic insulators. One element measures about 58 inches from end to end, another about 56 inches and the third about 43 inches. You'll not need the 43-inch element.

Cut the wires next to the rivets on the 43-inch element. Drill out the rivet holding the element to the boom and discard the element. Use a screwdriver and pliers to release one wire from beneath one of the rivets on the 58-inch element. Try not to damage the rivet. Pull the wire out and away from the rivet. Go to the remaining wire on the 58-inch element; its opposite end attaches to another rivet on the 56-inch element. Unwind the end of the wire from beneath the rivet on the 56-inch element and pull it towards the 58-inch element. You now have a single wire on the 58-inch element with one loose end. Pull that wire straight across to the opposite rivet that no longer has a wire under it. Use pliers and whatever force is necessary to loop the wire around and under the rivet head, as was the original wire. Seat the wire fully beneath the rivet head (see **Figs 13-10** and **13-11**). I was able to get the wire fully seated by pulling hard on the wire with my hand and squeezing the wire under the rivet head using the jaws of Vise Grip pliers. If you cannot get the wire fully wound and seated under the rivet, drill out the rivet and replace it with a bolt and nuts. Do not cut the wire off at the rivet. Pull the wire back toward the opposite rivet and cut it off leaving a pigtail about 1½ inches long. You may want to reseat the rivet by hitting it with a hammer. Just be sure to back up the

Fig 13-8—Completed 5-element, 2-meter Yagi, ready for installation.

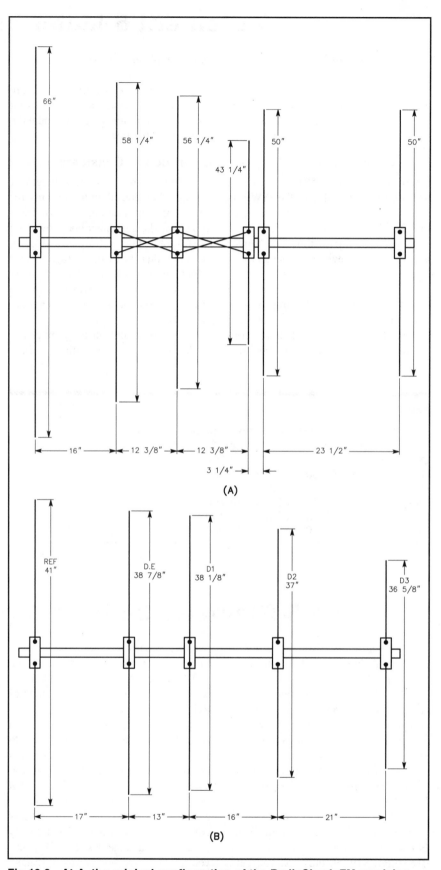

Fig 13-9—At A, the original configuration of the RadioShack FM receiving antenna. The element lengths and spacings at B are chosen for operation on 144 MHz. For operation on higher frequencies, shorten the elements even more; see text.

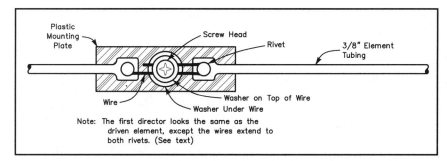

Fig 13-10—Drawing of the driven-element modification.

Fig 13-11—Here's the modified driven element.

rivet's head with a hard object before striking the rivet's opposite end. Be careful not to damage the plastic insulator. You have now turned a two-piece element into a one-piece element, and this will be the driven element.

Drill a mounting hole in the boom (for the one-piece element) 17 inches away from the center of the adjacent 66-inch element (reflector). Remove the 58-inch element from its original location and mount it at the new position using a bolt, two washers and a nut. Place one washer directly against the plastic insulator under the wire that connects the two 3/8-inch-diameter tubing halves together. Position the other washer on top of the wire so it bears down on the wire when the bolt is tightened. This puts the center of the element at the same electrical potential as the boom. Using the 1½-inch pigtail, bend it and place it between the two washers so there is a piece of wire on each side of the bolt. This prevents the washers from tilting and makes for a cleaner fit. Trim off any excess wire. (All of the foregoing is more difficult to describe than it is to perform! It doesn't take long to do once you understand what is going on.)

The next element (56 inches long; Director 1) is handled similarly to the preceding one. However, this element originally had two wires beneath each rivet head. One of those wires has already been removed. At the opposite rivet, unwind one of the two wires so that only one wire remains beneath each rivet. Pull one loose end of a wire straight across to the opposite rivet and force the wire into place under the rivet just as before. Pull the other loose wire end to its opposite rivet and force it into place. The two element halves should

now be connected together with two wires. The wires will be parallel to each other and on opposite sides of the rivet that secures the element to the boom.

Next, drill a hole in the boom 13 inches from the center of the 58-inch element (DE). Remove the 56-inch element from (D1) its original location and mount it on the boom at the new hole. Again, place a washer on opposite sides of the wires so that the washers squeeze against the wires as the bolt and nut tighten the element to the boom.

The remaining three elements (REF, D2 and D3) don't need to be modified; their individual dipole sections are already joined by metal plates. All you need to do is remove two of them from the boom, drill new mounting holes and mount them at their new locations. The first 50-inch element (D2) is placed 16 inches—(center to center)—from the adjacent 56-inch element. The end element (D3)—also 50 inches long—is placed 21 inches (center to center) from the new location of its

adjacent 50-inch element. All of the elements are now in place ready to be cut to length for 2-meter operation.

Element Trimming

For this job, a fine-toothed saw works well. (Caution: During the following steps, be sure that you cut half the total amount from each half [ie, each side] of an element.) For operation at the low end of the band (144 MHz), cut the 66-inch element to a total length of 41 inches (see Fig 13-9B). This element becomes the reflector. Cut the next element in line (the driven element) to a length of 38⅞ inches. Cut the next three elements (directors D1, D2 and D3) to lengths of 38⅛, 37 and 36⅝ inches, respectively. If you want to trim the elements for use at higher frequencies, cut ¼ inch off of each element for each 1-MHz frequency increase. For instance, cutting a total of ½ inch from each element tunes and maximizes the antenna for 146 MHz. (Again, cut half the total amount from each half of an

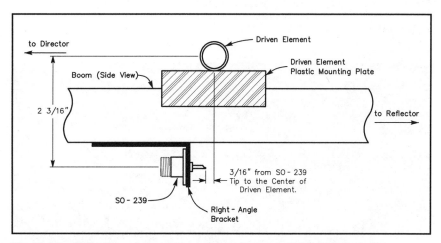

Fig 13-12—Side view of the driven-element area and SO-239 mounting bracket.

element section. For 146 MHz, the preceding example, that's ¼ inch from each half-element section.)

SO-239 CONNECTOR AND MOUNT

Refer to Fig 13-10 to **Fig 13-12**. Attach the SO-239 connector to the bottom of the boom beneath the driven element using an L-shaped piece of aluminum. Fabricate the bracket from a 3³/₈ inch length of aluminum cut from the 9 × 1 inch strip. Bend it at a right angle so that one side is about 1¼ inches long. Make the necessary holes to mount an SO-239 connector on the 1¼ inch long section and secure the connector to it. Fasten the bracket to the boom bottom using bolts and nuts, positioning the bracket so that the tip of the SO-239 center pin faces the reflector. Position the tip of the pin about ³/₁₆ to ¼ inch in front of the center of the driven element toward the director side.

Making the Gamma Match

Remove the outer insulation and braid from an 11-inch piece of RG-8 coax, leaving the center conductor and its insulation. Strip off ½ inch of the insulation and solder the center conductor to the SO-239 pin. At the pin, bend the wire at a right angle so that the wire is parallel to and about 2³/₁₆ inches away from the driven element along its length (see **Fig 13-13** and **Fig 13-14**). This lead forms the inner plate of the gamma capacitor. Next, select a piece of the scrap ³/₈-inch tubing you cut from one of the antenna elements and cut it to a length of 11 inches. Slip this tubing over the RG-8 inner-conductor insulation to form the outer plate of the gamma capacitor. Position the tube seam so it faces the ground when the antenna is at its operating position; this allows moisture an easy way out. To complete the capacitor construction, wrap the remainder of the l-inch aluminum strip around the driven element on one side and around the 11-inch tube on the other. Construct the strap so that the centers of the tubing sections are approximately 2³/₁₆ inches apart. Leave a tang on each side of the strap to accept a locking screw. Trim away any excess material.

Tuning the Gamma Match

Before applying RF to the antenna, connect an SWR meter to the SO-239 connector at the antenna, not at the transmitter end of your transmission line. This ensures that you are tuning just the antenna. For a quick adjustment of the matching network, you can try positioning the antenna straight up toward the sky, with the reflector sitting on the ground. Using this approach, however, I found that when I raised the antenna to a height of 10 feet on a metal mast, the gamma capacitor needed readjustment. If you're a perfectionist, it might ultimately be less work to tune the antenna while it's mounted in the clear a few wavelengths above ground or sitting in its intended operating position. If you're going to use a metal support mast, attach it to the antenna prior to tuning. Use a nonmetallic mast (wood, fiberglass, etc) if you're going to mount the Yagi vertically (so that the elements are in line with the mast); otherwise, antenna performance will suffer a bit. It's okay to use a metal mast when using horizontal polarization.

Reduce your transmitter's output power to about 1 or 2 W for safety, or use an antenna analyzer. Don't use more than a few watts—You don't need it. Set the transmitter frequency to that for which you cut the antenna. (Remember to ID your station during this adjustment period.) First, adjust the gamma strap (sliding it back and forth) on the driven element for the lowest SWR. Then slide the gamma tube (capacitor) back and forth within the strap for lowest SWR reading. You should be able to get a match by alternately making adjustments to the strap and gamma tube. I was able to tune my antenna to a 1:1 match. (An SWR of 1.5:1 or less is acceptable.) Recheck the SWR reading after finally tightening the strap to be certain that everything is still okay. Check by eye to ensure the gamma-capacitor tube is parallel with the driven element

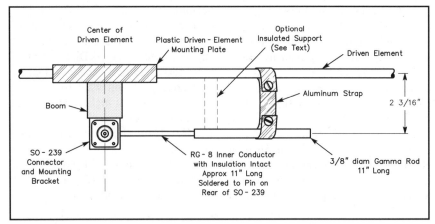

Fig 13-13—The 2-meter Yagi's gamma match. A piece of RG-8 coax and a length of tubing combine to create an inexpensive and rugged gamma-match capacitor.

Fig 13-14—The gamma match and driven element.

from one end to the other. It doesn't matter if the gamma-capacitor tube is slightly in front of or behind the driven element, but it should be parallel to it.

Performance

I don't have the proper equipment for making antenna-gain measurements. However, I made a crude comparison of the Yagi to a dipole using the following approach: First, I erected a 2-meter dipole on a 10-foot-long metal mast and adjusted the antenna for a 1:1 SWR. While feeding the dipole with a few milliwatts, I placed my H-T about 75 feet away from the dipole. The S meter reading on the H-T went full scale, so I removed the antenna from the H-T. The reading was still full scale. I then wrapped the H-T case with a shield of aluminum foil and the S meter reading dropped to S3. After that, I never touched or moved the H-T throughout the rest of the test. I rotated the dipole 90 degrees and, as expected, I got a zero reading on the H-T's S meter. I then turned the dipole back to its original position and rechecked the S meter. Again, it read S3. I used this reading as the dipole reference. Then, removing the dipole, I replaced it with the Yagi. I

pointed the Yagi directly at the H-T and fed it with the same power level used to feed the dipole. The S meter read full scale on my H-T! Because S meters are notoriously inaccurate and not calibrated, I have no way of knowing how much gain that indicates, but it's a lot! (A five-element Yagi on a boom this long is capable of producing a gain of about 10 dB.) When I turned the Yagi so that its reflector faced the H-T, the meter reading dropped to S4. That's a nice front-to-back ratio! I also checked radiation off the sides of the antenna. I was pleased to see an S0 meter reading from each side. [The ARRL Lab modeled Ron's Yagi using *YO* software and verified his claims.—*Ed.*]

SUMMARY AND ACKNOWLEDGMENT

After I finished my project, I decided that it might be a good idea to make sure that the gamma match worked okay when the elements were cut for 146 MHz because many readers might want to use the antenna for working distant FM repeaters. I sawed off ½ inch from each element and went through the tuning procedure again. I was still able to get a 1:1 match. Those wishing to use

the antenna for FM repeater work should orient the antenna elements vertically.

I wondered what effect moisture would have on the gamma capacitor. So, I poured water into one end of the gamma tube until it came out the other end. I rechecked the SWR and I found only a barely noticeable effect. I recommend you plug the ends of the tube with a dab of RTV or other non-corrosive sealant to keep out dirt and insects.

The driven element holding the gamma match will not fold for portable use if the bracket holding the SO-239 connector is bolted to the boom. One simple solution is to remove the bolts holding the bracket. Removal and replacement is made easier if you use wing nuts on the bolts. An optional, second support for the gamma-capacitor tube, made from nonmetallic material, provides better support for the tube during transportation.

My thanks to Larry, K3PEG, for instructing me about this type of gamma match fabrication. If you're looking for a good 2-meter antenna, try this one! It's inexpensive, easy to tune and is the simplest construction approach I've seen for quickly "homebrewing" a 2-meter Yagi.

A Compact 2-Element, 2-Meter Beam

This antenna by Lee Lumpkin, KB8WEV, and Bob Cerreto, WA1FXT, was described in January 2000 *QST*. I think you'll find desirable electrical and mechanical features in this beam. See **Fig 13-15**.

What do you get when you take an already-unusual design for an HF beam antenna, scale it to VHF and turn it on its ear? A vertically polarized modified Moxon, of course! Build this wire and PVC beauty to solve your 2-meter troubles in a jiffy.

I'd been looking for an antenna to monitor 2-meter simplex and Skywarn frequencies that was affordable and easy to install in my attic. Bob, WA1FXT, and I live in an area that sees Skywarn activation for tornado and severe thunderstorm watches several times a year. I also live in a house where my shack is in a new addition, separated from the rest of the house. When I'm in

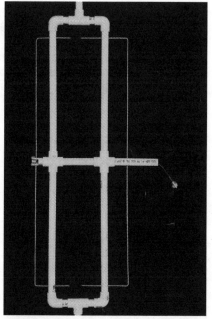

Fig 13-15—Photo of the completed 2-meter Moxon.

the older part of the house, I have a much better view of weather approaching from the west and north (the usual directions), but I can't hear the radios in my shack. I'm also out of touch with local 2-meter simplex frequencies when I'm not near the radio room. Bob has a similar situation at his home.

Finding the Design

Bob and I had been discussing HF and 6-meter Field Day antennas. One day, I visited L. B. Cebik's (W4RNL) Web site at: **http://www.cebik.com/**. The site is an excellent place to find antenna information and it's a valuable resource for those educating themselves about antennas. While considering his refinement of HF beams designed by Les Moxon, G6XN, I realized that these interesting gain antennas had the characteristics I considered ideal for a 2-meter attic antenna—smooth, wide front lobes with no notches, reasonable gain, relatively compact dimensions and ease of construction and feeding.

Modifying the Design

I cut and pasted W4RNL's dimensions for horizontally polarized HF wire Moxon beams into a spreadsheet and derived formulas for the dimensions. I oriented the antenna to achieve the vertical polarization needed for 2-meter FM and took the 10-meter dimensions and put them into Roy Lewallen's *EZNEC* antenna design and analysis program. Using the formulas I had derived from Cebik's plans, I rescaled the antenna for 2 meters and tweaked it a bit to overcome the large shift in the element length-to-diameter ratio. The resulting design characteristics contained a pleasant surprise. The single, smooth front lobe widened to about 135° along the horizon (the −3dB beamwidth). This vertically polarized variant was much broader than its horizontally polarized cousin was.

While tracking how the antenna's pattern changed at several points in the 2-meter band, I found a point about 500 kHz above the design frequency that had a single rear notch in the gain pattern at the cost of marginally higher SWR. This resulted in a cardioid-type pattern with a relatively narrow notch to the rear that was about 35 dB down from the maximum forward gain (which models at around 6 dBi in free space). Far from being a disappointment, this was a useful foxhunting antenna of manageable size. This was something Bob and I had both been looking for!

We needed a framework to support the wire elements, so I put the dimensions for the two wire elements into a CAD program and worked up a PVC framework to support them. When Bob saw the antenna pattern and construction plans he became excited about the antenna's possibilities—especially as a foxhunter.

Build One of your Own

Please note that the dimensional accuracy used here is overkill. If you cut your elements to within an eighth of an inch, your antenna should work like a champ, with no practical loss in performance. Put away the calipers and pick up a ruler! The most critical dimension

of these "modified Moxons" is the distance between the tips of the reflector tails and driven elements, which can be fine-tuned after assembly.

The first step in construction is to cut the ½-inch schedule 40 PVC pipes to the lengths needed for the support frame. The quantities and lengths are listed in the sidebar. If you're going to vary from the pipe lengths shown in the table, be sure to allow ¾-inch to accommodate the various PVC fittings.

After cutting the PVC to length (per **Table 13-4**), measure and drill the holes for the wire antenna elements. Use a drill press and a fence to center the holes in the pipe (or mark the holes and drill carefully by hand).

Place the tip of a center punch or a nail at the drilling point and tap with a hammer to dimple the surface. This will hold the tip of the drill bit in place and keep it from spinning off target as you drill.

Follow the diagram in **Fig 13-16** as you begin to assemble the antenna. Drill a hole completely through each of the four pipes labeled **C**, 1½ inches from one end. This will go at the end farthest from the antenna center. The hole drilled in pipe **F** should pass all the way through, ½ inch from the pipe end. Mark

one end of pipe **D**; that end that will be inserted into the PVC cross. Drill a hole completely through pipe **D** 2⅜ inches from the marked end. Make sure to orient the pipe properly when assembling the PVC frame or you will end up with a bowed reflector element (**A**).

Use solid #10 AWG copper wire for the antenna elements. Number 10 copper wire is a nominal 0.1-inch in diameter, but ours was a bit too large for a ⁷⁄₆₄-inch hole, so we used a ⅛-inch drill bit. This allows the wire to pass through easily without too much slop. If your wire slips through the holes after building the antenna, hold the elements in place with wire ties, heat shrink tubing, hot glue, RTV sealant or tape (anything that won't detune the antenna). If you're making a permanent outdoor antenna, use UV-resistant material to secure the elements.

The next step is to assemble the PVC frame. This is best done on a flat surface. Use a rubber or wooden mallet to persuade the pipes to seat snugly in the fittings, being careful to keep the wire holes in the correct plane.

Align the four vertical pipes (**C**) by sighting through the holes you drilled in each pipe for wire tails **a** and **b**, aligning them with the corresponding holes

---

PVC AND WIRE CUTTING SCHEDULE

Reflector element **A** consists of one piece of #10 AWG copper with a straight section and two tails bent at 90°. Total length is a single piece of 40-⁷⁄₃₂ inches.

Driven element **B** is two half elements fed in the middle. Total length is a nominal 37⁹⁄₃₂ inches, but build it according to the text. A slightly longer wire is required to wrap around the PVC and secure the feed point to the pipe. See Fig 13-16 for the drawing labels.

WIRE

Qty	Label	Description	Length
1	A	Reflector Element	29³⁄₃₂"
	a	Reflector Element Tail	5⁹⁄₁₆"
1	B	Driven Element	29³⁄₃₂"
	b	Driven Element Tail	4³⁄₃₂"

PVC

Qty	Label	Description	Length
4	C	Main Boom	15⁹⁄₁₆"
1	D	Tail Piece	6"
1	E	Middle Boom Spreader	5⅛"
1	F	Feed line Termination	2"
4	G	End Boom Spreader	2¹⁄₁₆"

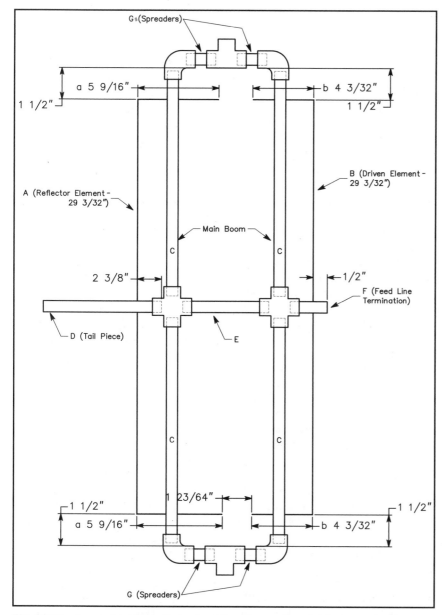

Fig 13-16—A construction diagram of the Moxon 2-meter beam antenna. See text and tables for details.

Table 13-4

Bill of Materials

10 feet	½-inch Schedule 40 PVC pipe
4	½-inch Schedule 40 PVC 90° elbows
2	½-inch Schedule 40 PVC crosses
2	½-inch Schedule 40 PVC tees
Approx 10 feet	No.10 AWG copper wire
1	PL-259 coax connector
1	UG-176U coax adapter
2	Wire ties
3	Amidon Ferrite Beads (FB-43-5621)
	Amidon Associates 240-250 Briggs Ave
	Costa Mesa, CA 92626
RG-8X coax	As needed
Misc	Plastic electrical tape

in the opposite vertical pipe. If necessary, a pair of pliers can be used to fine-tune the alignment by twisting the pipe in the fittings. The front and tail pipes, **F** and **D**, are aligned by sighting along the lengths of the vertical support pipes to be sure that the holes for wire sections **A** and **B** run parallel with the frame.

Next, prepare and install the wire elements. Straighten some #10 wire before starting the installation. After inserting the wire into the PVC frame, it's difficult to thoroughly clean the wire at the feed point (**F**), so be sure to clean it thoroughly beforehand. Oxidized wire makes it difficult to get a good solder joint, especially in this tight space. So use an abrasive plastic pad or fine steel wool to clean up the wire ends at the feed point to make for easier soldering.

First, install one half of the driven element (**B**). Take a longer piece of #10 wire (about 24 inches) and bend an inch at one end about 90°. Do this at the end you have already cleaned in preparation for soldering at the feed point. Bend about half of that 1-inch bend another 30° to 45° in the same plane. Pass the resulting "J" shape through the feed point hole in PVC pipe **F** from the outside (so the bends end up inside the pipe with about ½-inch protruding from the open end of the pipe). Hold the wire against the inside of the PVC pipe with pliers or a dowel and wrap the ½-inch of protruding wire back around the outside of the pipe and crimp it tightly against the outside of the pipe. See the close-up photo of the feed point to see the final result.

Once this is done, hold the wire parallel to the front vertical portion of PVC support frame C and bend it back at 90° at a point in line with the support holes in PVC pipe C, forming element tail **b**. This will be about 14¹/₈ inches from the outside of PVC pipe F.

Measure and cut the bent-back wire tail section (**b**) to 4³/₃₂ inches long. Leave extra and trim later if you wish. Pass this tail section through the support hole in the front vertical pipe (**C**) on the PVC frame. Install the other half of driven element **B** using the same steps and dimensions.

Now you need to feed the antenna with coax before installing the reflector element (wire **A**). Prepare the feed line by obtaining a three-foot RG-8X jumper (with PL-259s installed on each end) and cutting it in half. This speeds construction and makes it easy to build two antennas at once. You can, of course, make up your own RG-8X coaxial cable and PL-259 assembly.

Strip 1 inch of insulation from the shield and ¾-inch from the center conductor at the unterminated end of the coax. Use three type-43 ferrite choke beads (Amidon FB-43-5621) to keep RF from returning along the outer coax shield. Slip the beads onto the feed line and secure them with wire ties and electrical tape close to the stripped end of the coax taking care that they don't touch the bare copper braid, the center conductor or the wire elements at the feed point. The electrical tape should also help prevent this contact.

To improve access to the feed point, cut a section out of the side of the pipe at the feed point as shown in **Fig 13-17**. First cut into one side of pipe **F** just behind the feed point, perpendicular to the length of the pipe to a depth of about $1/3$ of the pipe diameter. Another cut in from the end of pipe **F**, along its length, but cutting in only about $1/3$ its diameter, leaves enough support for the center of driven element **B**. This leaves plenty of space for soldering.

We considered making these cuts before installing the driven element wires, but decided that the stresses involved in bending the heavy gauge wire around the PVC at the feed point might cause cracking. You may find that it's okay to make your access cut first. Be sure to use a fine blade, such as a hacksaw or dovetail saw.

Now run the feed line in from the rear of the center horizontal support pipe up to the feed point, through pipes **D**, **E** and **F**. Wrap the coax shield around one side of driven element wire **B** (inside pipe **F**) and the center conductor around the other end of the driven element wire, then solder both connections. Use paste flux and a 100-W iron of sufficient mass. Irons with less thermal capacity can't generate enough heat, or have their thermal energy conducted away too quickly by the #10 wire. Lengthy heating with a smaller iron is likely to melt the PVC.

Now it's time to put reflector element **A** into place. First, pass 45 inches (or more) of #10 wire through the rear

center support holes in PVC pipe **D**, being careful to go around the coaxial feed line rather than through it. Bend about six inches of wire at one end back at 90° toward the driven element and support frame (forming tail **a**) and trim it $5^9/_{16}$ inches from the bend. Then, pass this tail through the wire support holes in the rear vertical section (**C**) of the PVC support frame. Measure $29^3/_{32}$ inches from this first bend along reflector wire **A** and make the bend to form the other reflector tail. Trim this tail to $5^9/_{16}$ inches and pass it through its support hole in pipe **C**.

Everything is now in place, so square up the wire elements on the frame. One characteristic of Moxon antennas is a sensitivity to the relative positions of tails **A** and **B**, so make sure the tails are in line with each other and spaced at $1^{23}/_{64}$ inches. This was considered in designing the PVC support frame and the points at which it holds the wire elements. This design allows the wire tails to be held in line with each other, leaving the distance between the tips of the tails to be fine tuned and then taped, glued or otherwise secured to the PVC frame once the antenna is performing to spec.

We didn't cement our PVC frames because my antenna would be installed indoors and the joints were firmly seated without gluing. If you want to cement yours, we'd suggest assembling the frame to align the wire support holes and carefully making reference marks at the junctions of the pipes and fittings. This will allow you to quickly orient the PVC elements before the PVC glue sets up. If you're going to mount your antenna outside, gluing the PVC frame is a good idea. PVC glue sets up very quickly, so if you don't feel confident, you might want to insert small sheet metal screws into predrilled holes instead. Alternatively, you can build the PVC frame and glue it together before drilling the wire support holes.

You should try to run the feed line away from the antenna for a couple of feet before running it parallel with the main sections of the wire elements. Running it parallel to these sections at less than 19 inches or so may distort the pattern of the antenna and change its SWR.

Performance Testing

After building the first antenna, we

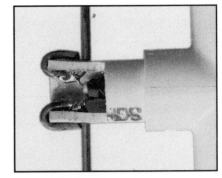

Fig 13-17—A closeup view of the connection between the coax and the radiating element.

decided to test its performance before building the second. We took the antenna to a clear spot in the yard and hooked it up to an MFJ-259 antenna analyzer through about 25 feet of RG-213 coax. Bob held the antenna up on a PVC mast while I ran through 2 meters with the analyzer—and I started to laugh.

Bob was dying with curiosity, so we traded places while he swept the band. The antenna came up on the frequency we expected, with an even broader bandwidth (see **Fig 13-18**). We decided to check the front-to-back ratio, but had no field strength meter at hand. Bob got in his truck and I aimed the front lobe of the antenna at him until his receiver dropped below S-meter saturation about a mile away.

While I turned the antenna and reported to Bob where he was in the pattern, a station in my normal fringe area called me. This station doesn't receive me full quieting on my base antenna (stacked $5/_8$-wave omni antennas at 33 feet, fed with about 2 W), but was hearing me now with the Moxon up only eight feet while running 350 mW!

Bob and this other station (11 miles in the opposite direction) reported S-meter readings in line with the computer-predicted pattern as I rotated the antenna in azimuth. At this point, we scrambled back to the garage to build a second antenna before we ran out of time!

The Hunt

About a week later, Bob and I got together for a foxhunt and to check out the front-to-back ratio in a more controlled manner. Bob, his son Matt, and I were on our first hunt together. Bob

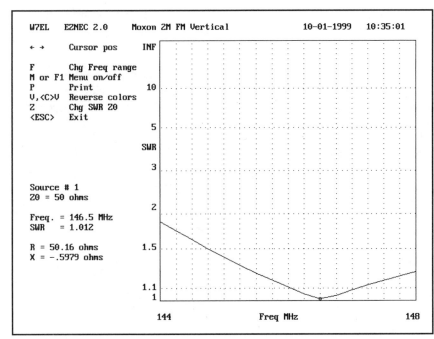

Fig 13-18—The predicted SWR bandwidth of our 2-meter beam, from 144 to 148 MHz.

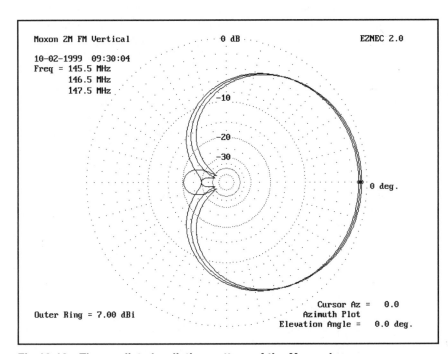

Fig 13-19—The predicted radiation pattern of the Moxon beam.

had borrowed a passive field-strength meter, but we were unsure of its linearity and were unable to get enough useful range out of it to measure the front-to-back ratio on the 2-meter Moxon.

Bob has a well-calibrated attenuator, so we made some measurements and checked the pattern and front-to-back ratio by switching the attenuator to give the same reading on the field-strength meter. The pattern turned out to be in line with the computer model, and the narrow rear notch was down 29 dB from the front lobe, exactly as predicted (see **Fig 13-19**). We also checked the antenna at 147 MHz, about 500 kHz above the design frequency of 146.5 MHz. Again, as predicted the rear notch deepened to about –35 dB.

We hunted using the rear notch in the Moxon pattern. We were thrown off several times by reflections from large metal buildings, a power plant that killed the signal, and the unfamiliar terrain. But we overcame the problems and were the third team to find the fox. We covered 19 road miles in the search for the fox, which was about six miles from the start as the crow flies. On one transmission, the fox was on a vertical omni with steady power when we were a couple of miles out. This gave us our best sample. The bearing we took on this transmission was within a couple of hundred feet from the fox's actual position.

The hunter who first found the fox (in half our time) and the team that found it a few seconds ahead of us were both using the same 4-element, balanced feed Yagi that I had used to win two California foxhunts. When tuned properly this Yagi has a single rear notch. The Moxon performed similarly, with the exception of its wider front pattern and reduced forward gain. We were very happy with its performance as a compact foxhunting antenna.

After we had designed and tested this antenna, we decided to see how it would act mounted on a standoff from a metal mast. We haven't checked thoroughly, but computer modeling suggests that at ¼ wavelength, the rear null is not nearly as deep. The cardioid notch pretty much disappears. At ½ and 1 wavelength, the pattern is pretty good, so choose your mounting offsets (from a vertical metal mast) accordingly. This was not a great concern to me because I used PVC tee connectors at the top and bottom of the frame to support the antenna with short sections of PVC pipe attached to the ridge beam and a ceiling joist in my attic. It has performed very respectably there, only 12 feet off the ground. I can make all of my regular 2-meter simplex contacts, and the antenna holds its own when accessing local repeaters.

RESULTING ANTENNA PERFORMANCE AND POTENTIAL USES

No antenna does everything well, but this design has a number of useful characteristics:

- A smooth, wide front lobe with modest, but useful gain (of about 6 dBi in free space) and none of the side lobe notches associated with most Yagi and quad beams of three or more elements.
- A single, deep rear notch (up to –35 dB relative to the maximum front lobe gain). This makes it useful for rejecting single-source interference and for foxhunting.

- A compact and simple design that is inexpensive and easy to build with minimal tools and skills.
- A very good direct match to 50-Ω feed lines.

You can use this antenna to: minimize or eliminate interference or intermod from pager transmitters or other stations while still receiving desired signals from most other directions, access desired repeaters while rejecting an unwanted repeater; and reach a broad swath of stations or repeaters with reasonable gain, and no need to rotate a beam or overcome multiple side-lobe nulls that accompany multi-element Yagis and quads. You should

also be able to foxhunt by placing the fox's signal in the single null and heading in the direction of greatest signal attenuation.

It should be noted that L. B. Cebik is responsible for refining the geometry of the Moxon beam to its full potential. Our antenna is a simple rescaling of his work. He is very generous in sharing his work with anyone who is interested. His work on this antenna was inspired by the designs of Les Moxon, G6XN, and Fred Caton, VK2ABQ, who started out with square HF wire beams using buttons to insulate the element tails. Visit Cebik's web site for a horizontal 10-meter version made from aluminum tubing.

A Pair of 3-Element, 6-Meter Yagis

Speaking of L. B. Cebik, this article, by W4RNL, appeared in February 2000 *QST* under the title "2×3=6." The formula is another way of stating two 3-element Yagi designs for 6 meters. One design is for gain—the other for wideband. If you're interested in a short-boom Yagi for this band, or if you're merely interested in the trade-offs that go into designing a beam, I think you'll find this interesting.

Yagi antennas provide good forward gain in a favored direction and excellent front-to-back ratio (F/B) for unwanted-signal rejection. A 3-element Yagi for 6 meters is a simple construction project and can make use of readily available materials. However, newer antenna builders are often faced with the question, "Which design should I use?"

To help you make the decision, let's look at two quite different designs. Each antenna is a bit over six feet long. One presses for maximum gain and a good F/B, but sacrifices bandwidth. The other achieves total coverage of 6 meters, but surrenders some gain in the process. By comparing the antennas' capabilities with your operating requirements, you can select the one that best suits your needs.

Despite the similar boom lengths, the two designs have quite different profiles, as shown in **Fig 13-20**. The

wideband model places more distance between the reflector and the driven element and decreases the driven-element-to-director spacing. In contrast, the high-gain model sets the director far ahead of the driven element and decreases the spacing between the driven element and the reflector. The reflector-to-driven-element spacing not only has an impact on gain, but affects the array feed-point impedance as well. In general, reducing the reflector-to-driven-element spacing lowers the feed-point impedance.

Gain

Let's first look at the high-gain

model to see what we can achieve and what it will cost. A three-element Yagi is capable of exhibiting a free-space gain of 8 dBi with a F/B greater than 20 dB. However, these figures can be sustained for a bandwidth of only little over ±1.5% of the design frequency. Across this span, the antenna's gain tends to increase, while the F/B peaks at over 25 dB near the design frequency.

Our sample high-gain Yagi is adapted from an optimized 20-meter design by Brian Beezley, K6STI. His original design covers all of 20 meters, but that band is narrow compared to 6 meters. When we scale the antenna for 51 MHz, its bandwidth is only about 1.5

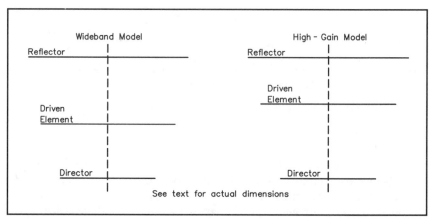

Fig 13-20—General outline of the wideband and high-gain three-element 6-meter Yagis.

MHz while retaining the desired operating characteristics. **Table 13-5** shows the antenna dimensions for a design using ½-inch-diameter tubing. Single-diameter elements are quite practical in VHF Yagis, but before we're finished, we'll see what to do should we decide—or need—to use two tubing sizes for each element.

Table 13-6 shows the antenna's anticipated performance characteristics, as modeled using *NEC-4*. The driven-element length is set near resonance on 51 MHz, and the feed-point impedance is about 25 Ω. That value isn't a direct match for the 50-Ω coaxial cable normally used in amateur installations. If we shorten the driven element, we can install a beta match. If we lengthen the driven element, we might use a gamma match or a T match. If we leave the driven element length as is, we could employ a ¼-λ, 37-Ω matching section made by connecting two lengths of RG-59 (or RG-11 for high-power operation) in parallel. All of these matching systems are described in *The ARRL Antenna Book*.

The table of projected gain and F/B values shows the rise in gain across the passband, as well as the peak F/B near the design frequency. Notice that the F/B drops rapidly as we approach frequencies only 1 MHz from the design center. For point-to-point communications at the low end of 6 meters, however, the narrow passband—combined with the higher gain—may be just what we need.

The target center frequency can be adjusted up or down within 6 meters by adjusting all three element lengths by the percentage of frequency change. To change the design frequency to

50.5 MHz to cover the 50 to 51-MHz range, increase all lengths by about 1%. If we stay at the low end of the band, we need not change the element spacing or diameter.

Builders who are more interested in raw gain than F/B can scale the performance at 52 MHz (or a bit above) down to the desired frequency. Simply scale the antenna dimensions, as given for the 51-MHz design frequency, to about 50 MHz or just a bit lower. You can adjust the driven-element length to resonance or use your favorite matching system. Changing the driven-element length to vary the feedpoint impedance by as much as 25-30 Ω has very little effect on the other performance figures.

BANDWIDTH

Suppose we want to cover the entire 6-meter band with a well-matched Yagi having relatively constant performance all the way. Although this 4-MHz span represents a ±4% bandwidth relative to a design frequency, we can redesign the Yagi to achieve this goal. However, we'll pay for the bandwidth with reduced gain and a lower peak F/B. The gain drops about 1 dB and the F/B is perhaps 5 dB off the peak.

From the same ½-inch-diameter

aluminum tubing, we can build a three-element Yagi with a free-space gain of about 7 dBi and a F/B of up to 21 dB. This antenna exhibits a feed-point impedance that permits direct connection to a 50-Ω coaxial cable (with a suitable choke to attenuate common-mode currents). The design dimensions shown in **Table 13-7** are adapted from a design for another band originally developed by Bill Orr, W6SAI.

The modeled performance parameters appear in **Table 13-8**. Notice that the gain curve is not a single rising line, but has a slight dip toward the low end of the band. The F/B peak has been set at the midband frequency because it tends to taper off fairly equally above and below the design frequency. Most notable are the feed-point impedance and SWR values. If we insulate the driven element from the boom, we can avoid the use of a matching network altogether.

The wideband model is suited to operators who want to cover the entire 6-meter band. However, effective use may require a mechanical scheme that lets you flip the beam from horizontal to vertical. In the vertical position, as shown in **Fig 13-21**, at a height of 30 feet above average ground, the pattern is wider and less strong than when the

---

Table 13-5

Element Lengths and Spacing for the High-Gain 6-Meter Design with ½-inch-Diameter Elements

Element	Length (inches)	Spacing from Reflector (inches)
Reflector	114.26	0
Driven Element	108.96	37.8
Director	102.43	77.94

Table 13-6

Modeled Performance of the High-Gain 6-Meter Design from 50 to 52 MHz

Frequency (MHz)	Gain (dBi)	F/B (dB)	Feed-Point Impedance (R ± j X Ω)	25-Ω SWR
50	7.92	16.55	26.9 − j 20.2	2.14
50.5	8.07	22.59	26.4 − j 11.6	1.57
51	8.24	25.86	24.9 − j 2.4	1.10
51.5	8.43	19.33	22.8 + j 7.8	1.40
52	8.64	14.66	20.3 + j 19.2	2.34

Table 13-7

Element Lengths and Spacing for Wideband 6-Meter Design with ½-inch-Diameter Elements

Element	Length (inches)	Spacing from Reflector (inches)
Reflector	116.80	0
Driven Element	108.10	40.7
Director	96.10	73.5

antenna is used horizontally. Still, these beams are both simple and inexpensive. Hence, you might want to build a high-gain model for the low end of 6 meters and a wideband model to cover the upper 3 MHz of the band.

Fig 13-22 overlays free-space azimuth patterns of both beams at their design frequencies. The patterns will give you a good idea of their relative performance potentials.

Stepped-Diameter Tubing

The beam dimensions for both models used uniform ½-inch-diameter elements. A common building practice is to use at least two tubing sizes in 6-meter beams. Most often, we start with ½-inch tubing at the center and use ³/₈-inch tubing for the element ends. Let's suppose we make the center portions of each element from 6-foot lengths of ½-inch tubing—3 feet of tubing on each side of the boom. What happens to the overall element lengths?

Table 13-9 compares the element lengths from the boom outward for each beam (commonly called "element half-lengths"). One model uses ½-inch-diameter tubing throughout, and the other uses ³/₈-inch-diameter tubing for the ends. The stepped-diameter lengths are chosen so that the antenna performance is essentially the same as with uniform-diameter elements. Note that the element lengths become significantly longer when we step the element diameter downward on the way to the element end. The amount of change differs for each element.

You can calculate the end lengths by subtracting 36 inches from the overall element length. However, be sure to add about three inches per end section to allow for telescoping the tubing.

I'll leave the remaining construction details up to you, since there are many acceptable ways to construct either of these Yagis. Again, *The ARRL Antenna Book* and articles in *QST* and recent editions of *The ARRL Antenna Compendium* are full of good ideas. Simply select those that best fit your available materials and individual skills.

Both of these Yagis—adapted from the work of veteran antenna designers—are good designs. Which you choose will depend on what you want to do on 6 meters during the present sunspot cycle and beyond.

Table 13-8

Modeled Performance Figures for the Wideband (50 to 54 MHz) 6-Meter Design

Frequency (MHz)	Gain (dBi)	F/B (dB)	Feedpoint Impedance (R ± j X Ω)	50-Ω SWR
50	7.00	14.90	48.4 − j 21.2	1.54
51	6.92	18.08	51.9 − j 9.9	1.22
52	6.96	20.31	51.9 + j 1.7	1.05
53	7.13	21.02	48.8 + j 15.0	1.35
54	7.44	18.40	43.0 + j 31.1	1.96

Table 13-9

Half-Element Lengths for Uniform Half-Inch and Stepped ½-Inch to ³/₈-Inch-Diameter Elements

High-Gain Design

Element	Uniform Diameter Length	Stepped-Diameter Length
Reflector	114.36	116.4
Driven-element	108.96	111.0
Director	102.43	104.0

Wideband Design

Element	Uniform-Diameter Length	Stepped-Diameter Length
Reflector	116.80	118.6
Driven-element	108.10	110.0
Director	96.10	97.6

Note: All dimensions are in inches. For the stepped-diameter elements, the inner 36-inch length uses ½-inch-diameter tubing, with ³/₈-inch-diameter tubing used for the remainder of the element

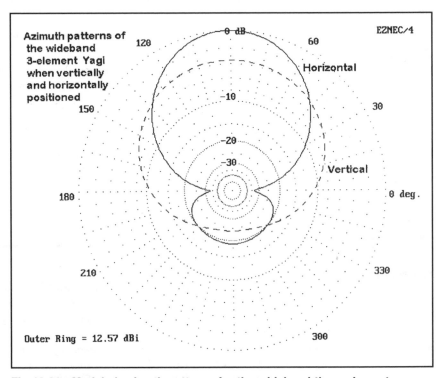

Fig 13-21—Modeled azimuth patterns for the wideband three-element 6-meter Yagi in horizontal and vertical positions at 30 feet above average earth.

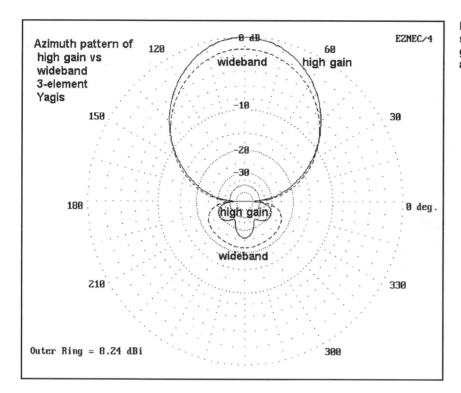

Azimuth pattern of high gain vs wideband 3-element Yagis

120 0 dB 60
wideband high gain

EZNEC/4

150 -10 30

-20

-30

180 high gain 0 deg.

wideband

210 330

Outer Ring = 8.24 dBi 300

Fig 13-22—Overlaid models of free-space azimuth patterns for the high-gain and wideband 6-meter designs at their design frequencies.

Homebrewing a 6-Meter Yagi

ARRL Senior Lab Engineer and RF guru Zack Lau, W1VT, wrote this article for January/February 1998 *QEX*. I think you'll find lots of good ideas in Zack's article. In other words, even if you don't build an exact copy, you find a lot of useful techniques here that you might want to incorporate into your own projects. Here's what Zack said.

Six meters is a great band for home built Yagis. The elements are reasonably small, but not so small that building tolerances are critical. With careful construction and detailed instructions, it is certainly feasible to build no-tune Yagis up to 432 MHz, but I have my doubts about 903-MHz Yagis made out of aluminum rods and tubing. This is especially true if you factor in misinterpretations made when copying someone else's design.

At the other end of the spectrum, tuning is often necessary to compensate for environmental effects. Many people can't mount a 40-meter antenna far enough away from other objects to eliminate detuning effects. See for yourself how bad this is with a 2-meter mo-

bile station and an SWR meter—then scale things up dimensionally by a factor of 20. Thus, for proper performance, low-frequency antennas often need to be tuned in-place. When they're moved, retuning is often required.

Most 6-meter Yagis are horizontally polarized and cover only the SSB/CW portion of the band. Building for horizontal polarization is much simpler with small Yagis, because interaction with vertical supports is minimized. While it might be nice to cover the entire band, the typical sacrifice in antenna performance hasn't justified the work involved in coming up with a clever design. At least I haven't seen anyone publish such a design.

These days the electrical design of antennas is easy. There are plenty of Yagi designs and computer modeling programs out there. I picked this design out of Lawson's book *Yagi Antenna Design* (no longer in print) because it has good gain and pattern for just four elements. I wanted few elements for portable work—more elements mean more assembly/disassembly time. That's a big

factor when you are surrounded by black flies and other obnoxious insects. An extra element or two does give you a bit more design flexibility. You can often get the beam to work well over a wider bandwidth with more elements, while keeping the boom length constant. Extra bandwidth helps the antenna to work well despite the effects of rain, though few Yagis work well when covered with ice. You don't get more gain by adding more elements, however; maximum gain is pretty much a function of boom length. This is why W5UN's 24-foot-boom Yagi for 2-meter EME has just 11 elements. They just aren't needed for this particular application.

According to *Yagi Analyzer*, the simple program that comes with *The ARRL Antenna Book*, the antenna has 10.6 dBi of free-space gain with the unwanted lobes suppressed by 20 dB—a reasonably clean pattern. I like to use dBi because it is relatively unambiguous. DBd measurements are problematic because some people just subtract 2.15 dB from the isotropic gain reference number, while others reference an actual dipole in the same location. Thus, one who is modeling antennas over ground can get dBd numbers that vary by as much as 6 dB, due to ground gain effects and definition differences.

To simplify the electrical design, I used insulated elements spaced ¼ inch above the boom. This makes the boom interaction minimal, so it isn't necessary to factor in a boom correction. Many element-mounting methods allow the boom to interact with the elements, requiring the elements to be slightly longer than predicted by computer modeling programs.

I did a bit of research on the best material for the mounting plates; Lexan seems to be the best choice. Lexan is the same stuff used for bulletproof windows, so it doesn't shatter like cheaper plastics. Unlike acrylic, it is UV resistant. UV resistance is important for anything you intend to put out in the sunshine for long periods—unless you want something that self-destructs. Lexan has disadvantages: It lacks optical clarity and costs more than other plastics. I used oak blocks to attach the elements to the mounting plates, as shown in **Fig 13-23** and **Fig 13-24**. A ½ inch "bullet" drill makes tight fitting holes in the blocks. After pounding the tubing through the blocks, I painted the wood for weather protection. The paint also serves to glue the blocks to the tubing, though the fit was so tight that this isn't necessary.

To make field assembly easier, I decided to pin the element clamps to the boom. This requires precision drilling of the boom, lest you end up with elements that aren't in the same plane. A square boom is much easier to drill correctly, but I haven't really looked for a source of telescoping square tubing. Two of the element pins also hold the three boom sections together.

It's more traditional to use U-bolts and saddles, but many people have problems with the elements rotating out of alignment. This usually results from using "universal" saddles, which aren't matched to the tubing being used.

You can get much better performance by machining saddles that maximize the contact area. I've made them out of 1 inch square tubing to fit standard 1¼ inch mast sections. It may be a little easier to make them out of chan-

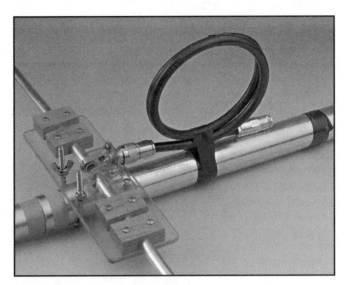

Fig 13-23—Driven element of the Yagi.

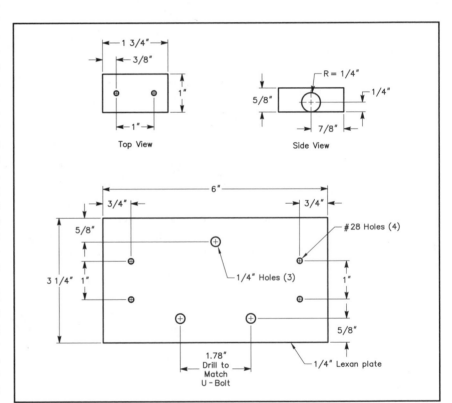

Fig 13-24—Hardwood element mounting block and Lexan plate.

nel stock. This is a tedious process with a round file, but a lot cheaper than using a miniature milling machine with a rotary table. **Fig 13-25** and **Fig 13-26** show the basic design of the saddles. I've also made some wooden versions using a Forstner bit (designed for cutting clean holes), but haven't thoroughly tested them.

Here's another significant mechani-

cal problem: What's the best way to make portable elements that fit inside a small car? Fortunately, aluminum tubing is conveniently sold in sizes that telescope together—0.058-inch-wall tubing works quite well for this purpose.

The challenge is joining them together. I did it the hard way, slotting the tubing and making custom clamps out of aluminum plate. I've made the

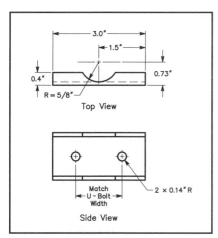

Fig 13-25—Custom saddle dimensions.

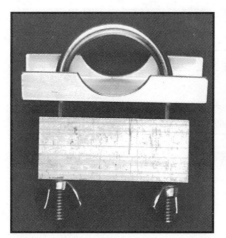

Fig 13-26—Machined clamp to match 1¼ inch mast.

Fig 13-27—Machined element clamp.

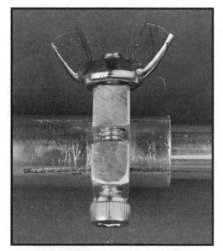

Fig 13-28—Element clamp holding tubing together.

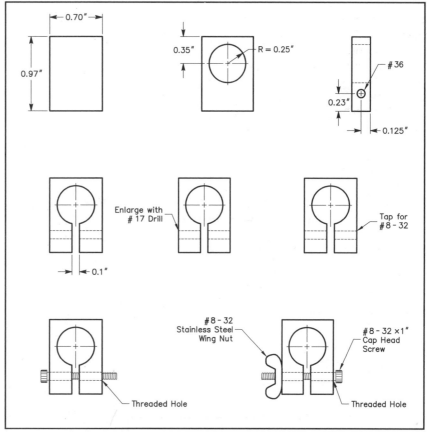

Fig 13-29—½ inch tubing clamp construction steps.

slots with a bandsaw, but I get much better results with a metal reinforced wood fixture that guides a hacksaw blade. A fixture using a miter box and hacksaw might work even better.

Figs 13-27 through **13-29** show an element clamp I've designed. I make them out of scraps of ¼ inch 606l-T6 aluminum plate. Number 8 stainless-steel wing nuts work quite well; they allow quick assembly by hand. (I've also tried #6 hardware, but it is a little too small. I needed a flat washer to reduce the friction when using the smaller #6 hardware.) A version using #10 hardware might be advisable for someone with bigger fingers.

If the wing nuts get lost, it is still possible to use the clamps, by unscrewing the 1 inch screws and screwing them in backwards with an Allen wrench. Keep an Allen wrench handy by taping it to the boom.

You could simply drill holes in the assembled elements and put screws through the holes. The disadvantage is that you can't tweak the lengths, but that isn't a problem if you are copying a design that doesn't need adjustments. Adjustment-

free antennas make quite a bit of sense for portable work, since it isn't unusual for things to shift during transport.

You don't want to waste time figuring out the proper settings. To help identify the element pieces quickly, I color coded them by painting the element tips. I also painted the boom to assist in putting the elements in the

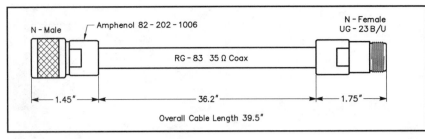

Fig 13-30—λ/4 matching section.

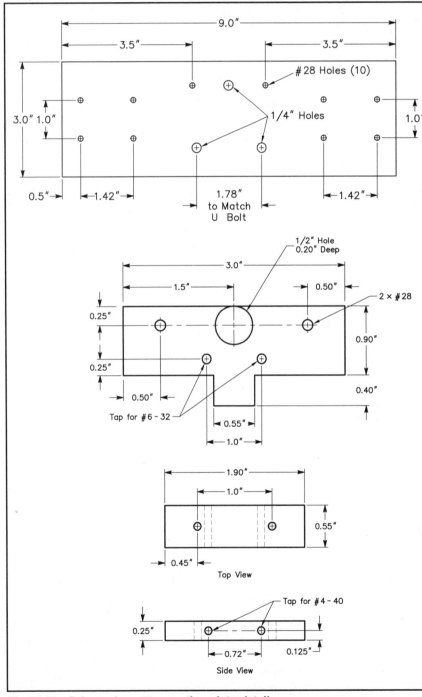

Fig 13-31—Driven-element mounting-plate details.

proper location. Colored tape also works, as long as you don't have to slide a clamp or U-bolt over it. Tape can stop a clamp's movement or get shredded in the process. Paint will probably be scratched up the first time you use the antenna—so don't worry too much about how it looks.

You can also use stainless-steel hose clamps in place of my machined versions. If you go this route, it's a good idea to use clamps made entirely of stainless steel; some clamps have parts that rust.

In keeping with the idea of a simple design, I used a λ/4 of somewhat exotic RG-83 coax to feed a split driven element, as shown in **Fig 13-30** (before coiling to form the balun). I'm not sure if anyone besides Times Microwave makes this coax, but it is available from the Wireman. Because the antenna is balanced, I provide a balun by making a two-turn coil out of the matching section. To accommodate the large #10 center conductor of RG-83, I used a 9913 N male connector on one end and drilled out the center pin of a female UG-23/U connector for the other. Many standard N connectors are designed for #11 or #13 wire and won't fit without modification. Some people have filed down the center conductor of the coax to fit such connectors.

Alternatively, one could parallel connect two lengths of 75-Ω coax (connecting both the shields and center conductors at both ends) to make 37.5-Ω coax. This does shift the optimum feedpoint impedance, however, from 24.5 to 28 Ω. A perfectionist might want to tweak the electrical design of the Yagi a bit to fit this.

The driven-element connection is simpler—I swaged a pair of terminal posts to some brass strips and some un-clad fiberglass circuit board. The brass strips are then attached to the driven element with #4-40 screws. The coax is taped to the fiberglass to provide strain relief for the soldered connections to the terminal strips. For the other end, I made an L bracket out of brass to hold a UG-58A/U panel jack. I soldered the shield to the brass and the center conductors to the center pin. Like the driven-element connection's insulator, I made the brass L long enough to securely tape the coax and provide strain relief.

Solid-dielectric coax seems to be

reasonably consistent in terms of velocity factor, so the trimming often necessary with other types may not be necessary. Still, there's a good way of accounting for discontinuities such as coax connectors: Substitute a 24 Ω resistor for the driven element and use an antenna analyzer to figure out what frequency the matching network is cut for—and then re-cut it to the proper length. Make sure the resistor is reasonable noninductive; that's something the antenna analyzer can also test. If you do this with a 10-foot length of coax, you can build three matching sections and not need to unsolder any connectors. You first measure what frequency the 10-foot section works at, and then the shorter 3-foot sections. Since a ¾ λ matching section performs similarly to a λ/4 section, you might use this fact if your measurement technique doesn't cover much lower frequencies.

Fig 13-31 shows the pieces of Lexan I use to attach the UG-58 panel jack to the mounting plate. The half-inch hole in the T-shaped piece is a little tricky—I drilled it just deep enough to hold the hex bolt head. This captures the screw and prevents it from turning when you screw on a wing nut. The smaller pieces go on top of the larger pieces and the T-shaped piece keeps the element halves separated. The little top piece is for mounting the N connector. I use pieces of copper strap to attach the connector to the element halves. These straps are 0.3 × 2.0 inches long, with mounting holes drilled 0.2 inches from each end. Attach them to the driven element and N connector with #4-40 hardware. For the connections to aluminum tubing, I drill a #43 hole ¼ inch from the ends. Then I enlarge the closer hole with a #33 drill and the far end with a #4-40 tap. The straps are then attached with ⁹/₁₆-inch long #4-40 screws and #4 lock washers. It helps to coat the ends of the straps with solder to reduce corrosion. Finally, I coated the electrical connections with nonacidic Dow 3140 RTV.

The exact specification of Yagi dimensions can be a bit confusing. Often, one gets a taper schedule like that in **Table 13-10**.

For the *cognoscenti*, this is enough to build the antenna. Beginners need a bit more explanation. First, it is often

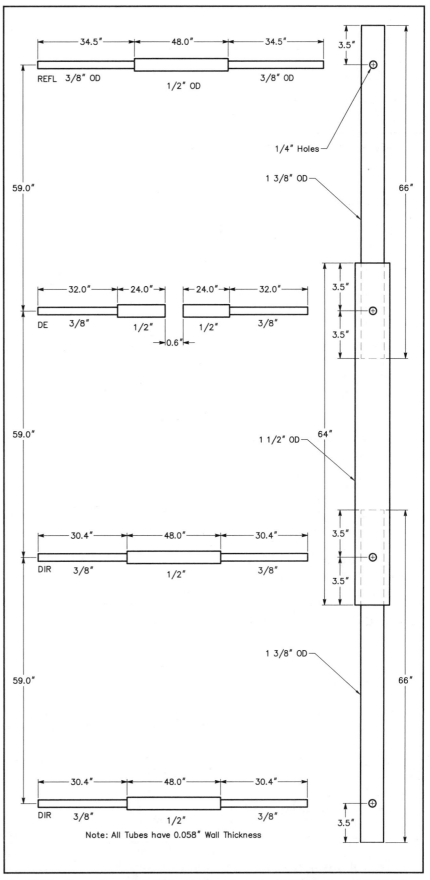

Fig 13-32—Four-element 6 meter Yagi made out of 0.058-inch wall 6061-T6 aluminum tubing. Tubing dimensions are outer diameters.

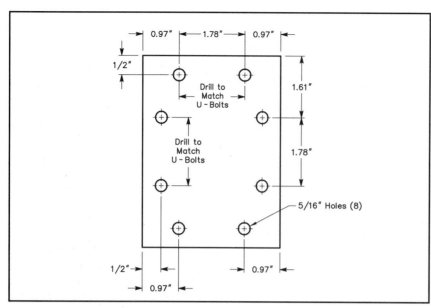

Fig 13-33—Boom to mast plate.

Table 13-10
Taper Schedule (inches)

	0.500" OD	0.375" OD	Spacing Between Elements
Ref	24	34.5	0
DE	24	32.0	59.0
DIR1	24	30.4	59.0
DIR2	24	30.4	59.0

See Fig 13-32 for details.

Table 13-11
Measured SWR

Antenna Height = 16 feet

SWR	Frequency (MHz)
1.9	49.18
1.5	49.45
1.4	49.64
1.0	49.84
1.0	50.04
1.2	50.20
1.4	50.25
2.1	50.36

Antenna Height = 11 feet

SWR	Frequency (MHz)
2.0	49.31
1.2	49.82
1.0	50.03
1.0	50.10
1.0	50.14
1.2	50.21
1.2	50.25
1.4	50.29
2.0	50.40

quite efficient to work with half elements when modeling Yagis, because the assumption that you have a symmetrical antenna enables the software writers to come up with a program that runs faster and handles bigger antennas. Thus, the taper schedule specifies just half an element, although this may be a poor way to actually build an element. Also, the schedule doesn't include any overlap required to actually join the elements—it's just the electrical model. Typically, I'll add about three inches to the smaller tubing since it effectively uses up four 6-foot sections of $^3/_8$-inch tubing. Finally, unless stated otherwise, spacing dimensions given by programs are center to center distances.

Fig 13-32 shows a drawing of the antenna—I moved the boom off to one side for clarity. Remember that the boom is just a mechanical support. I designed the element clamps for minimal interaction, so it really isn't part of the electrical design. Thus, it would work just as well—or maybe even better—if you could magically suspend the elements in mid-air, without real supports that interact with the antenna.

Table 13-11 shows some SWR measurements made in the ARRL HQ parking lot with an SWR analyzer and a cable with 0.3 dB of loss. Cable loss makes the SWR look better. To correct for it, one can convert SWR to return loss and subtract out twice the cable loss, because the reflected power makes a round trip through the coax.

Fig 13-33 is a drilling guide for a boom-to-mast plate made out of ¼-inch 6061-T6 aluminum plate. I made this plate a long time ago and used it be-

cause it was available. Simple V-shaped saddles seem to work adequately for the boom saddles as there is much less torque to move things out of alignment.

Two Portable 6-Meter Antennas

Markus T. Hansen, VE7CA, wrote this article, which appeared in *The ARRL Antenna Compendium, Vol 5.* I believe you'll enjoy reading about his portable 2-element quad and his portable 3-element Yagi.

Being a ham for over 32 years has provided the time to try many different aspects of this great hobby. Traffic nets, DX, FM mobile, equipment homebrew-

ing and, of course, antenna experimenting have supplied hundreds of hours of enjoyment. Only recently did I become interested in VHF. It began when I found a used Yaesu FT-726R VHF/UHF all-mode transceiver at a reasonable price. With it, I could try my hand at satellite communications and grid collecting on the 144 and 432-MHz bands. Then the opportunity came along to add a 6-meter

module and I jumped at it. Several local hams had been telling me about propagation modes I had not experienced: *sporadic-E skip* and *auroral propagation.* As soon as the 6-meter module arrived, up went a dipole.

My first experience working California, Nevada and other distant stations by sporadic E, with only 10 W to a dipole at 20 feet was exhilarating. However, it wasn't too long before I realized that local hams with better antennas were working stations I couldn't even hear. Hearing them work double-hop into Mexico and the East Coast spurred me to action. It was time to build my own gain antenna.

I could have settled for a store-bought Yagi but I have always enjoyed building my own antennas. There is a certain amount of satisfaction saying: "My antenna is home built." So I decided to start with a two-element quad.

After a visit to our local lumber store I came home with a three-foot length of 2×2 clear cedar and four 10-foot lengths of ½-inch fir dowel. A few evenings in the garage and a two-element quad emerged, ready for tuning. I attached the coax and tuned the reflector for maximum front-to-back ratio, hurrying because the band might just be open.

I noticed a big improvement over the dipole! Despite the improvement, I still found a local ham using a four-element Yagi working stations I couldn't work. Either I needed more power or more antenna gain. Although I could build a 100-W amplifier, I still had to be able to hear them before I could work them, so I decided to make the quad bigger.

I went back to the lumber store, returning with a six-foot length of 2×2 clear cedar and six lengths of ½-inch fir dowel. I kept the two-element quad up for comparison with my new three-element quad. This time, the director and reflector were hand-tuned for maximum forward gain. The new quad

was mounted on a 26-foot pole outside the ham shack and the "armstrong method" was employed to rotate the array. Next, I built a four-element Yagi on a 12-foot boom and put it up on the tower at 52 feet. From my home station I could work just about every station that the locals could and I had a lot of fun on 6 meters.

If you spend enough time hanging around dyed-in-the-wool, hard-core, VHF/UHFers you will find something very peculiar about their behavior. When they talk about contesting they are thinking of high and lofty places—they don't mean the tower in the backyard. They are talking about faraway places on top of the highest mountain peaks man and vehicle are capable of reaching. In other words, if you do not possess a portable gain antenna for your favorite VHF/UHF band, you are not a true VHF/UHFer. Not only does an antenna have to be portable, it must be easily assembled and disassembled, just in case you have to move quickly to another, supposedly superior, location.

I still liked the idea of a two-element quad, which is easy to assemble, inexpensive to build and just seemed to want to work. The only trouble is that it is a three-dimensional affair. However, it can be made to be quite rugged, and the wire elements are easily repaired in remote locations. As a first attempt at a portable 6-meter gain antenna, I decided to build a quad that would be easy to disassemble and carry in the back of our family van.

A Portable Two-Element 6-Meter Quad

My primary objective was to construct a two-element quad using material found in any small town. I did not want a complicated matching network. The Gamma matches commonly used on quads do not hold up well when you are setting up and taking down these antennas in the field. I planned on adjusting the distance between the driven and the reflector elements so that the intrinsic feed-point impedance was 50 Ω.

When I built my first 6-meter quad, the driven element length was derived from the formula 1005/freq. The reflector was made about 3% longer. Starting with a spacing of 30 inches, I went through the process of moving the elements closer together and adjusting the driven element for minimum SWR and the reflector element for maximum front-to-back ratio with a tuning stub. This took several hours and when I finished I had an element spacing of 24 inches. This produced an SWR under 1.2:1 over a large portion of the 6-meter band. During these adjustments, the antenna was mounted 12 feet high, as this was the height I intended to use for portable operations. The dimensions were later confirmed using a computer modeling program known as *AO*, the Antenna Optimizer, by Brian Beezley, K6STI. See **Table 13-12**.

Fig 13-34 shows the dimensions for the boom and the boom-to-mast bracket. The boom is made from a 27¼-inch length of 2×2. (The actual dimension of 2×2 is closer to 1¾ by 1¾ inches but it is commonly known in lumber yards as a 2×2.) Use whatever material is available in your area, but lightweight wood is preferred, so clear cedar or pine is ideal. Drill the four

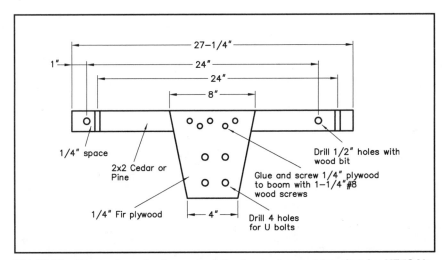

Fig 13-34—Dimensions for boom and the boom-to-mast bracket for VE7CA's portable two-element 6-meter quad.

Table 13-12

Gain Comparisons, Computed and Measured

Antenna	Computed* (dBd)	Measured (dBd)
Quad	4.06	4.2
Yagi	5.68	5.8

*Computed using YO for Yagi, and AO for dipole and quad.

½-inch holes for the spreaders with a wood bit, two at each end, through one of the faces of the 2 × 2 and the other through the other face. The boom-to-mast bracket is made from ¼-inch fir plywood and cut to the dimensions shown in Fig 13-34.

The spreaders are ½-inch dowel. Our local lumberyard had a good supply of fir dowels but other species of wood are available. The exact material is not important. Maple is stronger but expensive. Fiberglass would be ideal but it is not always available locally. Cut two of the ½-inch dowels to a length of 83⅝ inches for the driven element spreaders and two to 88 inches for the reflector spreaders. **Fig 13-35** is a photo showing one end of the boom with the two spreaders inserted. The mast was made from two six-foot lengths of 1¾-inch fir dowel. Again, use whatever you may have available. I did not have any aluminum tubing large enough for a mast and wood dowel is a good alternative. Waterproof all wooden parts with at least two coats of exterior varnish.

While you are at the lumber yard or hardware store look for plastic pipe that fits over the end of the ½-inch spreaders. You will need a one-foot length, with some to spare. Cut it into seven equal lengths, approximately one inch long, and one to a length of 1½ inches. Drill a 1/16-inch hole through the seven equal lengths ¼ inch from the ends, and two holes one above the other ¼ inch apart on the 1½-inch sleeve. I used #14 hard-drawn stranded bare copper wire for the elements. Do not use insulated wire unless you are willing to experimentally determine the element lengths, since the insulation detunes each element slightly.

Cut the reflector element 251 inches long and slip one end of the wire through the holes you drilled in four of the plastic sleeves. Don't attempt to secure the wire to the plastic sleeves at this point. Cross the end of the reflector elements one inch from their respective ends and twist and solder together. The total circumference of the reflector element should be 249 inches when the ends are connected together.

Cut the driven element wire to 241 inches and slip three of the one-inch sleeves onto the wire. Again, don't secure the wires to the sleeves yet. Then the ends are passed through the two holes in the 1½-inch pipe. Wrap the ends around the pipe and twist them back onto themselves to secure the wire. The coax feed line is attached directly to the two ends at this point. The circumference of the driven-element loop from the points where the coax is attached should be 236⅝ inches. Solder the coax feed line to the driven element and waterproof the coax with silicone seal. I used RG-58, as it is lightweight. The length required for a portable installation is typically not very long, maybe 20 feet, so the loss in the small cable is not excessive. Near the feed point, coil the coax into six turns with an inside diameter of two inches. I found this an effective method of choking any RF from flowing on the outside of the coax shield.

Begin assembling the quad by pushing the two reflector spreaders, without wires attached, through one end of the boom and the two shorter driven-

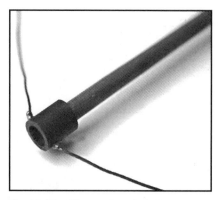

element spreaders through the holes in the other end of the boom. Center the spreaders and mark the spreaders with a black felt-tip pen next to the boom. Now insert a 1½-inch #8 wood screw or a threaded L-hook into the boom so that it just touches one of the spreaders. Take the screw or L-hook out and file the end flat, then reinsert it so that it is just snug against the spreaders. I only used two L-hooks for the two vertical spreaders; the horizontal spreaders are held in the proper position by the tension of the wire loops. If you use an L-hook, you can unscrew it with your hands—you won't have to worry about leaving the screwdriver at home.

You are now ready to assemble the wire loops. Take the reflector loop and place the four plastic caps over the ends of the reflector spreaders. Equalize the wire lengths between the spreader so that the loop is square. Now, secure the plastic sleeve pipes by tightly wrapping wire around the sleeve and the wire element and soldering the wire in place. See **Fig 13-36**, a photo showing one of the plastic sleeves slipped over one of the spreader ends, with the wire element through the hole and fastened in place. Follow the same procedure with the driven element.

Fig 13-37 is a picture of the quad's boom, with the plywood boom-to-mast bracket fastened with wood screws and glue. Two U-bolts are used to attach to the mast. When the quad is raised, the shape of the loop is commonly known as a diamond configuration. The mast consists of two six-foot lengths of doweling joined together with a two-foot length of PVC plastic pipe, held together with wood screws.

Make a slot the width of a #8 wood screw about one inch deep from the top of the plastic PVC pipe and then put the top mast into the plastic pipe. Insert a one

Fig 13-35—Photo of one end of the VE7CA quad with the two spreaders inserted.

Fig 13-36—Photo showing one of the plastic sleeves slipped over the end of a spreader to provide a mechanical mounting point and support for the wires.

Fig 13-37—Photo of the two-element quad's boom, with the plywood boom-to-mast bracket secured with wood screws and glue.

Fig 13-38—Ready for action! VE7CA has set up his quad next to the family van.

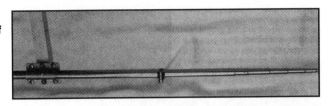

Fig 13-39—Photo showing a piece of aluminum tubing used as a center section to join the two telescoping tips together.

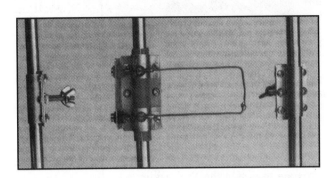

Fig 13-40—A view of the center sections of the three Yagi elements with their mounting brackets.

Table 13-13
Three-Element Yagi Dimensions

Element	Spacing Along Boom (inches)	Center Section Ele. (inches)	Telescoping Length (inches)	Total Length (inches)
Reflector	0	22¾	51½	125¾
Driven	28	9¾*	48⁵/₈	58³/₁₆
Director	63³/₈	14½	51¼	117
Hairpin	#14 wire	4 long	1⁵/₈ spacing	

*Driven element uses two sections insulated at center.

inch #8 wood screw into the bottom of the slot you cut into the top of the pipe and tighten only enough so that the top mast can be removed without unscrewing it. I drove a nail into the end of the lower mast and left it exposed an inch or more. This end is placed in the ground and the nail holds the pole in place. A strip of wood approximately 1 × 3 and long enough to cross over the roof rack of our family van is used to hold the center of the antenna mast to the roof rack of the van with small diameter rope. See **Fig 13-38** for a photo of the quad in action next to the family van.

To disassemble the quad, lay it on its side, slip the plastic sleeves off the ends of the spreaders and roll up the wire loops. Loosen the L-hooks holding the vertical spreaders in place. Push the spreaders out of the boom, loosen the U-bolts and free the mast from the boom.

That is all there is to it. It takes about two minutes to put it up, or take it down. I have found it quite sturdy, surviving several storms with high winds.

A THREE-ELEMENT PORTABLE 6-METER YAGI

The idea to build a Yagi antenna resulted when we traded the family van for a compact car. I needed something

that would fit into the trunk of the car. At close to seven-feet long, the quad spreaders were too long. After computer modeling a three-element Yagi on a five-foot boom, I found that I could pick up about 1.5 dB gain over the short-boom two-element quad. A five-foot boom fits into the trunk or across the back seat of the car, but I had to do something about shortening the nine-foot elements!

Several options were considered. Loaded elements were too complex and tedious to tune. Splitting the elements in the center would work if an easy, reliable method could be devised to quickly fasten and unfasten the elements from the boom. Since my philosophy for portable equipment is to keep it as simple as possible, I continued to look around for good alternatives for elements.

One day I noticed a box of portable-radio telescoping antenna elements at our local radio parts store. To my delight, they were 54 inches long

when fully extended. I left the store with six telescoping elements and a big smile on my face. On the way home I stopped by a scrap-metal yard and rummaged around in some bins of aluminum tubing. A 60-inch length of aluminum tubing that fit over the end of my telescoping elements was found and purchased. There are many different sizes of telescoping antenna elements, with different diameters. This is where you will have to use your scrounging skills! **Fig 13-39** shows how the tubing is used as a center section to join two telescoping elements together. It also serves to extend the total length of each element, since two telescoping elements themselves are not long enough to resonate on 6 meters. Each center section is slotted at both ends with a hacksaw, and stainless-steel hose clamps are used to secure the telescoping elements. See **Table 13-13**.

Since the telescoping elements are severely tapered ⁷/₁₆ down to ¹/₁₆ inch), I

Fig 13-41—Photo detailing attachment of the reflector to the square-section boom, using two #10 bolts and wingnuts.

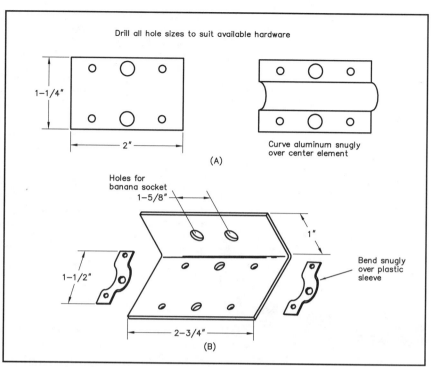

Drill all hole sizes to suit available hardware

1–1/4"

2"

(A)

Curve aluminum snugly over center element

Holes for banana socket
1–5/8"

1"

1–1/2"

2–3/4"

(B)

Bend snugly over plastic sleeve

Fig 13-42—At A, details for the reflector and director element-to-boom brackets, made of ¹/₁₆-inch plate aluminum. At B, details for the driven-element bracket. These are screwed to the square boom.

used the *YO* Yagi Optimizer modeling program to design the Yagi, taking all tapers into account. After numerous trial runs on YO a satisfactory design was derived on a 65-inch boom. By splitting the driven element in the center and employing a hairpin match, I was able to obtain an SWR below 1.16:1 from 50.05 to 50.2 MHz. **Fig 13-40** shows the center sections of the three elements with their mounting brackets.

I decided to use a square boom so that I would have one flat surface to work with. **Fig 13-41** shows how the reflector is attached to the end of the boom with two 1½-inch 10-32 bolts and wingnuts. **Fig 13-42A** provides the dimensions and details for the reflector and director element-to-boom brackets, which are formed from ¹/₁₆-inch plate aluminum. The driven element is split in the center and is insulated from the boom. Fig 13-42B shows details for the driven-element bracket. **Fig 13-43** is a photo of the driven element with the hairpin matching wire and the banana plugs used to connect the coax to the driven element. You could use a female PL-259 connector if you wish. I used #14 solid bare copper wire for the hairpin. It is very durable—even after being severely warped in the car trunk, I can bend it back into shape quickly and easily.

The boom is ³/₁₆-inch square aluminum, 65 inches long. This material was found at a local hardware store. To detach the elements, just loosen the wing nuts and remove the elements from the boom. I used a similar method to attach the support mast to the boom.

As with the quad design, I decided to use a choke balun, consisting of a coil

Fig 13-43—Photo of driven element, complete with hairpin match and the banana plugs used to connect the coax cable to the driven element.

of coax next to the antenna feedpoint. This chokes off current flowing along the shield of the coax so that the antenna pattern will not be distorted on this balanced feed system. To determine the size of the coax coil, I first plotted the antenna pattern feeding the antenna with a straight length of coax. Just like *The ARRL Antenna Book* predicts, the pattern was definitely skewed to one side. I then coiled up the coax for a total of six turns with an inside diameter of 2 inches. Six turns were sufficient.

To tune the hairpin match, assemble the Yagi on its mast and extend the elements. Spray switch contact solution on a cloth and wipe any dirt and grease from the elements. Push the elements together and apart a couple of times so that the contact solution cleans the elements thoroughly. Attach the antenna mast to your vehicle or use whatever method of support you intend to use in the field. Connect an SWR meter and a transmitter to the coax feeding the antenna. I used two alligator

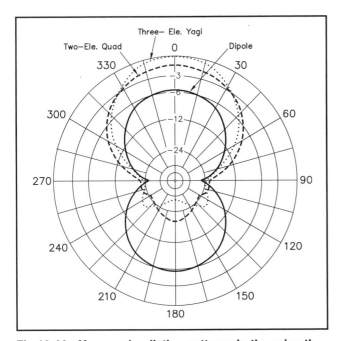

Fig 13-44—Measured radiation patterns in the azimuth plane for three 6-meter antennas: the portable two-element quad, the portable three-element Yagi and a reference dipole.

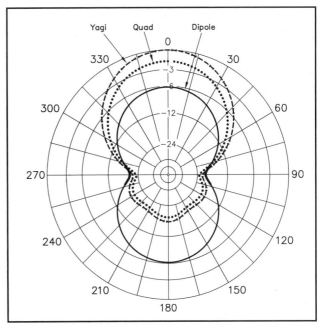

Fig 13-45—Computed radiation patterns for the same antennas in Fig 13-42. The computations are remarkably close to the actual measured patterns!

clips soldered together to slide along the two hairpin wires to find the position for the lowest SWR. The dimensions computed by computer were correct!

I can take this antenna out of the trunk of the car and assemble it in less than two minutes. One caution: the telescoping elements when fully extended are quite fragile. I have not broken one as yet, but carrying a spare element just in case would be a good idea.

Are These Antennas Effective?

In order to evaluate the two portable antennas, I decided to carry out actual field antenna-pattern measurements. The reference antenna was a 6-meter dipole. A single-transistor, battery-operated crystal oscillator was used as a source. It was placed 200 feet from the antennas under test.

The test location is a large, level grass soccer playing field. The antenna mast was tied to a wooden stepladder in the center of the playing field. A homebrew direct-conversion receiver, step attenuator and a VU meter with a 600 to 8-Ω audio transformer matching the VU meter to the audio output jack of the receiver made up my test equipment.

On a 12-foot mast, I mounted a 6-meter dipole tuned for the 50.13 MHz test frequency. Turning the dipole through

360°, VU meter readings directly in dB were plotted on an ARRL ANTENNA RADIATION PATTERN worksheet. Fortunately, the dipole pattern turned out to be textbook symmetrical, indicating that the test site was acceptable for further antenna measurements.

I then removed the dipole and mounted the three-element portable Yagi on the same mast. With the Yagi pointed at the test oscillator and 30 dB of attenuation in line, the receiver audio level was set so that the VU meter read zero. I did not adjust the audio gain control further or move the location of the test oscillator until all antenna measurements were made. Rotating the Yagi through 360°, I stopped every 10° and plotted the VU meter readings on an ARRL ANTENNA RADIATION PATTERN worksheet. As I rotated the Yagi and the VU meter reading decreased to −10 dB, the in-line attenuation was decreased by 10 dB.

After completing the Yagi measurements, I removed it and put up the two-element quad. In a similar manner, I recorded the VU readings as I rotated the quad through 360°. Finally, the dipole was placed back up on the mast and the antenna pattern plotted on the same plotting sheet.

Fig 13-44A and **B** show the results

of the actual field measurements. **Fig 13-45A** and **B** show computed elevation and azimuth patterns of the three antennas. I was amazed at how close the actual field measurements were to the computer analysis.

Concluding Remarks

Do these antennas perform in the field? Yes, they do. In the 1994 ARRL Field Day, the two-element portable quad was instrumental in helping VE7NSR (the North Shore Amateur Radio Club) capture the number one position in the 1A class for Canada.

I have used the three-element portable Yagi on numerous occasions in the field and found it a very effective portable antenna. Side-by-side comparisons between the Yagi and the quad indicate that the Yagi outperforms the quad, as expected.

Constructing Amateur Radio antennas is still one area in this great hobby where the results always seem to outweigh the effort. Employing a simple design eases construction, keeps the cost low as well as increasing the likelihood that the design will perform properly. I hope the construction and design techniques outlined in this article will provide readers with the incentive to build their own antennas.

14 Towers

With Visions of Sugarplum Towers Dancing in My Head...

By Dean Straw, N6BV

Yes, the subtitle above is a really bad paraphrase of "The Night Before Christmas" poem. Haven't we all had our Christmas dreams? But let me tell you a little story about a kid and his continuing antenna dream. I was first licensed in 1959, when I was a 12-year old barefoot kid in Hawaii. My first antenna was a 20-meter vertical I cobbled together with #24 wire taped to a bamboo pole. My ground system consisted of a single ground rod. (As others have confessed about their own first-ever verticals, I was not alone in being naïve about the real requirements for radial ground systems.) I fed this magnificent skywire with a home-brew pair of 6L6s that acted as a frequency doubler to 20 meters, starting from a 40-meter war-surplus FT-243 crystal.

My lash-up worked OK, especially since my KH6 call gave me at least 10-dB "call-sign" gain compared to other stations calling from more garden-variety locations. Back then I was always dreaming about bigger antennas. I dreamed of crashing through massive pileups with a single call, of running hundreds (maybe thousands) of exotic DX stations, all clamoring to get into my log. My secret mantra became "big beam… big beam" and I repeated that to myself, all the time.

When I was a kid, my ultimate vision of a "big beam" was a 3-element monoband 20-meter Yagi on a tower.

And I actually did achieve that dream, in a modest sort of way, with a rotating tower made of heavy duty telescoping water pipes, topped with a second-hand 20-meter Yagi on an 18-foot boom. This rather scary contraption reached all the way to 30 feet above ground. My father and brother helped me install that system, but not without some real excitement raising it to the vertical position with the heavy Yagi attached. To this day, my Dad and brother regard me as something of a nut case when it comes to my antennas.

Anyway, we finally got it installed, trued up and working properly. But there were some nagging problems. You see, I had decided to be really clever and had mounted the rotator at ground level for easy servicing. Unfortunately, the base of my ersatz rotating tower was located right outside my parents' bedroom window, and the grinding noises made while rotating the beast tended to limit my late-night DXing!

Fast-forward some 40 years and I'm still dreaming about big antennas. However, my ambitions have grown, probably in proportion to the graying of the hair on my head. Now, I dream about 6/6/6-element stacked monoband 20-meter Yagis on 150-foot towers. Those ambitions have yet to be fully satisfied, I should point out, but at one time I did have a pretty neat stack of tribanders when I lived in New Hamp-

shire. Even though I now live in the middle of bustling San Francisco doesn't mean I can't continue to dream about someday having big antennas!

YOUR OWN DREAMS

While I've been reminiscing about my own beginnings as an HF operator, I should point out that devotees of the VHF/UHF bands are not immune to day-dreams about big towers and rotary Yagis either. They dream of living on mountaintops, something that contest enthusiasts and die-hard DXers also dream about. Whatever your ham-radio interests, you too can dream!

Let's say that you've recently gotten your feet wet on HF, operating with horizontal dipoles suspended from trees. Or let's say that you're smarter than N6BV used to be, and you learned about how to install a good ground-radial system. Because of this, you've been having a lot of fun using ground-mounted verticals.

Still, you have this nagging feeling that you'd like to be *louder*. Maybe your buddy in the next town always beats you out to the DX, and he has a triband Yagi on a 50-foot tower while you have your measly dipole or vertical. Whatever the motivation, you want to get into the ham-radio "big leagues." In other words, you are now seriously contemplating putting up your own *steel tree*—your first tower. This tower will, of course, be festooned with at least one rotary Yagi on the top, maybe more than one.

PLAYING THE DEVIL'S ADVOCATE

Chuck Hutchinson and I agonized over this chapter for quite a while, because putting up a tower does not fall neatly into the category of being "simple"—and remember, the title of this book is *Simple and Fun Antennas for Hams*. Planning, putting up and then maintaining a tower is a major undertaking. And I haven't mentioned paying for it yet either.

Pardon the slightly twisted metaphor, but I'm going to play the Devil's Advocate here. And I'm going to throw some cold water over your hot dream. If after that treatment your dream still comes through, wet but full of enthusiasm and drive, then fine and dandy. You should go for it!

I'm going to have to paint this picture with a broad brush, because each person has a unique situation compared to anyone else. Some of you are lucky enough to live out in the country (like my dear friend K8CH), with acres of land to work with, no zoning and very few neighbors. Others live smack dab in the middle of a big city, surrounded by hundreds, perhaps thousands, of neighbors.

I'm also going to tell you outright that no single book is going to give you all the possible information and helpful tips you will find valuable when putting up your own tower. Since you will be spending *a lot* of money when this is all said and done, it behooves you to set aside perhaps $100 for books and reference materials. [And despite my partisanship as Editor, I am going to suggest that your antenna library must have the latest edition of *The ARRL Antenna Book*.]

So here we go. What should you be considering as you pursue your tower dream? Let me suggest that the main categories are:
• Performance issues
• Environmental issues
• Legal issues
• Cost issues

Performance Issues

The conventional wisdom among hams about their antennas is encapsulated in the following two tongue-in-cheek aphorisms (sometimes known as *hamisms*):
• "If your antenna didn't fall down last winter, it was too small."
• "Higher is better."

There are some wry truths in both of these statements. The first saying has, no doubt, created a few cases of heartburn for ham attorneys. While I like to kid around, I am a very serious advocate of safety. So if I err anywhere dealing with antennas, it is on the side of caution. In other words, I prefer to *overdesign* and *overbuild* to achieve a specific level of performance, rather than putting something up in the air and simply hoping that it will stand up to the elements.

Concerning "higher is better": A higher antenna is often a better performer than a lower one, because it usually will emphasize low-angle performance. But this is not necessarily always so, mainly due to the sometimes-surprising effects of local terrain. Several years ago, Jerry Hall, K1TD, and I wrote a white paper that is posted on the *ARRLWeb* site (**http://www.arrl.org/field/regulations/local/antplnr.pdf**). This describes in some detail the tradeoffs in performance versus height for HF antennas from 3.5 to 30 MHz. The title is: "Antenna Height and Communications Effectiveness." The paper's main audience is city planners and people who might be involved in your getting that all-important building permit, which we'll discuss later.

The foreground terrain at your own location in directions of interest can have a profound effect on how your signal is launched into the ionosphere. Since each terrain is different (unless you live on truly flat ground), you should do a detailed terrain analysis if you really want to determine the optimal heights for your various HF antennas. *The ARRL Antenna Book* has a lot more detailed information on this subject of performance versus height.

Now, for the last several paragraphs I've been cautioning you that radio performance can be different at every location because of unique local terrain. I'm going to backtrack here because I want you to have a feel for the range of possibilities. As an old professor of mine was fond of saying, "We need some illustrative examples" (which as a good southerner he pronounced, "il-**lust**-ra-tive").

If I had to recommend a single height for decent HF capabilities on the ham bands, I'd pick 70 feet. This is a full wavelength high on the "queen" of the DX bands, 20 meters. It is also two wavelengths on 10 meters, which can be a little high for some propagation paths. On the other hand, 70 feet is only a half wavelength high on 40 meters, which is rather low for long-distance communications on this band.

Finally, 70 feet is only a quarter-wavelength high on 80 meters. Unfortunately, you can't have everything in one installation. And for you VHF/UHF operators, a 70-foot high antenna installation is an excellent choice for almost anything you would like to do, particularly if you're already on a nice hilltop.

Now, I'm going to go somewhat farther out on the proverbial limb (carrying my trusty handsaw, of course) and recommend that an even more ambitious dream antenna system would involve a 100-foot high tower. Now you can really start to cook on the bands lower than 7 MHz!

So let's work with sample towers at these two heights for the rest of this chapter. I'm going to assume that the 70-foot tower will be a medium-duty setup, using popular Rohn 25 tower, with a small multiband Yagi (14/21/28 MHz) on the top and wire dipoles for 3.5 and 7 MHz. Performance will be good, even if not optimal for all frequencies.

The 100-foot tower system will be more substantial, using larger Rohn 45 tower, with a large multiband (14/21/28-MHz) Yagi on top, together with a 2-element shortened 40-meter Yagi above it. I'll assume an 80-meter wire dipole is used here too. Performance will be better with this system, even if still not absolutely optimal for all frequencies.

Environmental Issues

The term "environmental issues" covers a lot of territory. The first environment you are going to encounter as you plan your dream installation is that of your *family*. For most of us, that includes a spouse and probably some children. The person who, rightfully, holds a lot of sway when it comes to things like hobbies and towers and antennas is your spouse. If you're really lucky, your spouse is also a ham, but even that blessed circumstance doesn't guarantee domestic tranquility when it comes to aesthetic matters—such as, "Boy, that thing is ugly!"

Some words to the wise: Make sure your spouse is fully aware of your plans, and fully approves of your plans! "United we stand, divided we fall." Oops, I shouldn't mention the word "fall" in a discussion about towers. "United we stand, divided we never get an antenna" is closer to reality.

The second environment you'll be working in is your *neighborhood*. As should be obvious from the word, there are people involved, your neighbors. Perhaps you've already noticed in the past that when you've waxed rhapsodic about your dreams for big beautiful antennas to your friends and neighbors, sometimes you've encountered resistance. Strangely, these people don't quite have the same passion for metal trees that we hams have. Such is life.

So, another word to the wise: "Keep your friends close, but your enemies closer." Get to know your neighbors and know who might be adamantly opposed to your dream antenna. Believe me, you really do want to know who your opposition will be when you go through an ordeal like a public hearing in order to receive a building permit. But it's still best to keep your neighbors as friends in the first place.

Back when I put up my fairly large antenna system in rural New Hampshire, I made it a point when we first moved in to go out and meet the neighbors and tell them about my dreams for a new antenna system. Several of them even helped me dig holes and move around large rocks (New Hampshire is not called the Granite State for nothing.) When it was all said and done, they had vested interests in my antenna, having helped build it themselves. They were wonderful neighbors and I miss them still.

The third environment you'll be mired in, like it or not, is that of the *politics in your town* (or city or county, whatever form of government you are under). Let's settle on the descriptive term *city hall* for what you'll be facing—with all the subtle (and not-so-subtle) connotations that come with this term. Dealing in this environment means knowing in general what's going on in

your town or city with respect to antenna-related ordinances or bylaws. If you can get to know the people who are on the town Planning Board or the folks who work in the Permits Department down at City Hall, it will be better for you, but you don't have to be a political pro to understand the political environment within which you must operate.

The fourth environment you will find yourself in, and one that can help you a lot in fulfilling your dream antenna system is your local *ham club*. At the local club you'll find people who have already been down this path. They probably know lots about antennas, and hopefully they know lots about towers. After all, they've put up antennas and they've put up towers. They've run the gauntlet going through the legal niceties necessary to get building permits.

The local ham club can be a wonderful resource for you, and the really amazing part is that it's free. Hams love to describe what they've had to do to solve their problems or to achieve their dream stations. Be friendly and open; listen and learn.

Some local clubs even hold "tower universities," often just before ARRL Field Day. They train people how to safely and sanely install towers and antennas. Some local clubs have purchased community antenna tools, such as gin poles, climbing belts, pulleys, guy-wire tension-measuring devices or heavy-duty ropes. As I say, local clubs can be great resources for the antenna dreamer.

Legal Issues

Need I really say this? This is a litigious society. Before you put up what looks to you to be a wonderful improvement to neighborhood aesthetics, you better have all your legal ducks in a row. This means, as I've tried to indicate several times in the preceding sections, you must get a *building permit* for your antenna/tower installation. When you come right down to it, this is the real legal issue for your dream antenna—get the permit.

Here's another ARRL book that is an absolute must-have in your antenna library: *Antenna Zoning for the Radio Amateur* by Fred Hopengarten, K1VR. Fred is a prominent communications attorney who has been involved with helping hams get building permits for

the antenna systems for many years. Fred's book costs $49.95, about 20 minutes of time for a lawyer. It's an incredible investment for that low price; believe me, even if only to provide your own attorney with all the background he/she needs to represent you most effectively and quickly.

Cost Issues

Now I'm going to get your attention. What is this dream of yours going to *cost*? At prices for new equipment in early 2002, a 70-foot, guyed Rohn 25 tower, with a small tribander and rotator, will set you back about $3,000, including concrete but without labor. For a 100-foot, guyed Rohn 45 tower with a large tribander, a 2-element 40-meter beam and rotator, the cost will be about $5,000, again with concrete but without labor. And that's the good news, especially if you and your friends do the labor.

Here comes the part that will rile you, so don't shoot the messenger, please. Remember those legal issues mentioned above? You can figure on about the same level of costs for legal-related expenses to obtain a building permit in many cities. This is if you're lucky and don't run into determined opposition from neighbors with deep pockets and hotshot lawyers.

That comes to a total of about $6,000 for a legal, installed medium-sized dream, and $10,000 for a more substantial version. Perhaps you might want to take a break and think about this some more at this point.

Do You Really Want to Continue?

Now, I must hasten to add that you may be really fortunate and live in a "tower friendly" town. Since you have also been a good neighbor, you could parlay these two advantages into a much cheaper dream installation. You could also save significantly if you can put up a used tower or used antennas that are in good, safe condition. Count yourself as being truly blessed if you find yourself in this happy situation.

Anyhow, I've said what needed to be said. I've done the Devil's Advocate thing. You've got the straight facts (hopefully, worst-case facts) to help you decide whether you can afford to proceed with your dream antenna system or whether you want to stick with using trees or ground-mounted antennas.

PRACTICAL TIPS ON PUTTING UP A TOWER

Now let me move on to less depressing matters. I'll give some details about actually putting up a tower, some practical tips that aren't listed in most other books.

The Good Fear Factor

I've been putting up, taking down and maintaining ham-radio towers for about 35 years. I can tell you without hesitation that as I start my climb upwards my mental state is one of being *fearful*. I think that fear is an entirely reasonable thing to feel, considering that if I fall from 20 feet or more, I will most likely die. Sobering thought, isn't it?

If fear were to really overwhelm me, such that I couldn't work effectively because I was too busy clutching the bottom five feet of a tower, I would quit climbing altogether. But *good fear* breeds caution, and caution breeds a healthy respect for moving slowly and deliberately on the tower. After maybe five minutes of careful, deliberate climbing, fear becomes confidence, but

confidence that is nonetheless firmly connected to caution! I try very hard to think out my moves in advance of making them, all the time I'm on the tower.

Chapter 1, Safety, in *The ARRL Antenna Book* contains a lot more information about tower safety. Remember the discussion earlier about local ham clubs? Make sure you learn from the accumulated experience of the veteran tower climbers in your club. Also listen with discernment, lest any of the grizzled old-timers might have developed some bad habits over the years!

Climbing Belt

Let me be very blunt. If you decide to climb a tower without a climbing belt, your mama raised a *fool*. A really good belt can be bought for less than about $150. Your life is worth a lot more than that, isn't it? Buy a climbing belt and use it, always.

Fig 14-1 shows the belt that Chuck Hutchinson uses. Note that the open end of the snap-action safety hooks (at the ends of the lanyard going around the tower) point outwards. This means that even if you bump up against something like a guy wire, the hook won't release automatically, causing you to fall off the tower.

I have two lanyards on my belt: a long one that can be adjusted to go completely around Rohn 25 or 45 tower, and a shorter one with a so-called "Gorilla Hook" at one end for quick attachment to the tower. I clip this short lanyard to the tower before unclipping and moving the main lanyard at points like guy-wire attachments or at antenna side-mount brackets, where I must undo the main lanyard. If I should slip, I'd fall a maximum of about one foot before being fetched up by the short lanyard. This would be an exciting one foot, to be sure, but a non-fatal one.

Take note also of Chuck's handy Klein tool bag, shown clipped to one of the attachment points on his belt. (Note that this is not attached to one of the belt's D-rings, which should be strictly reserved for the lanyard hooks.) After Chuck belts in at a working height on his tower, he moves the tool bag clip to one of the tower rungs. You can also see the rawhide thong with a T-bar at the bottom used to hold electrical tape.

Fig 14-2 shows Chuck in his "Look, Ma, no hands" mode. He is playfully demonstrating how to test the belt and lanyard—at ground level—before he climbs up the tower. Test your gear before climbing up the tower.

Fig 14-1—Close-up of Klein climbing belt used by K8CH. It's crucial that the snap-action safety hooks at the end of the lanyard (the part going around the tower) point outwards. That way, even if you accidentally open the hook (by bumping into a guy wire, for example), the hook still stays in place and you don't fall off the tower. Note the Klein tool bag hooked to Chuck's belt—not to the D-rings used exclusively for the lanyard hooks.

Fig 14-2—"Look, ma, no hands!" Chuck Hutchinson tests his belt, while standing on the ground.

Power Lines

Don't even think of getting anywhere near overhead power lines, with either the tower itself or any antenna. Remember, antennas and towers are 3-D objects—They have dimensions of length, breadth and height. If any one of these dimensions manages to get across a High Voltage power line you could become what a friend of mine grimly calls a "crispy critter." Stay away from power lines.

Clothing and Water

Since moving back to a 25×100-foot lot in San Francisco, I no longer have my own tower and antennas. So I usually operate out at the contest superstation of Ken Keeler, N6RO, in Oakley, CA, about 40 miles east of San Francisco. I am one of the climbers working on Ken's five towers, three of which are 130+ feet high. Summertime temperatures out at N6RO can go above 100° F. During the winter, we're lucky that temperatures are a lot more moderate, rarely going below about 40° F. At either end of these two extremes gloves are very useful. I prefer leather work gloves, but others prefer "kid gloves" (as in goat) because they are thinner and it's easier to feel objects like nuts or bolts through them.

Even in relatively low temperatures, dehydration can occur, so be prepared to drink water at regular intervals on the tower. As Rod Peterson, K4QG, pointed out in his Nov 2000 *QST* article "Another Look at Tower Work": "Don't worry about 'disposing' of the water either. While working hard on a hot summer day you'll have little inclination to visit the powder room." Our tool bucket at N6RO always has a bottle of water in it.

In hot, humid Jamaica on a DXpedition in 1998, we drank lots of Gatorade to keep us full of electrolytes so we wouldn't cramp, a trick that long-distance runners have used for years. If in fact you find yourself cramping up on the tower, that's an almost sure indication that you need to rest and to get some water and electrolytes. Stop whatever you are doing and drink. I've cramped up on a tower in really hot weather and it's scary.

Another tip that fits under the category "clothing"—Wear work shoes

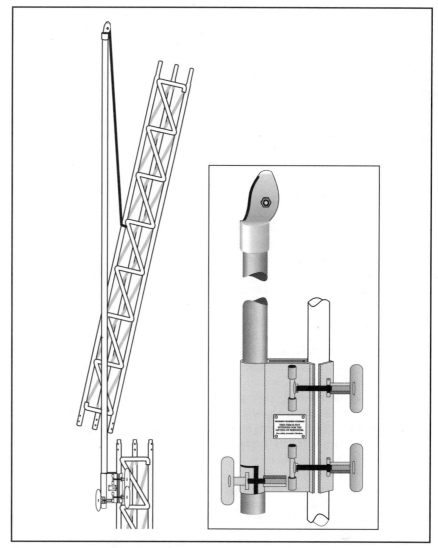

Fig 14-3—Drawing of Rohn "Erection Fixture" EF2545, also known commonly as a "gin pole."

with heavy soles. Tennis shoes definitely don't work well for prolonged periods standing on a tower rung. And here's another piece of necessary "clothing." Everyone on the ground must wear a hard hat. Even a small nut or a bolt dropped from 70 feet could be a lethal projectile buried in someone's head. Climbers too should wear hard hats, particularly if two of them are on the tower working together.

The Gin Pole and Tips on Tower Building

An essential piece of hardware for working on towers is a *gin pole*. The dictionary describes this as "a device for moving heavy objects." See **Fig 14-3**, which shows a drawing of the Rohn "Erection Fixture" EF2545. This gin pole was designed to work with the nominal 10-foot long sections of Rohn 25 or 45 towers.

I'm going to assume in the following discussion that you are installing Rohn 45, which weighs about 70 pounds. This is a lot of weight, and you must refrain from adding to that during installation. That means, for example, that you *do not* attempt to lift a 10-foot section with the guy wires attached! Neither should you attempt to lift the top section with the rotator and rotor shelf installed. The gin pole (and your ground crew) will not appreciate all that strain.

The main working part of the gin pole is the pulley mounted at the top of the 12-foot long heavy-wall aluminum tubing. This pulley has a rope going down to the ground crew through the center of the aluminum tube. At the base of the tower, the pull rope should be run through a *snatch block* attached to the tower just above ground level. This block allows the pull rope to be pulled out horizontally away from the tower base. That helps protect ground crew should a tool be dropped by the people on the tower.

An adjustable, sliding clamp towards the bottom of the aluminum tubing is clamped to the tower using a swinging L-bracket-type clamp with two clamping bolts. These have T-bar handles that can be tightened by hand. In fact, this gin pole can be moved and deployed without any tools. The clamp is positioned on the top of the tower section onto which the next tower section is to be installed. Once clamped to the top of the tower, you would loosen the T-bar handle that tightens the clamp against the sliding aluminum tube and slide the tubing up to its maximum extent.

In practice, the following steps are taken as each 10-foot section of tower is installed, one-by-one. I'm assuming here that the gin pole starts out on the ground, with at least one person belted in at the top of the tower. I'm also assuming that the pull rope has been threaded through the aluminum tube and the top pulley, with a knot tied to prevent it from falling back down the tube.

1. The clamp holding the aluminum tubing is loosened so that the pulley on the tube can be lowered to where it is just above the bottom clamp. Then the T-bar handle for the tube clamp is tightened.

2. The climber lowers a tag rope for the ground crew to tie to the gin-pole pull rope. (This tag rope has been looped through a temporary pulley clipped to the top of the tower. It is also used to pull up tools and other materials.) The ground crew then pulls the gin pole up to the climber, using the tag line rope. Friction of the rope against the top of the pulley-head assembly will prevent the gin-pole assembly from slipping down. [Note that some climbers prefer to "walk" the gin-pole up the tower rather than having it pulled up from the ground below. They free up their hands for climbing and for

temporarily holding the gin pole by using their belt lanyard looped around the tower as they climb.]

3. Once the gin-pole head reaches the top of the tower, the climber clamps the gin pole clamp securely to the top of the tower.

4. The T-bar handle for the tube clamp is loosened, and the aluminum tube is extended to its maximum height, as shown in Fig 14-3. Make sure you have tied the free end of the rope coming through the top pulley temporarily to the top of the tower, or else you'll have to lower the gin pole and go through this step again.

5. The free end of the pulley rope is then dropped to the ground, often using a weight such as a medium Crescent wrench or perhaps a hammer to keep the rope from waving about as it dangles down the tower, tangling with every imaginable thing as it proceeds downwards. It's amazing how even a tiny breeze can make an unweighted rope dance like that.

6. The ground crew then ties the free end of the rope *above* the balance point of the tower. For Rohn 25 or 45 there are eight horizontal cross

Fig 14-4—Climber is guiding the new section onto the top of the existing one. The gin pole attached to the left leg is bearing the weight, as the climber gives verbal instructions to the ground crew pulling on the gin-pole rope. (*Photo courtesy Mike Hammer, N2VR.*)

braces per section. You want the crew to tie the rope to the fifth horizontal brace from the bottom. Please remember that you want the bottoms of the tower sections' legs to be pointed downwards, not flipped over, when the bottom of these legs approach you at the top of the tower section the climber is standing on.

7. Once the bottom of the rising tower section is just above the top of the legs of the bottom tower section, the climber guides the tower down onto the top of the three legs, while calling out to the ground crew instructions about *slowly lowering* the new section down onto the legs. See **Fig 14-4**, which shows the climber guiding the new section of Rohn HBX tower onto the previous section's legs. This process is considerably easier to accomplish if each section of tower has been put together on the ground to make sure that the legs fit together easily. There's nothing more frustrating that trying to manually force-fit tower sections together at the top of a tower. It seems that freight companies don't always handle heavy tower sections very gently and legs easily get bent out of alignment. I number tower sections in the order they've been test-fitted together on the ground, marking them with a laundry marker pen. I also spray a small amount of WD-40 up inside mating tower legs after test-assembling them to help prevent galling and to ease fitting sections together. [Don't do this to excess—WD-40 is slippery and messy when it runs out of the bottom of tower legs.]

Another caution: Make sure before you start installing any tower that the correct ends of the bottom section's legs, "male" rather than "female," are pointed upwards. A good friend (who will go unnamed) had to have Rohn make and send him a special "gender-bender" flange to turn females into males, since he had installed the base upside-down in the concrete base. You don't want to do that.

8. Once the new tower section has been guided down onto the male ends, the six pinning bolts are inserted and tightened with nuts. Note that Rohn uses two different sized bolts, with the larger diameter

one on the bottom.

9. If this section of tower is one where guy wires are to be placed, they can be brought up using the gin pole rope and positioned on the tower. I also should point out that the maximum spacing for Rohn 25 is 30 feet between guy-wire sets, and 40 feet for Rohn 45. Thirty feet of unguyed Rohn 25 tower is wobbly, though safe. I prefer to come down off the tower when setting guy-wire tension, since I do not like to be on a wobbly tower when the ground crew is moving around yanking on guy wires. I also greatly prefer working on Rohn 45 tower, which is substantially more secure feeling and easier to stand on, with its legs 18 inches apart, while Rohn 25 legs are only 12 inches apart.

10. Finally, you reposition the gin pole for the next section of tower. The T-bar at the clamp is loosened, the tube is dropped down to the level of the clamp, and the climber walks the gin pole up to the top of the section just installed and clamps it there, ready to pull up the next tower section.

One other thing to remember about tower work: The climber is the boss. The climber is the only one who can see everything going on at the top of the tower and below on the ground. Work out in advance voice commands from the climber to the ground crew below.

Inclement Weather

Another caution about tower climbing: If it is raining (or even worse, if it is snowing), your tower will be slippery. I do not like to climb when a tower is slippery, although I've had to do it on occasion when something breaks during a contest. Still, my usual caution is multiplied by at least a factor of two when it rains!

The Rotator

Rotators are without a doubt the weakest link in any installation of a rotary beam antenna. Rotators are mechanical devices that move, and unfortunately this means that they also *break*. In planning your tower/antenna installation you should make provisions for repairing the rotator. Specifically,

this usually means mounting a separate bearing plate above the rotator so that the full weight of the rotating mast and the beam(s) is supported by this bearing plate. That way, you can remove the rotator when (not if) it breaks and lower it down the tower for repair.

If you can't replace or fix the rotator immediately, you will have to devise some means to prevent the mast/beam from turning in the wind, since this will wrap and unwrap the feed coax around the mast until said coax is sheared off. I used to use a set of L-bracket clamps that could be bolted to the tower legs, with muffler clamp U-bolts to hold the mast from rotating. However, this was always clumsy since with a triangular tower nothing really lined up correctly, and I definitely preferred to replace the rotator with another one while I repaired the first one.

And don't forget to provide a loop of coax to allow your beam to rotate properly. See **Fig 14-5**, which shows a rotator loop taped to the rotating mast and the tower for an elliptically polarized UHF Yagi array. Make sure you position the rotator loop so that it doesn't snag on anything.

Fig 14-6 illustrates a different technique for making a rotator loop, where the loop is wound several times as it as-

cends the rotating mast. It can thus wrap and unwrap as the rotator turns.

The Mast

Remember how proud you were when you finished installing your tower and beam? How pleased you were with how your antenna boom was perfectly horizontal! Then one night your heart sinks as you come home in a blinding wind and rainstorm to find your beam pointing upwards (or downwards) at a crazy angle of 45°. Welcome to the sad world of people who have bent their masts. You now have an expensive and potentially quite dangerous job of replacing the bent mast and most likely your bent and broken beam antenna.

Perhaps the most penny-wise, pound-foolish thing (aside from not wearing a safety belt when climbing) you can do in a tower/beam installation is to put the beam too high on the rotating mast above the top of the tower. You might also come to the same sad result by cutting costs using inadequate material for the mast.

The problem comes down to a simple mechanical engineering concept called *bending moment*, defined as "the tendency to cause rotation about a point or an axis." Let me give you the bottom line here: *You really don't want to bend*

Fig 14-5—Rotator loop for an elliptically polarized UHF Yagi array. The feed coax is bundled with a control cable for the polarization relay.

Fig 14-6—Another technique for making a rotator loop. The feed coax is wrapped several times as it ascends the rotating mast. It wraps and unwraps as the rotator is turned.

your mast. To prevent bending the mast you have a number of good engineering choices:

- Use a stronger mast with a heavier wall thickness.
- Use a bigger mast with a larger diameter.
- Use a stronger mast made of stronger material.
- Use a smaller beam or mount your beam closer to the top of the tower.
- All of the above.

I have seen hams try to use thin-wall fence-pole tubing or inexpensive water pipe for rotating masts. Sometimes they get away with this, but often they don't. See Chapter 22 in the 19th Edition of *The ARRL Antenna Book* for detailed information about masts.

Talk to members of your local ham club and listen to their horror stories about bent masts. Better yet, hire a mechanical engineer to evaluate your overall system. But don't try to cut corners or costs by trying to get by with a cheap mast.

Putting the Beam on the Tower

In general, I am a fan of building a beam antenna on the tower. At one time, when I had a fair amount of practice doing it, I could put together a HyGain TH7DX tribander on a tower in less than 30 minutes. But many people prefer to build their antennas on the ground and then move them to the top of their towers for installation.

For really large antennas (like full-sized 40-meter Yagis, for example), the first-class way to go is to hire a crane. Some hams even have used helicopters to put their monster Yagis on the top of tall towers, but I suspect that this may be just a little beyond the scope of most readers of this book about simple ham antennas.

Again, I strongly suggest you look long and carefully at the procedures shown in the 19th Edition of *The ARRL Antenna Book*.

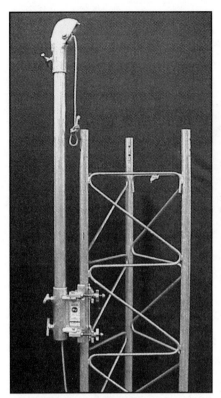

Fig 14-7—A photograph of the WBØW gin pole, shown mounted on a short section of Rohn 45 tower. (*Photo courtesy WBØW.*)

Lightning Protection

Your installation should be protected from lightning, even if you live in an area where lightning occurs only rarely, such as Northern California. Nonetheless, we have one or sometimes two lightning storms each year.

Ground each tower leg. Install so-called lightning arrestors in the coax and install protection for the wires in your rotator control cable too. Having bolts of lightning leaping around in your ham shack is not a pleasant experience. Nor is it an inexpensive experience either, what with all the damage resulting in your electronics and in your house due to the resulting fire. See Chapter 3 for details on how K8CH built his cable entrance panel.

Fig 14-8—An innovative way to decorate a tower! Morning glories can grow to astounding heights, it turns out. (*Photo courtesy K4BXU.*)

Weatherproofing

Both Chuck and I have discussed weatherproofing several times in preceding chapters. I buy and use dozens of rolls of electrical tape in my antenna projects. Tape is cheap! Remember that the final wrap of tape on a coax should be going upwards, like the overlapping shingles on a roof, in order to shed water.

15 HF Beam Antennas

In Chapter 2 I said, "If you measure antenna performance on a dB per dollar scale, the dipole comes out a big winner." I also said, "I like to think of my dipoles as one-element Yagis."

In this chapter you'll find mostly 2-element Yagi beams. In other words, this is the next step up in performance. And it really is a *big* step!

You'll find a number of rugged designs in this chapter and you also will find lightweight, light-duty designs suitable for portable operation. Some of the antennas are built of aluminum tubing, while others are made using copper wire. I hope you find something that will meet your needs.

A Rugged, Easy-to-Build, 2-Element, 17-Meter Yagi

The title states the major considerations that went into the design of this Yagi antenna. Let me explain further. I live on a small hill that is mostly surrounded by open fields, and that means that the wind blows unimpeded on my antennas. For that reason, I want an antenna that can handle at least 90 mph winds. A rating of 80 mph might be good enough, but I've seen wind gusts close to that speed within the last year. As you can see, for me *rugged* is a necessity.

From the beginning, my plan has been to share this design with you so that you could build one too. I know that some of you have limited resources available, and that others have no desire to be a machinist. For that reason, this antenna requires no special tools or assemblies.

The Parts

Perhaps the most obvious component of a Yagi is aluminum tubing. I've based the elements and boom on 6-foot lengths of aluminum tubing, which are available from Texas Towers and can be shipped via UPS. (They also sell 12-foot lengths, but those have to be shipped by freight.) Elements are made from 6063-

T832 drawn aluminum tubing with a 0.058-inch wall thickness. These tubes telescope inside one another very nicely. For the boom, I chose 2-inch OD 6061-T6 extruded aluminum tubing with a 0.120-inch wall thickness.

I used Penetrox to lightly coat the element tube ends where they telescoped inside other tubes. (You may substitute Noalox or Contax.) This prevents oxidation of the aluminum, and small metallic particles help to maintain electrical conductivity through the joints. It also has the excellent side effect of making it much easier to disassemble the elements, should that ever become necessary.

Stainless steel U-bolts connect elements, boom and mast to each other. DX Engineering (**http://www.dxengineering.com/**) sells complete saddle clamps with all necessary hardware included. The saddles provide a solid grip on the parts being joined. DX Engineering also sells pre-drilled plates for mounting elements to boom and boom to mast.

The center insulator for the driven element is a length of 0.75-inch fiberglass rod. This is available in 8-foot lengths from Max-Gain Systems

(**http://www.mgs4u.com/**).

Driven-element insulators are made from short lengths of 1-inch PVC conduit. This is available from Home Depot and other building supply dealers and is marked as "sunlight resistant."

I used 49 aluminum pop rivets to assemble the elements. The feed-point connections are made with #8 hardware. You'll find a list of the major parts in **Table 15-1**.

Element Design

The elements are spaced 5 feet and 8 inches from each other. That's about as much as you can get on a 6-foot boom, and it's adequate.

For a short Yagi like this one, element strength is the key factor in determining the antenna's ability to handle winds. I thought about using an un-reinforced element such as the one shown in **Fig 15-1**. Would it be strong enough? I calculated the strength using equations from the ARRL book, *Physical Design of Yagi Antennas* by Dave Leeson, W6NL (formerly W6QHS). The results were not encouraging, as the element is only good for 78-mph winds—and with a quarter-inch of ice that drops to 61 MPH.

Table 15-1
Major Parts for the 2-Element 17-Meter Yagi

Qty	Item
2	1-inch OD 6063-T832 Drawn Aluminum Tubing 0.058-inch wall, 6-foot length
3	0.875-inch OD 6063-T832 Drawn Aluminum Tubing 0.058-inch wall, 6-foot length
4	0.75-inch OD 6063-T832 Drawn Aluminum Tubing 0.058-inch wall, 6-foot length
4	0.625-inch OD 6063-T832 Drawn Aluminum Tubing 0.058-inch wall, 6-foot length
4	0.5-inch OD 6063-T832 Drawn Aluminum Tubing 0.058-inch wall, 6-foot length
1	2.0-inch OD 6061-T6 Extruded Aluminum Tubing 0.12-inch wall, 6-foot length
1	2 8 × 3.5 × 0.19-inch element-to-boom plate (6061-T651 aluminum—DX Engineering ETB190)
1	8 × 10 × 0.25-inch boom-to-mast plate (6061-T6 aluminum—DX Engineering BTM810)
8	2-inch saddle clamp (DX Engineering SAD200)
2	1.25-inch saddle clamp (DX Engineering SAD125)
1	1-inch saddle clamp (DX Engineering SAD100)
2	3-inch lengths of 1-inch PVC conduit
49	$1/8$-inch aluminum pop rivets

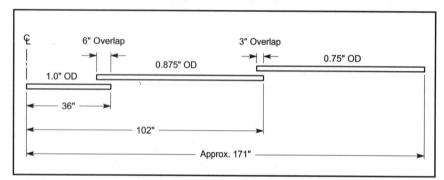

Fig 15-1—An un-reinforced element for 17 meters. Half of the element is shown in the drawing. The other side is a mirror reflection of this half.

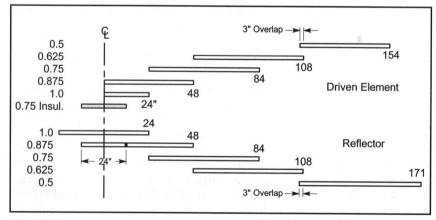

Fig 15-2—Dimensions for the reinforced elements of the 17-meter Yagi. See text for additional details.

What if I used larger, hence stronger tubing? The math reveals that the increased wind load of the larger tubes more than offsets the increased strength. What about smaller, less wind resistant tubes? Turns out that the strength decrease is greater than the wind resistance change. In other words, Fig 15-1 shows a very-close-to-optimum un-reinforced 17-meter Yagi element using 0.058 wall thickness tubing. It all meant that I needed to reinforce the elements.

In consultation with Dean Straw, N6BV, we came up with the element design and dimensions shown in **Fig 15-2**. These elements will handle 112-mph winds—and even with a quarter-inch of ice they will still handle 81 mph. Luckily, high winds and ice loads rarely happen simultaneously, so this design should be adequate for my needs.

Construction

Start by cutting the elements as shown in Fig 15-2. When you begin element assembly, use fine sandpaper to clean that portion of each element section that will telescope inside another (next larger size) section.

After sanding, apply a thin coat of Penetrox (or equivalent) to those same portions. Push the sections together, twist and move back and forth a little bit. This will lightly coat the inside of the large section.

Use three $1/8$-inch pop rivets at each tubing joint as shown in **Fig 15-3**. In that 24-inch length of 0.875-inch OD tubing at the center of the reflector, use a single rivet to hold the piece in place at the middle of the larger (1.0-inch) center piece.

At the center of the driven element, leave a $3/4$-inch gap between elements. Wrap a couple of turns of electrical tape around the fiberglass insulator at the center. This will protect it from solar (UV) radiation damage. For feed-line connections, drill the driven element halves and insulator $1^1/16$ inch each side of the center (holes $2^1/8$ inch apart). These holes should be $5/32$ inch diameter for #8 hardware.

Cut two 3-inch lengths of 1-inch PVC conduit. (These will be used to insulate the driven element.) Be sure to use sunlight resistant PVC—if it is, it is marked on the conduit. With a hacksaw, cut a slot down the length of each

Fig 15-3—Example of a riveted element joint. See text.

PVC insulator. Make a second cut parallel to and $3/16$ inch from the first cut. This will allow the insulator to firmly close against the driven element.

Fig 15-4 shows the reflector and its plate mounted to the boom. Use 1-inch U-bolts and saddles to fasten the reflector to the mounting plate. Be sure to put some oil on the U-bolts *before* you install the nuts. Stainless steel is prone to seize up if you don't apply some lubricant to the threads *every time* you move the nuts. Trust me on this, there is nothing more frustrating than to have the nut freeze on a U-bolt as you are installing your Yagi at the top of your tower.

Fasten the plate to the boom with 2-inch U-bolts and saddles. Don't forget to lubricate the threads.

The driven element mounting scheme is shown in **Fig 15-5**. You'll need 1.25-inch U-bolts and saddles to fasten the driven element and its insulators to the mounting plate. Add the boom-to-mast plate and its four 2-inch

U-bolts and saddles and the basic beam is finished as you can see in **Fig 15-6**.

Feeding and Matching Your Yagi

For a 50-Ω feed-point impedance, you'll need 0.50 μH of inductance across the feed point. An easy way to do that is to use a *hairpin match*, called that because it does look like a hairpin. The hairpin also allows you to ground the center of the element. Dimensions are given in **Fig 15-7**. You can use #12 solid copper wire to make the hairpin. A lug mounted at the hairpin center is used for making a connection to the boom, to provide some measure of lightning protection. This connection can be made with a sheet-metal screw. Because you will be joining dissimilar metals, be sure to clean the contact areas and apply a thin coat of Penetrox. In **Fig 15-8** you can see how the hairpin and

Fig 15-6—The assembled Yagi only lacks a feed line to be ready for installation.

the feed line attach to the driven element. I used six ferrite beads to make a choke balun. These are available from Palomar Engineers as their BA-8 kit (**http://www.palomar-engineers.com/ Balun_Kits/balun_kits.html**). Alternatively, you can wind 8 feet of the feed line into 7 turns to make your choke

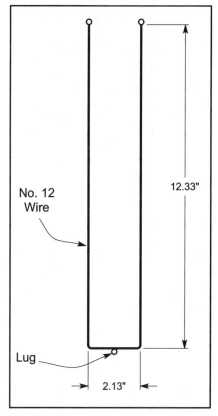

No. 12 Wire

12.33"

Lug

2.13"

Fig 15-7—Dimensions for the hairpin matching network.

Fig 15-4—The reflector is mounted to the boom by means of a flat aluminum mounting plate and four stainless-steel U-bolts with pillow blocks.

Fig 15-5—Driven element mounting detail. PVC insulators are needed to keep from shorting the element to the boom.

Fig 15-8—Feed-point detail with feed line attached. The choke balun wrapped with electrical tape consists of six ferrite beads over the RG-213 coax.

Fig 15-9—The installed 17-meter beam. After initial testing, the 75-meter dipole (mounted at the top of the mast in this photo) was moved below the beam, and the lower dipole was removed.

balun. Use electrical tape to hold it in place. The chapter on coax feed lines presents techniques for preparing the coax for connecting to an antenna.

Installation

With help from my wife Sylvia, K8SYL, I installed the Yagi at the top of my 30-foot tower, which is bracketed to the garage. (See **Fig 15-9**.) The center of K8SYL's 75-meter dipole was mounted at the top of the mast above the beam on the tower. My 40, 20 and 15-meter dipole (described in Chapter 2) was a couple of feet below the Yagi.

I ran the feed line to my radio to check out the beam. As I tuned the band, I found a DX station. To my joy Yassar, TA3D, came back to my first call, and we exchanged 59 signal reports. To my disappointment, however, the SWR was nearly 3:1. Further, my transceiver was putting out less than 50 W. The internal antenna tuner could handle that, but the SWR should be very close to 1:1. I had to determine the reason and correct the problem.

I lowered the Yagi and sat it a few feet above the ground pointing straight up. In that position, the SWR looked good. You've probably already guessed what was wrong when the beam was on the tower. If you thought it was interaction with those dipoles, you're right.

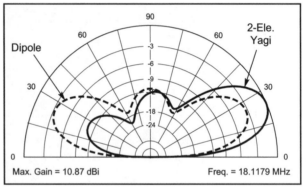

Max. Gain = 10.87 dBi   Freq. = 18.1179 MHz

Fig 15-10—Computed elevation pattern of the 2-element 17-meter beam (solid line) at 30 feet compared to a dipole (dashed line) at the same height.

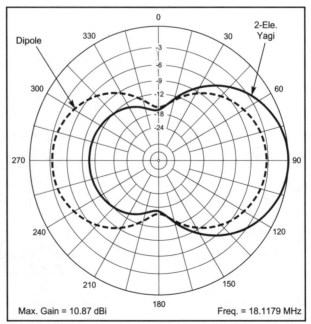

Max. Gain = 10.87 dBi   Freq. = 18.1179 MHz

Fig 15-11—Computed azimuth pattern at 25° elevation of the 2-element 17-meter beam (solid line) at 30 feet compared to a dipole (dashed line) at the same height.

I took down the 40, 20 and 15-meter dipole and lowered K8SYL's 75-m dipole to a position about 3 feet below the Yagi. Voila! The SWR was now less than 1.2:1 anywhere in the band.

Results

Even at 30 feet high, this Yagi is an excellent performer. You can see in **Fig 15-10** and **Fig 15-11** how this Yagi compares to a dipole. I've made QSOs with many DX and domestic stations. This antenna has brought me a lot of fun.

SHORT-BOOM 2-ELEMENT HF YAGIS

Perhaps you'd prefer a less rugged version of the 17-meter beam, or maybe you'd like to have a Yagi for another band.

If so, the following should be of interest. Dean Straw, N6BV, and I have designed this family of small 2-element beams for you. Make the elements from 6063-T832 drawn aluminum tubing with 0.058-inch wall thickness. You'll notice that these beams use nothing longer than 6-foot lengths of aluminum tubing. That's because those lengths will ship via UPS with no special handling required. Make an exception for 20 meters, where you'll want to have an 8-foot boom. (Good news is that the good folks at Texas Towers tell me that they can ship up to 9-foot long packages by UPS. Also, they will cut a 12-foot length into unequal lengths for you. Shipping will cost you a bit more, however.) On the subject of booms, I like to use 2-inch OD 6061-T6 aluminum tube

with a 0.12-inch wall. It's very strong—no doubt stronger than I need.

Here are a couple of guidelines for assembling the beam elements. When joining two pieces of tubing, use 3 inches of overlap. When doubling the thickness of a section, extend the inner piece of tubing about an inch beyond the next joint toward the element center.

Since only one half of each element is shown, the first section nearest the boom will actually be made up of a continuous length of tubing for the reflector. For example, the first section of the 10-meter version is made of 0.625-inch diameter tubing that is 72 inches long, our standard 6-foot length, centered at the boom.

We've calculated hairpin-matching networks for each of the beams. I prefer to use a hairpin match because it's easy to ground the center of the hairpin to the boom using a solder lug. However, if you prefer to use a coil at the center you may center tap the matching coil and ground the tap to the boom. In case you want to use a coil, we've calculated approximate coil dimensions for #12 wire. You should squeeze the turns together or pull them apart a bit to tune the antenna for best SWR.

10-Meters

You'll find the half-element design for the 10-meter Yagi in **Fig 15-12**. This element will withstand winds of 96 mph. With a 1/4-inch of ice on the element it will withstand winds of 68 mph. The reflector for this beam breaks the guideline of 3 inches overlap, with only a 2-inch overlap. Nevertheless, this should work just fine.

Use an element spacing of 66 inches. The matching network is a hairpin formed of #6 wire and is 2.5 inches wide and 23 inches long. Alternatively, you could use a coil with 0.84 µH inductance. Make the coil with 4 turns, 2.5-inch diameter and 1.875 inches long.

12-Meters

You'll find the half-element design for the 12-meter Yagi in **Fig 15-13**. This element will withstand winds of 100 mph. With a 1/4-inch of ice on the element it will withstand winds of 73 mph.

Use an element spacing of 68 inches. The matching network is a hairpin formed of #6 wire and is 2.5 inches wide and

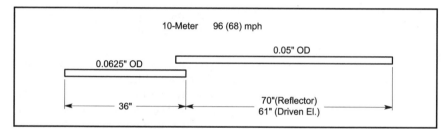

Fig 15-12—Half-element design and dimensions for the two-element 10-meter Yagi. The wind-survival rating is 96 mph (68 mph with 1/4-inch of ice). Dimensions are given in inches.

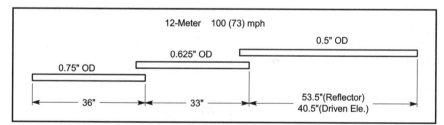

Fig 15-13—Half-element design and dimensions for the two-element 12-meter Yagi. The wind-survival rating is 100 mph (73 mph with 1/4-inch of ice). Dimensions are given in inches.

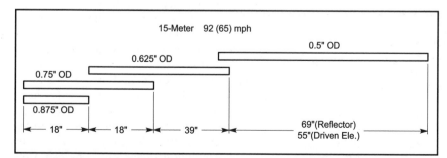

Fig 15-14—Half-element design and dimensions for the two-element 15-meter Yagi. The wind-survival rating is 92 mph (65 mph with 1/4-inch of ice). Dimensions are given in inches.

16.57 inches long. Alternatively, you could use a coil with 0.59 μH inductance. Make the coil with 4 turns, 2-inch diameter and 1.8 inches long.

15-Meters

You'll find the half-element design for the 15-meter Yagi in **Fig 15-14**. This element will withstand winds of 92 mph. With a ¼-inch of ice on the element it will withstand winds of 65 mph.

Use an element spacing of 68 inches. The matching network is a hairpin formed of #6 wire and is 2.5 inches wide and 13.83 inches long. Alternatively, you could use a coil with 0.49 μH inductance. Make the coil with

4 turns, 1.875-inch diameter and 2 inches long.

17-Meters

You'll find the half-element design for the 17-meter Yagi in **Fig 15-15**. This

Table 15-3
Coil Dimensions of 2-Element Wire Yagi Matching Inductances

Inductance (μH)	Diameter (Inches)	Length (Inches)	Turns
0.54	2	2.05	4
0.57	2	1.875	4
0.73	2	2.3	4

element will withstand winds of 89 mph. With a ¼-inch of ice on the element it will withstand winds of 64 mph. This element is very close—arguably close enough—to my 90-mph goal.

Use an element spacing of 68 inches. The matching network is a hairpin formed of #6 wire and is 2.5 inches wide and 12.625 inches long. Alternatively, you could use a coil with 0.44 μH inductance. Make the coil with 4 turns, 1.75-inch diameter and 2 inches long.

20-Meters

You'll find the half-element design for the 20-meter Yagi in **Fig 15-16**. This element will withstand winds of 83 mph. With a ¼-inch of ice on the element it will withstand winds of 60 mph.

You could use an element spacing of 68 inches. The matching network is a hairpin formed of #6 wire and is 2.5 inches wide and 11.2 inches long. While compact, this antenna will only cover the upper (phone portion) of the band. The SWR at 14.0 MHz is over 4:1. For that I reason I do not recommend that you use this boom length on 20 meters.

If you use an element spacing of 92 inches (an 8-foot boom), you'll be able to cover the entire band with an SWR of less than 2:1. You'll need to shorten the driven element tip to 50.5 inches (instead of 51), and the hairpin needs to be 2.5 inches wide and 16.53 inches long. Alternatively, you could use a coil with 0.57 μH inductance. Make the coil with 4 turns, 2-inch diameter and 1.875 inches long.

Wire Yagis

Of course, you don't need to use aluminum tubing to build a Yagi. Wire will also work. Oh yes, you'll have to provide supports, but some of you may want to try a wire Yagi.

Dean Straw, N6BV, designed a series of wire Yagis just for you. These were meant to use straight elements—*not* inverted V elements. The dimensions in **Table 15-2** are based on #14 wire. The values in the table are half-element values—in other words, from the center to the element tip. For tip-to-tip (overall) lengths, you'll have to multiply the table values by two. Coil dimensions for matching inductances are given in **Table 15-3**.

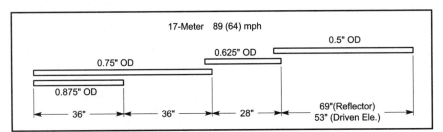

Fig 15-15—Half-element design and dimensions for the two-element 17-meter Yagi. The wind-survival rating is 89 mph (64 mph with ¼-inch of ice). Dimensions are given in inches.

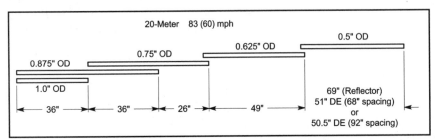

Fig 15-16—Half-element design and dimensions for the two-element 20-meter Yagi. The wind-survival rating is 83 mph (60 mph with ¼-inch of ice). Dimensions are given in inches.

Table 15-2
Half-Element Dimensions for 2-Element Wire Yagis

Band (Meters)	Reflector (Inches)	Driven Element (Inches)	Spacing (Inches)	Matching Inductance (μH)
10	105.0	98.75	66	Not Needed
12	118.25	111.0	70	0.54
15	140.4	151.5	68	0.57
17	164.6	154.5	69	0.54
20	210	199	92	0.73
40	420	400	234	Not Needed

Note: The reflector and driven-element dimensions are from the center to a tip. These dimensions will have to be doubled to determine tip-to-tip dimensions.

Basic Beams for 12 and 17 Meters

L. B. Cebik, W4RNL, is well known as an antenna guru and educator. He is also an ARRL Technical Advisor in the area of antennas and antenna modeling. I can attest that his theory is sound and his designs are solid. This article appeared in August 2000 *QST*. Even if you choose to build one of the earlier Yagi designs in this chapter, you ought to read Cebik's discussion and examine his construction techniques for good ideas.

Small directional beams are a popular choice for 12 and 17 meters. There, the lower signal density requires less gain and front-to-back ratio (F/B) than we need on other HF bands for successful operation. Although we can scale and adapt beams for 15 and 10 meters and press them into duty for 12 and 17 meters, we might save a bit of tower space and trouble by looking at alternative designs suited to these narrow bands.

The Driver-Director Alternative

The most common form of two-element Yagi used on 20 through 10 meters is the driver-reflector type. The antenna offers modest gain and F/B with an easily matched feed-point impedance. In a fairly straightforward way, we can design driver-reflector Yagis to cover the entire span of 20 and 15 meters and at least the first megahertz of 10 meters.

An alternative and much neglected two-element Yagi design uses a driver and a single director. On 20, 15 and 10 meters, this beam type is used only by those who wish to operate solely in either the CW (or data) or the SSB portions of the band. Driver-director Yagis are inherently narrow-band arrays that sustain their characteristics for a bandwidth that is less than 1% of the design frequency.

However, driver-director arrays have some advantages. **Fig 15-17** shows one of them: a shorter boom length. As we reduce the element spacing, the gain of driver-director Yagis increases (up to a limit). The feed-point impedance also decreases with closer spacing. A practical spacing limit is between 0.07 and 0.08λ, leaving us with a feed-point

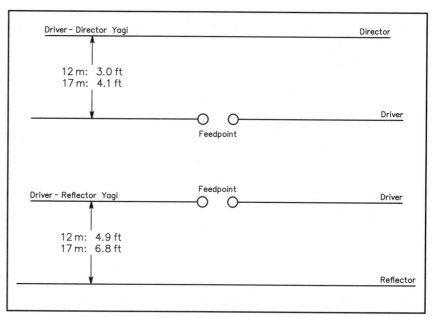

Fig 15-17—A comparison of driver-reflector and driver-director types of two-element Yagi arrays.

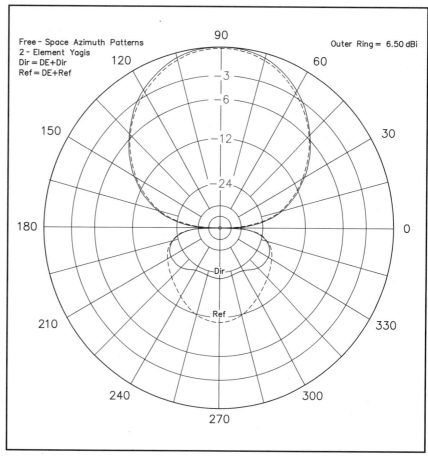

Fig 15-18—Overlaid free-space azimuth patterns of 17-meter two-element driver-director (solid line) and driver-reflector (dashed line) arrays.

impedance in the 20 to 25-Ω range. This impedance range minimizes power losses due to natural assembly resistances and lets us use standard matching networks, such as the gamma or beta. In contrast, a driver-reflector Yagi requires an element spacing between 0.125 and 0.15λ to optimize most parameters. In short, a driver-reflector Yagi will be 1.5 to 2 times longer than a comparable driver-director design.

The driver-director design offers a second benefit over the driver-reflector Yagi: increased F/B. **Fig 15-18** overlays free-space azimuth patterns for the two designs for 17 meters. With respect to gain, there is little difference between the designs, with the driver-director array having a slight, but not operationally significant, advantage. In the F/B department, however, the driver-director array shows nearly a 10-dB improvement.

The so-called "WARC" bands (30,

17, and 12 meters) are very narrow, with 17 and 12 being 100 kHz wide (18.068 to 18.168 MHz and 24.89 to 24.99 MHz, respectively). These bandwidths fall well within the operating bandwidth limits of driver-director Yagis. Driver-director Yagis may be very well suited for these bands, with performance improvements over other designs and savings in boom length and wind loading.

Monoband Beams for 12 and 17 Meters

I designed a pair of driver-director Yagis for 12 and 17 meters using antenna-modeling software, in this case, *NEC-4.1*, *MININEC* and *NEC-2* would have been equally satisfactory. My procedure involved two steps: creating a basic design with a uniform-diameter model and then adjusting the dimensions for the use of an "element-taper schedule." An element-taper schedule specifies in decreasing sizes the tubing

diameter used for each element from the center to the tip. At HF, uniform-diameter elements add unnecessary weight to the antenna. Moreover, available nesting aluminum tubing sizes (I recommend 6063-T832) make construction convenient.

Table 15-4 presents the dimensions of the basic uniform-diameter models, using 0.5-inch-diameter elements. The dimensions for each antenna are set so that the driver shows a reactance of about – j 25 Ω. This reactance facilitates the use of a beta match hairpin, which is actually a shorted section of transmission line and provides an inductive reactance across the feed-point connections. The table lists alternative lengths according to the impedance of the parallel line fabricated for the beta line.

The anticipated performance as predicted by the NEC models appears in **Table 15-5**. We can expect a free-space gain of about 6.5 dBi, with a F/B

Table 15-4
Basic (Uniform-Diameter) Element Dimensions for 17 and 12-Meter Driver-Director Yagis

All dimensions are in inches.

17 Meters: 0.5-Inch-Diameter Elements

Driver Length	314.4
Director Length	304.6
Element Spacing	49.6

Beta (Shorted Transmission Line) Length

Impedance	Length
600 Ω	6.6
450 Ω	8.8

12 Meters: 0.5-Inch-Diameter Elements

Driver Length	228.0
Director Length	221.3
Element Spacing	36

Beta (Shorted Transmission Line) Length

Impedance	Length
600 Ω	4.8
450 Ω	6.4

Table 15-5
Anticipated Performance Parameters: 17- and 12-Meter Driver-Director Yagis

Frequency (MHz)	Free-Space Gain (dBi)	F/B (dB)	Pre-Match Feed-Point Impedance (R ± j X Ohms)	Post-Match Feed-Point Impedance (R ± j X Ohms)
17 Meters				
18.068	6.3	20.6	21 – j 30	60 + j 16
18.118	6.5	21.9	20 – j 27	55 + j 6
18.168	6.7	20.8	18 – j 23	46 – j 3
12 Meters				
24.89	6.5	21.7	19 – j 29	62 + j 10
24.94	6.6	21.6	18 – j 26	56 + j 2
24.99	6.7	20.2	17 – j 24	49 – j 4

Note: When remodeling for an element taper schedule, adjust element lengths to achieve these performance figures.

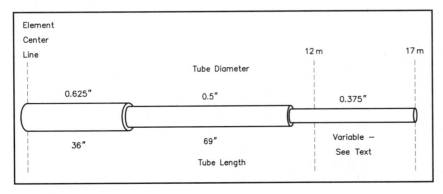

Fig 15-19—The element diameter-tapering schedule used in all of the antennas described in this article. Note that only a half-element is shown, with the other half being a mirror image of the portion displayed. The tip length will vary from element to element, with 12-meter tips being very short and 17-meter tips being quite long.

Table 15-6
Adjusted Stepped-Diameter Element Dimensions for 17 and 12-Meter Driver-Director Yagis

All measurements are in inches.

17 Meters

Driver Length	321.4	Tip Length	55.7
Director Length	311.4	Tip Length	50.7
Element Spacing	49.6		
Beta (shorted transmission) line length (1-inch-spaced #12 AWG wire)	10.3		

12 Meters

Driver Length	231.6	Tip Length	10.8
Director Length	224.6	Tip Length	7.3
Element Spacing	36		
Beta (shorted transmission) line length (1-inch-spaced #12 AWG wire)	7.3		

See the text and Fig 15-19 for the element-tapering schedule used for this example. Final dimensions may vary with changes in the element-tapering schedule.

ratio of over 20 dB. I have listed the anticipated pre-matched and post-matched feed-point impedances for both antennas. In the NEC models, the beta match consists of a shorted transmission line placed in parallel with the feed point.

One error often made by beginning antenna builders is to simply copy model dimensions using whatever materials may be available. This route often leads to mediocre beam performance. Before we translate the model into a physical antenna, we must adjust the dimensions for the element-taper schedule.

Fig 15-19 shows the taper schedule used in the test antennas. The centermost section uses 36 inches of ⁵⁄₈-inch-diameter tubing, starting from the element centerline. The next tubing section is a 6-foot length of ¹⁄₂-inch-diameter material, with 69 inches showing. The overlap is about 3 inches: much more overlap adds unnecessary weight, while much less weakens the junction. The element tip sections are made from ³⁄₈-inch-diameter tubing. The 12-meter tips are quite short, while the 17-meter tips are quite long.

The element lengths and tip sections are listed in **Table 15-6**. The taper schedule used here is for test purposes only. Although the final elements appear to be strong, many builders prefer to use a more aggressive taper schedule for additional strength. That is to say, they use more different tubing sizes, beginning with a larger

diameter. This technique results in shorter lengths of each tubing size, a practice that can yield stronger elements. Part of my reason for using longer lengths of fewer tubing size stems from a desire to reuse the tubing in other test antennas.

If we keep the same spacing as we used with the uniform-diameter model, the element lengths for the tapered elements will be longer to achieve the same performance and feed-point impedance. On 12 meters, the elements will be four to six inches longer than on the uniform-diameter model. On 17 meters, the elements will be over six inches longer on the tapered-element model.

If we choose a more aggressive tapering schedule, we may expect the elements to be even longer relative to the uniform diameter model. This holds true even if we begin with larger-diameter tubing. The required extra length to make a tapered-diameter element electrically equivalent to a uniform-diameter element is not simply a function of the average diameter. Instead, it is a complex function involving the tubing diameters and the rate of decrease along the element length. In general, for any beam you wish to reproduce using a variant-tapering schedule for the elements, it pays to remodel the antenna using the materials planned for the physical version. Modeling software, whether devoted strictly to Yagis or more generally applicable (such as NEC), provides the best known guidance for Yagi construction. In many cases, I have built

Fig 15-20—A close-up view of the polycarbonate boom-to-element plate, saddle U-bolts, fiberglass stiffening rod, and driver connection points of the beams in this article. The construction of parasitic elements is similar, but the element is continuous across the plate.

Fig 15-21—The 12-meter driver-director beam during initial construction, using a stand and short mast to raise the elements to a good working height.

Yagis directly from careful models and have had to make either no adjustments or only the most minimal adjustments.

In the case of the 12 and 17-meter band driver-director Yagis, the only required adjustment made was to the beta-match shorted line. My test line consisted of #12 AWG copper wire spaced as close as possible to one inch. The match-line spacing was dictated by the spacing of the stainless-steel bolts on the driver used for both the beta and the female coax connection. Because the characteristic impedance of a one-inch-spaced #12 line is close to 385 Ω, the line length increased slightly from the NEC model: to a little over 10 inches on 17 meters and to a little over 7 inches for 12 meters.

My test models used poly-carbonate (Lexan) plates to mount the elements to the boom. **Fig 15-20** is a close-up of the driver boom-to-element plate, with the coax connector and its connections before adding the beta match. There is no allowance in the models for "plumber's delight" construction in which the elements make electrical contact with the boom. For short-boom antennas, I often use either PVC or aluminum tubing as the boom and have found no difference for these antennas when using insulated elements. **Fig 15-21** shows the 12-meter version of the antenna during initial construction, using a four-legged support stand to bring all of the antenna components to a good working level.

Field adjustment of the antennas is a two-step procedure. After verifying that the element structures and spacing correspond to the model, use one of the available SWR analyzers to read both the feed-point resistance and reactance without the beta match line. The readings should correspond closely to the model reports. If not, then adjust the elements until they do. This should involve no more than a small change of the driver tip lengths. A driver-director Yagi is just a bit more finicky than a driver-reflector beam in driver length adjustment, but mounting the antenna on a long mast and propping it on a step-ladder can ease the task. Position the antenna to point upward as straight as possible and get it as high off the ground as you can while still being able to reach the driver for adjustment. Al-

though the result may not hold precisely when the antenna is at its operating height, the setting will generally be close enough to permit final adjustment only to the beta-section length or width, since widening the beta match is equivalent to increasing its length.

Now, at near-ground level, add the beta match and adjust its size for a nearly perfect 50-Ω match at the center of the band. Secure the connections. At the antenna's operational height, you should be able to refine the adjustment with nothing more complex than a little widening or narrowing of the line.

I have omitted other building details, since there are so many preferred variations. My element-to-plate U-bolts are stainless steel and use saddles, as do the plate-to-boom U-bolts. The driver has an 18-inch-long insert of $1/2$-inch-diameter fiberglass rod that aligns the split element sections and prevents tube crushing from either the U-bolts or the connection bolts. I use a $1/4$-inch-thick aluminum plate for the boom-to-mast mounting, with U-bolts sized for the mast and the boom. Tubing sections can be locked together with stainless steel hose clamps, aircraft-grade pop rivets, or sheet-metal screws. Deburr drilled holes to ensure that you can separate the element sections later in the life of the beam. In addition, a thin coating of a conductive

antioxidant at each tubing junction is advisable.

Two Beams in One

The individual two-element Yagis for 12 and 17 meters can be stacked on a single mast and fed individually. However, the two antennas tend to interact, even with a separation of up to 12 feet. The 17-meter Yagi will show a small increase in gain, but a larger (5-dB) decrease in F/B at some separations. The 12-meter beam shows a reduction in gain with an increase in the feed-point impedance (with the beta line installed). A separation of about 8 feet appears to be as close to optimal as you might get.

Even though the individual antennas are lightweight, many builders prefer to have their beams lined up in one plane. Therefore, finding a way to combine two beams in a single dual-band array appears desirable. At the same time, if we can reduce the number of feed lines to one, we will have simplified everything possible.

One of the simplest techniques for feeding two beams with a single line is to use open-sleeve coupling, a technique developed and patented by Tom Schiller, N6BT. In effect, we connect the feed line to the lower-frequency driver. On the lower band, the driver acts normally as part of its array of elements. On the

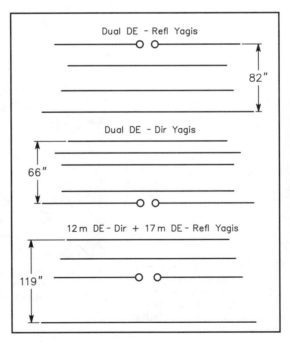

Fig 15-22—Outline drawings of some possibilities for open-sleeve coupled 12 and 17-meter arrays. See the text for the reasons why the top two have been rejected for this article, even though they might be capable of good performance.

higher band (or bands, in the case of triband beams), we simply feed the lower-frequency driver with the higher-frequency signal. Closely spaced to the lower-band "master" driver is a shorter "slaved" driver for the upper band. It receives virtually all of the higher-frequency energy and operates as the driver for its own array of elements.

Finding the correct length and spacing for the slaved driver can be tedious without some guidance. The object is to adjust the length and spacing so that the master driver shows the proper feed-point impedance at not only its own lower frequency, but at the higher frequency as well.

Assuming we want to have both beams pointed in the same direction, there are several approaches to combining the two beams using open-sleeve driver coupling. Three such approaches are outlined in **Fig 15-22**. One scheme combines two driver-reflector Yagis, with the 12-meter elements nestled inside the 17-meter pair. A second scheme combines driver-director Yagis, with the 12-meter driver immediately in front of the 17-meter driver. Note that the 12-meter beam has three elements. When a higher-frequency director lies behind or in front of a director used for a lower frequency, it tends to yield poor results. The answer is to use two directors. Although the single director will not yield standard two-element (driver-director) performance, the pair of directors does. The inner and outer director combination yields standard two-element performance—and sometimes a little bit more.

However, I have rejected both of these schemes for the present effort, although either one would produce a very compact dual-band Yagi. Both designs are very finicky. Models indicate that adjustments of less than a quarter inch in either element length or spacing for the 12-meter drivers can upset performance. Although such tolerances can be obtained in a commercially produced beam, home construction rarely permits such precision.

Less critical is the lower scheme in Fig 15-22. This array uses a driver-reflector design for 17 meters with a driver-director design for 12 meters. The overall length is about 10 feet, with the master driver positioned just forward of the center of balance, where the boom-to-mast mounting plate attaches. The design has an added advantage. We can select any desired impedance for the upper-band beam simply by changing the spacing and length of the slaved driver until the master driver shows the desired impedance with a 12-meter signal. With a driver-reflector beam for 17 meters, we can choose element spacing that gives us an acceptable match when directly connected to 50-Ω coaxial cable. With proper design, we can forget a matching network altogether.

As we did for the individual beams, let's design the dual-band beam a step at a time. The first step is to design it with uniform-diameter elements. **Table 15-7** shows the resulting dimensions for the combination array. Note that the 12-meter driver is spaced from the 17-meter driver by 4.3 inches. This distance is close enough to worry any antenna designer using NEC software, because NEC has a known problem with closely spaced wires of different lengths. So I ran the problem on *MININEC* as well. It indicated that the slaved 12-meter driver needed to be about one inch shorter and a quarter-inch closer to the master driver than the NEC numbers in the table. This is one of several clues we shall later use to field-adjust the beam to perfection.

In good designs using open-sleeve coupling, the upper-band elements have virtually no effect on the impedance for lower-band signals. Hence, once the lower-band elements are set, they require no change as we adjust the upper-band elements. Unfortunately, the rejected schemes did require some changes in the lower-band element lengths, which then required some readjustment of the upper-band lengths—another daunting aspect of their demands for the home builder. The design in Table 15-7 is quite stable, and adjusting the 12-meter elements leaves the 17-meter elements unaffected.

Table 15-8 shows the modeled performance of the antenna in free space. Especially important is the column of feed-point impedance numbers. The spacing of the 17-meter

---

Table 15-7
Basic (Uniform-Diameter) Element Dimensions for a 17 and 12-Meter Dual-Band Yagi
All measurements are in inches.

Element	Function	Length	Distance from Reflector
1	17-m Reflector	326.4	——
2	17-m Driver (fed)	307.2	81.6
3	12-m Driver (slaved)	234	85.9
4	12-m Director	222	119.2

Table 15-8
Anticipated Performance Parameters: 17- and 12-Meter Dual-Band Yagi Frequency Free-Space F/B Feed point

Frequency (MHz)	Free-Space Gain (dBi)	F/B (dB)	Feed-Point Impedance R ± jX (Ohms)
17 Meters			
18.068	6.5	11.3	43 + j 2
18.118	6.4	11.4	46 + j 6
18.168	6.3	11.5	49 + j 8
12 Meters			
24.89	6.5	27.1	61 + j 5
24.94	6.5	31.9	53 + j 6
24.99	6.6	33.8	44 + j 8

Note: When remodeling for an element taper schedule, adjust element lengths to achieve these performance figures.

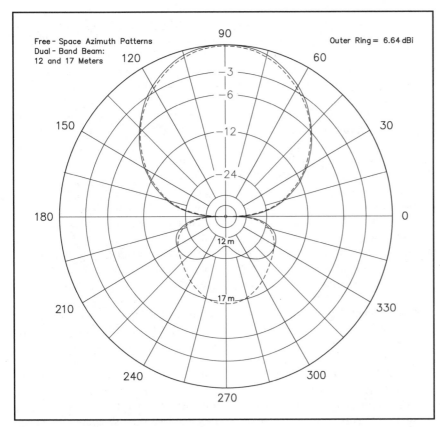

Fig 15-23—Overlaid 12 and 17-meter free-space azimuth patterns for the dual-band beam described. Compare these patterns to those in Fig 15-18.

Table 15-9
Adjusted Stepped-Diameter Element Dimensions for a 17 and 12-Meter Dual-Band Yagi (Two Versions)
All measurements are in inches.

Test-Model Taper Schedule

Diameter	Length
0.625	36 (from element center)
0.5	69
0.375	tip (see below)

Element	Length	Tip Length	Distance from Reflector
1	334.0	62.0	——
2	313.8	51.9	81.6
3	239.0	14.5	85.9
4	225.4	7.7	119.2

Alternative Taper Schedule

Diameter	17-m Length	12-m Length
0.75	48 (from element center)	12 (from element center)
0.625	33	18
0.5	33	48
0.375	Tip (see below)	Tip (see below)

Element Number	Element Length	Tip Length	Distance from Reflector
1	338.4	55.2	——
2	314.4	43.2	81.6
3	241.7	42.8	86.2
4	228.0	36.0	119.2

elements was selected as a compromise between obtaining the highest gain for this type of two-element Yagi and having a low 50-Ω SWR. On 12 meters, the impedance magnitude changes direction relative to the 17-meter progression as we raise frequency. In addition, the rate of change is much more rapid. The fast impedance change presents a major challenge to commercial antennas using this feeding technique for 20, 15 and 10-meter Yagis. However, for 17 and 12-meter use, the amount of change is well within tolerances for a good 50-Ω match. All we need to add at the feed point is a standard 1:1 choke balun, which can be a coil of coax or a ferrite-bead balun of W2DU design. This precaution suppresses common-mode currents on the feed line.

Because this design uses a reflector for the lower band, we see a distinct difference in the F/B for the two bands. **Fig 15-23** provides the same information in more graphic form by overlaying the azimuth patterns for the two bands. Although not operationally significant, the 17-meter driver-reflector combination has a modicum more gain and better F/B than the beam might have if used independently. The shorter 12-meter elements have a slight director function on 17 meters. Likewise, the 17-meter elements function (although minimally) as reflectors on 12 meters, elevating the F/B on that band relative to the use of the 12-meter elements as an independent beam. The phenomenon has acquired the name "forward stagger," indicating the design principle of placing higher-band elements forward of lower-band elements for best performance.

We are now ready to translate our basic design into a practical one that uses stepped-diameter tubing for the elements. The test model used the same tapering schedule as the independent beams—because it used the same elements with only the tips adjusted. **Table 15-9** gives the required overall element lengths and the tip lengths for each of the elements in the final array.

To quickly illustrate that changing the tapering schedule may also change the element lengths, the table also identifies a second version of the beam. This version has the same modeled performance as the basic and the test models. However, it uses a more aggressive tapering schedule. It begins with ³/₄-inch diameter tubing and progresses to ³/₈-inch-diameter tubing. The progressions differ for the two bands to yield the strongest elements of each overall length. Note that the required element lengths are all longer than those for the test model, despite the fact that the center element sections have a larger diameter than those of the test model. Moreover, the NEC model indicates that the driver spacing should be slightly greater, although field adjustment determines the final spacing.

Construction and Adjustment of the Dual-Band Beam

Construction of the test antenna is simply a doubling of the element mounting tasks described for the monoband driver-director Yagis. If element-mounting plates are used for the two drivers, the plate edges that face each other should be trimmed so that driver spacing can be adjusted to its final value. Because the spacing (depending on the element sizes used) may be less than four inches center-to-center, the plates should extend no more than two inches from the element centers. For 12 and 17 meters, metal or polycarbonate plates need not be more than about four inches wide for good mounting strength.

For this beam, cut and assemble the reflector, master driver and director to length. Then preposition and tighten these elements before installing the slaved driver. The slaved 12-meter driver is the only element that requires patient adjustment. Much of the work can be accomplished with the beam supported by a mast set horizontally so that the reflector is 5 to 10 feet off the ground and the beam is pointed straight up. Check the feed-point impedance and double-check the element dimensions and spacing. If the feed-point impedance is close to the modeled values and the beam passes the dimensional checks, then the 17-meter portion of the beam will perform up to the modeled standard. **Fig 15-24** shows the entire two-band array during construction on a crank-up assembly that I use to make adjustments and tests.

Recheck the length and install the slaved driver, but don't lock down the tips or the spacing. Using the modeled spacing as the starting point, measure the feed-point impedance on the master driver with a 24.94-MHz signal. You may find a resistance that is either higher or lower than the desired level and a reactance that may be either inductive or capacitive. The combination you discover dictates whether you will adjust either the spacing or the element length. Here is the guideline for this particular antenna:

1. Increasing the element length decreases the feed-point resistance and makes the reactance more inductive (or less capacitive). Decreasing the element length does just the opposite, increasing the feed-point resistance and making the reactance more capacitive (or less inductive).

2. Closing the spacing decreases the feed-point resistance and makes the reactance more capacitive (or less inductive). Opening the spacing increases the resistance and makes the reactance more inductive (or less capacitive).

If this is your first open-sleeve coupled beam, be extra patient. It is easy to forget the guidelines and adjust the wrong parameter. If that happens and the feed-point values appear to be going awry, return the slaved element to its original length and spacing and start the procedure again. Make very small changes between feed-point measurements until you get a good feel for how much each increment of change affects the feed-point impedance.

Once you have set the slaved driver to give a proper impedance or SWR curve on 12 meters, recheck the 17-meter feed-point impedance. It should

Fig 15-24—The dual-band beam during mounting to a crank-up mast fixture used at W4RNL for initial testing and adjustment of small arrays. See the text for a technique to keep the two driver elements parallel to each other.

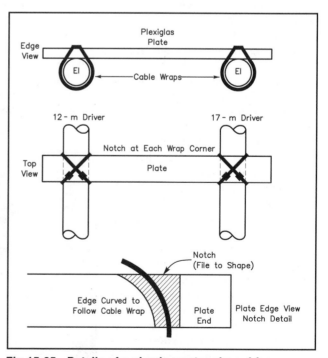

Fig 15-25—Details of a simple master-slave driver alignment plate with cable-wrap binders.

not have changed by an amount requiring readjustment of the element. Also, check the spacing between the slaved driver and the director. Set the spacing to within about a quarter inch of the model to ensure good performance across the 12-meter band. Moving the driver up to an inch might dictate one more round of slight adjustments to the slaved driver for the best SWR curve.

These adjustments should hold when the antenna is raised to its operating height. However, recheck the feed-point impedances on both bands to be certain.

Because the spacing between drivers is somewhat critical, you may experience some SWR fluctuations in gusty winds that push the two drivers back and forth. (The difference in element droop between the two drivers, shown in Fig 15-24, gives an indication of how the wind may also change the element spacing from a parallel set of lines.) You can minimize the fluctuations by locking the two drivers together with a simple Plexiglas or acrylic plate, as shown in **Fig 15-25**. The plate can be about an inch or so wide and long enough to allow about one-half inch of overhang past each driver. You can use material up to one-quarter inch thick, but one-eighth inch will normally work well. File notches into the plate so that crossed cable wraps lock the plate in place when tightened. The filing suggestion in the figure is a reminder to avoid a sharp edge where the cable ties bend across the plate. UV-resistant cable wraps are the most durable.

Place these plates about three to four feet from the element center on each side of the array. Do not lock the cable ties to the tubes with adhesive. It is important for the tubes to be free enough to move lengthwise in the clamps so that they are never overstressed by winds. The plates simply maintain the spacing between the drivers, forcing them to wobble in the wind in unison.

Like all beams, the dual-band array needs at least annual inspection and preventive maintenance. Check the feed-point connections, the tubing junctions, all junction plates and hardware and the weather seals you place over coax connectors. While you are up on the tower, check the rotator and its connections as well. If you make your checks by lowering the beam, feel free to clean the tubing as well. Annual maintenance is also a good time to remove old bird and insect nests from any of the crevices they like to use.

Summary

Relatively high performance is easy to obtain on 12 and 17 meters, where beams are light and inexpensive to build. These beams provide some of the highest performance available for their degree of complexity. They require a bit more patient adjustment than simple driver-reflector beams, but the size reductions and performance improvements may make the effort worthwhile.

Two Elements on 10 Meters

Al Alvareztorres is part of the ARRL Lab crew. His specialty is answering technical questions and he answered a good one when he wrote this article for April 1999 QST. See **Fig 15-26**.

Living in a condo has many advantages, none of which is being able to mount a tribander on a 60-foot tower. So I make do with a long, thin random wire that works nicely as long as the New England wind, snow and ice don't conspire to give my hamming a holiday (which happens more often than I'd like). And although it's somewhat directional on the higher bands, I haven't figured out how to rotate 200 feet of wire without the neighbors becoming suspicious. One answer is to operate mobile. A bumper-mounted vertical is fine for casual operation, but it leaves a lot to be desired when mountain topping for rare DX. With a solar maximum just around the corner, I decided that a portable 10-meter beam was necessary.

The beam had to fit in the trunk of my Subaru (limiting the largest component to about four feet in length) and had to be easy to assemble and erect on site by one person. In this article I'll describe the antenna and provide some construction tips that may help you avoid some pitfalls if you take on this worthwhile project.

The Boom

From past experience I know that TV masts make good booms for smaller antennas. They're lightweight, strong and readily available at most RadioShack and home stores. The light-duty stuff is plenty strong and comes in five-foot lengths. That was my starting point.

At 28.4 MHz, for an antenna made of tubing and not supported at the ends, a half wavelength is 491.8 divided by 28.4 MHz, or 17.3 feet. To accommodate my "Subaru factor," four feet divided by 17.3 feet produces a boom length of

Fig 15-26—The completed AA1DO Yagi mounted on a portable tripod.

Fig 15-27—Two pieces of angle aluminum are attached to the boom with two nuts, bolts and lock washers. Your drilling must be accurate, so use a drill press if possible. In addition to drilling the boom holes, you'll need to drill four holes in each angle piece: two for accepting the boom-mounting bolts and two for the U-bolts that will hold the element.

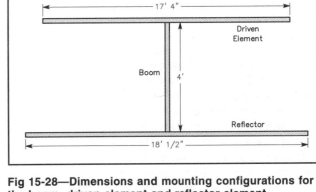

Fig 15-28—Dimensions and mounting configurations for the boom, driven element and reflector element.

Fig 15-29—Use hose clamps to compress the slotted ends of the telescoping elements and keep everything in place. Marking the exact positions of the sliding tubes makes it much easier to assemble the antenna in the field.

0.116 wavelength, a size that gives a nice gain and a feed-point impedance that can be easily matched to your coax line.

The TV mast (with the crimped end lopped off) fits in my trunk and allows two elements to be mounted 4 feet apart and fed with RG-58 coax. So far so good. I would be building a two-element beam.

Now, how to mount the elements to the boom and the boom to the mast (another 5-foot TV mast section)? In the past I had used a U-bolt and clamp arrangement, but this technique requires care in keeping the elements parallel to each other and to the ground. This is fine for permanent installations, but not something to be bothered with while operating portable.

I decided on right-angle pieces

permanently mounted to the boom (see **Fig 15-27**). I used ¹/₂-inch 1 × 2 aluminum angle scrap because it "looked about right." Your local hardware store has aluminum angle in various dimensions and lengths. I cut six, 3-inch pieces of angle to make the U-bolt mounting brackets—two to hold each element and two to hold the mast.

Drilling the two holes in the angle's smaller dimension—the part that attaches them to the boom—isn't critical as long as you drill the holes on the boom the same distance apart. The angles will be permanently mounted to the boom using 2-inch bolts, nuts and lock washers. When you mount them, be careful not to crush the tubing. It's not terribly strong, but it is lightweight. We're going for portability here!

The holes in the larger dimensions should be tailored to allow the mounting of the 1¹/₄-inch U-bolts for the elements and the 1³/₄-inch U-bolts for the mast. Because the element mounts must be as parallel as possible and the boom mount must be at right angles to them for maximum efficiency (and so your antenna doesn't look like it's under the influence), make the boom holes with a drill press if possible.

Now for the Elements

Most beam antennas are made with aluminum tubing because it's strong, lightweight and available in sizes that "telescope" into each other. The telescoping feature is important. It helps in transportation and makes tuning the antenna a snap.

The beam's driven element should be 17.3 feet. The length of a reflector for a two-element Yagi with 0.116-wavelength element spacing should be 18 feet ¹/₂-inch. See **Fig 15-28**.

I needed 35 feet of tubing (plus some to fit inside each telescoping joint for support). Because the tubing comes in 8-foot lengths, this worked out to five lengths of assorted sizes. The three telescoping sizes available at my local hardware store were 1 inch, ⁷/₈ inch and ³/₄ inch—perfect! Because the 1-inch section was going to be the center part of the two elements, I picked up U-bolts and nuts while I was there. You'll also need eight hose clamps sized to fit your tubing.

This is how the material was cut up. One 1-inch tube was cut in half, yielding two four-foot lengths. The two ⁷/₈-inch tubes were cut in half to yield four 4-foot lengths. One ³/₄-inch tube was cut in half to yield two 4-foot lengths. From the remaining ³/₄-inch tube I cut off an 8-inch piece (for later use in the gamma match) and cut the remaining length in half to yield two lengths a little over 3.5 feet each. I then took the 1-inch tube and cut a slot in each end to a length of about 1¹/₂ inches. Pushing the tube endwise into a band saw makes a really nice double-slot arrangement. I did the same at one end of each ⁷/₈-inch tube. When the elements are assembled, hose clamps will pinch the slots closed and keep the element sections in place (see **Fig 15-29**).

Construction Time

In the garage I erected a 3-foot tripod. I then cut a small piece off the unswaged end of the second 5-foot TV mast (so it would fit in the trunk) and installed it into the tripod. I mounted the boom on the mast with U-bolts and clamps and attached the two 1-inch tube sections to each end of the boom with U-bolts and centered them for balance. I then slid the unslotted ends of the four ⁷/₈-inch tubes into the ends of the 1-inch tubes, holding them in place with hose clamps. I inserted unslotted ends of the four remaining tube sections in place (using the two shorter ³/₄-inch tubes on the driven element). You won't believe how big a 10-meter beam seems when it's inside a garage!

Some Last Element Details

I drilled a hole at the center of the driven element and installed a bolt to attach the shield of the coax. I drew a ring around both 1-inch tubes with permanent markers to show the exact center for easy assembly. I used black when marking the driven element and red on the reflector. That way, in the field I wouldn't have to stop to figure out what was what (that's also why I cut slots into only one end of some of the element sections).

Feeding the Antenna

As you may have noticed, this antenna uses "plumber's delight" construction. The driven element isn't split into two legs like a conventional dipole. In this case, the driven element is one piece, and everything is shorted to the boom, to the mast and to ground. To top

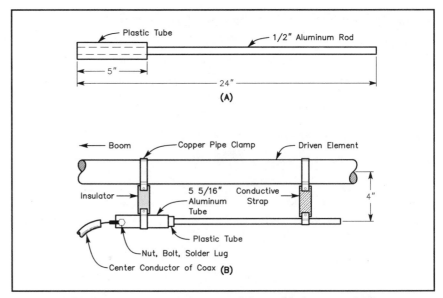

Fig 15-30—Making your own gamma match is easier than you think. Construct the variable capacitor element by sliding a 5-inch piece of ¹/₂-inch diameter plastic tubing over a 24-inch piece of ¹/₂-inch diameter aluminum rod (A). Then, slide the plastic-sleeved end of the rod into a 5⁵/₁₆-inch long, ³/₄-inch diameter aluminum tube and attach the entire assembly to the driven element (near the boom) using one plastic insulator and one conductive strap as shown (B). Note that the assembly must be separated from the driven element by 4 inches, center-to-center.

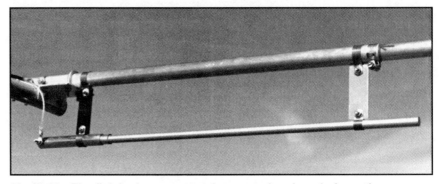

Fig 15-31—The finished gamma match mounted and ready for action.

it off, the beam is fed with unbalanced coax. So, how does it work? Like magic! And the magic words are gamma match. There are actually several ways to feed a plumber's delight antenna, but the gamma match is probably the simplest.

How a gamma match works is beyond the scope of this article. In short, the braid of the coax is connected to the center of the driven element (since this is where the voltage null occurs in a half-wave conductor). The center conductor of the coax is connected to the same driven element through a capacitor some distance away from the center. In the old days we used tuning

capacitors from discarded AM radios. Tuning caps are as scarce as hen's teeth nowadays, so I decided to try a technique I'd come across in the 1974 *ARRL Antenna Book*—incorporating the capacitor into the structure of the gamma match.

Building the Gamma Match

I took the 8-inch piece of ³/₄-inch tubing that I had set aside before and cut it to 5⁵/₁₆ inches. I cut a piece of ⁵/₈-inch plastic tubing to a length of 5 inches and cut a ¹/₂-inch aluminum rod (tubing will work) to 24 inches. Sliding the plastic tubing onto the ¹/₂-inch rod

Fig 15-32—The shield braid of your coaxial cable attaches to the driven element using a nut, bolt and solder lug. The center conductor, however, must attach to the end of the gamma match capacitor, as shown here.

until their ends were flush, I now slid this assembly into the 5⅝₁₆-inch tube until ½ inch of the plastic tube was left exposed (see **Figs 15-30** and **15-31**). I now had a capacitor! See **Fig 15-32**.

I drilled a hole near the end of the 5⅝₁₆-inch tube and installed a small bolt for the center conductor of the coax. This assembly was mounted to the driven element so that the larger end (the one with the bolt) was directly under the center of the element and the two tubes were four inches apart center-to-center.

The gamma match is held on by an insulated strap at the end closer to the center of the driven element and by a conductive aluminum strap at the other

end. The locations of the straps aren't critical at this point. The straps themselves can be made of any sturdy insulating and conducting materials. I used flat plastic stock and flat aluminum stock (1 inch by ¹⁄₁₆ inch worked fine) held in place by copper clamps (designed to hold copper pipes to a wall). These clamps come in all sizes, are easily bent to the proper size, already have holes in them for attaching to the straps and are inexpensive. Mechanically, everything looked good! But would it work?

Tuning the Antenna

I was fortunate that it was a beautiful summer day and that I had my wife, Donna, AA1DQ, to help me. I disassembled the monster in the garage and reassembled it on the lawn. Everything went together nicely in about 15 minutes. I attached the braid of the coax to the driven element and the center conductor to the gamma match. The fact that it was only four feet off the ground would have little effect on the tuning, although the overall performance would be affected by the high angle of radiation. Leaving the hose clamps over the element slots loose, I adjusted the driven element length to about 17 feet and the reflector to about 18 feet ½ inch.

I would make the adjustments while Donna, visible through the shack window, keyed the transmitter and recorded the SWR readings. It goes without saying that visual (or some other positive) contact is

imperative for safety. She could see that I was clear of the antenna before keying the transmitter.

I find that it's best to keep a written record when tuning an antenna (even if it's only a dipole) so that I know where I am and which way I'm going. I make a chart with frequency on the Y axis and antenna length on the X axis. I then enter the lowest SWR point (resonance) at the appropriate X-Y position. As I change the length I can easily see what's happening.

If you find that the SWR at your chosen frequency is unacceptable, begin adjusting the gamma match by sliding the center bar in or out. If you can't achieve a match, slide the entire matching section toward or away from the center of the driven element. As a last resort, adjust the driven element length. This will also have an effect. Remember to keep records. Otherwise you may get your adjustments all out of whack and won't know where you are. When you're done, tighten the hardware on the gamma match, as it will not be moved again.

I was lucky. After only a few adjustments I obtained a 1:1 match at any chosen frequency (28.0 to 28.5 MHz). A match of 1.3:1 was attainable beyond these frequencies (up to 28.6 MHz). Your results may vary.

I was overjoyed. The beam showed very good side rejection and a respectable front-to-back ratio. I marked the element sections at their contact points with a ring using the same permanent markers. When erecting the system I could simply slide the sections to the rings and tighten the hose clamps. There was nothing left to do but try it out on Beseck Mountain. Along the way I got some foot-long metal tent pegs to hold the tripod steady.

The Verdict

The antenna has been used several times mountain topping and contesting. It performs well and can be erected by one person in about 15 minutes. It was well worth the effort. I have since gotten another section of mast and, with two people, it can easily be put up at 10 feet.

I haven't experimented with the reflector length yet to see the effect on the gain and the front-to-back ratio. As they say, "If it ain't broke, don't fix it!"

Table 15-10
Bill of Materials

Qty	Description
2	5-foot light-duty TV mast
1	1-inch × 8-foot aluminum tube
2	⁷⁄₈-inch × 8-foot aluminum tube
2	³⁄₄-inch × 8-foot aluminum tube
1	¹⁄₂-inch × 4-foot aluminum rod
1	1-foot section of clear vinyl tubing
1	2-foot length of aluminum angle
2	1³⁄₄-inch U-bolts
4	1¹⁄₄-inch U-bolts
8	Hose clamps to fit on 1-inch tubing
6	2-inch bolts & hardware
2	1¹⁄₂-inch bolts & hardware
4	¹⁄₂-inch bolts & hardware
1	3-foot tripod
3	1-foot metal tent pegs

A Portable 2-Element Triband Yagi

This antenna may be just the thing for your summer cottage, campsite, Field Day or even your home station. Markus Hansen, VE7CA, wrote about this for November 2001 *QST*. I think you'll find the antenna and the story behind the antenna interesting. See **Fig 15-33**.

Several years ago I entered the ARRL November Sweepstakes CW contest in the QRP category, operating from a portable location. It turned out to be a very frustrating experience with only 3 W of output power and dipole antennas. After the contest I decided that the next time I entered a QRP contest it had to be with gain antennas.

My philosophy has always been to try to keep life as simple as possible. In other words, I look for the easiest way to accomplish a goal that guarantees success. Don't get me wrong: Dipoles work particularly well considering the time and effort put into making them. But adding a reflector to a dipole antenna increases the overall gain about 5 dB, depending on the spacing between the elements. This extra gain makes a significant difference, especially when you are dealing with QRP power levels. My 3-W transmitted signal would sound like a 9.5-W powerhouse just by adding another piece of wire! And it would be inexpensive too.

With Solar Cycle 23 in full swing, having an antenna with gain on 15 and 10 meters also became a consideration. Another parameter was the sale of the family van, which meant the new antenna had to fit into the ski boot of our car. Keeping these constraints in mind, I used a computer antenna-modeling program, trying different design parameters to develop a triband 2-element portable Yagi using wire elements.

The basic concept comprises three individual dipole driven elements, one each for 10; 15 and for 20 meters tied to a common feed point, plus three separate reflector elements. The elements are strung between two 2.13-meter (7-foot) long, 2 × 2-inch wood spreaders, each just long enough to fit into the ski boot of the car. Use the lightest wood possible, such as cedar, pine or spruce to keep the total weight

Fig 15-33—The VE7CA portable Yagi deployed for DX action.

of the antenna as light as possible. Fiberglass poles would also work, or PVC pipe reinforced with maple doweling to ensure they don't bend. (Wood has the benefit of being easy-to-find and very affordable).

Adding a reflector element relatively close to the driven elements lowers the feed-point impedance of the driven element, so a simple hairpin match was employed to match the driven elements to a 50-Ω feed line. **Fig 15-34** shows the layout and dimensions of the antenna.

The Hairpin Match

The matching system is very simple and foolproof. You should be able to copy the dimensions shown in **Fig 15-35** and not need to retune the hairpin match, unless you plan to use the antenna in the top portions of the phone bands. The dimensions in Fig 15-35 produced a very low SWR—under 1.3:1 over the CW portions of all three bands. However, even in the lower portions of the SSB bands, the SWR doesn't rise above 2:1. SWR measurements were made at the end of a 25-meter (82-foot) length of RG-58 coax feed line.

Some may wonder why I used such a long feed line. First, when operating from a portable location it is better to be long than short. Nothing is more frustrating than finding that the coax you took along with you is too short. Further, when I change beam direction I walk the antenna around the antenna support,

thus requiring a longer length than if I went directly from the antenna to the operating position.

If you are concerned about line loss you can run RG-58 down to the ground and larger-diameter RG-8 or RG-213 to the operating position. You may also find that in your particular situation a shorter length of coax will do. An 18-meter (59-foot) long piece of RG-58 has a loss of about 1 dB at 14 MHz, which is entirely acceptable considering the convenience of using coax cable.

Adjusting the Hairpin Match

If after raising the antenna the SWR is not as low as you want in the portion of the bands you plan to operate, first double-check to make sure that all the elements are cut to the correct length and that the spacing between the driven elements and reflectors are correct. Next you can adjust the hairpin match. Connect either an antenna SWR analyzer or a transmitter and SWR meter to the end of the feed line and pull the antenna up to operating height. Determine where the lowest SWR is on 15 meters. By moving the shorting bar on the hairpin match up or down you can adjust the lowest SWR point to the middle of the portion of the 15-meter band you prefer. If your preference is near the top end of 15 meters you may have to shorten the 15-meter driven element slightly. After adjusting the 15-meter element and hairpin match, adjust

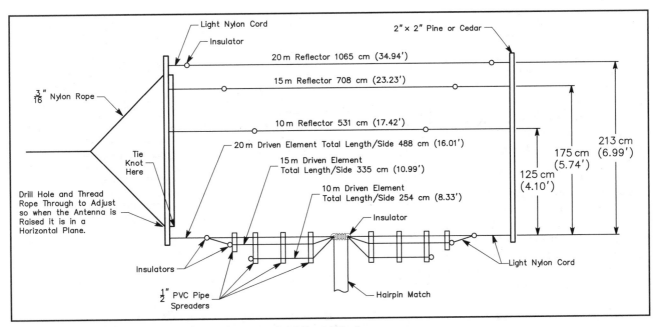

Fig 15-34—Dimensions for VE7CA's 2-element wire triband Yagi.

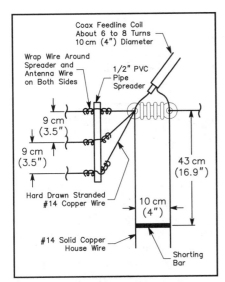

Fig 15-35—Close-up view of the feed point.

the 10 and 20 driven-elements lengths separately, without changing the position of the shorting bar on the hairpin match.

The hairpin match is very rugged. You can attach the feed line to it with tape, roll it up, pack the antenna away and even with the matching wires bent out of shape it just seems to want to work.

Antenna Support

Adhering to my constraint to keep things as simple as possible, I only use one support for the antenna, typically a tree. When the antenna is raised to its operating position it is a sloping triband Yagi. To achieve this, attach a rope to each end of the 2 × 2s to form a V-shaped sling, as shown in the Fig 15-34. Attach a length of rope to one sling and pull the antenna up a tree branch, tower or whatever vertical support is available. Tie a second length of rope to the bottom sling and anchor the antenna to a stake in the ground. By putting in two or three stakes in the ground around the antenna support, you can walk the antenna around to favor a particular direction. To change direction 180°, give the feed line a pull and the array will flip over. So simple but very effective!

Local or DX

One of the features of a sloping antenna is that you can adjust the take-off (elevation) angle. For example, if you are interested in North American contacts (whether for casual QSOs or the ARRL November Sweepstakes contest), then sloping the antenna away sideways from the support structure at 45° with the feed point approximately 8 meters (26 feet) above the ground, will yield a 20-meter pattern similar to **Fig 15-36A**. Here, the maximum lobe is between 10° and 60° in elevation. The pattern of the antenna in a flattop horizontal configuration at 9.1 meters (30 feet) is overlaid for comparison. You can see that the tilted beam has better low-angle performance, but at higher angles has less gain than its horizontal counterpart. Fig 15-36B shows an overlay of the azimuth patterns for these two configurations at a 10° takeoff angle.

If DX is your main interest, then you want to position the antenna even closer to vertical to emphasize the lower elevation angles. **Fig 15-37** shows the pattern on 20 meters when the antenna is tilted sideward 10° away from vertical, again compared with the other orientations in Fig 15-36A. The feed point is 6 meters above ground and the model assumes fresh water in the far field, which is the case at my portable location.

Remember that the radiation pattern is quite dependent on ground conductivity and dielectric constant for a vertically polarized antenna. A location close to saltwater will yield the highest gain and the lowest radiation angle. With very poor soil in the near and far field, the peak radiation angle will be higher and the gain less.

I have had the opportunity to test this out at my portable location. Using two trees as supports, I am able to pull the antenna close to horizontal with the feed point about 7 meters above the ground. In this position, with 20 meters open to Europe, I have found it difficult to work DX on CW with 3 W of output power. How-

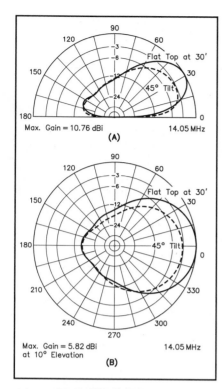

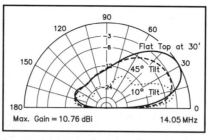

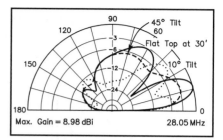

Fig 15-36—At A, comparison of elevation patterns for VE7CA Yagi as a horizontal flat top (solid line) and tilted 45° from vertical (dashed line). At B, comparisons of azimuth patterns for a 10° elevation angle.

Fig 15-37—Comparison of elevation patterns for VE7CA Yagi as a horizontal flat top (solid line), tilted 45° from vertical (dashed line) and tilted 10° from vertical (dotted line).

Fig 15-38—Same antenna configurations as shown in Fig 15-34, but at 28.05 MHz. On 10 meters, the flattop configuration is arguably best, but the 45° tilted configuration is not far behind.

ever, when I change the slope of the antenna so that it is nearly vertical I not only hear more DX stations, but I find it relatively easy to work DX.

I have tried this many times, since it is simple to lower one end of the antenna to change the slope and hence the radiation take-off angle. The sloping antenna always performs much better for working DX than a low horizontal antenna. Recently, I worked nine European countries during two evenings of casual operating, even though the highest end of the antenna was only about 10 meters high, limiting the slope to about 45°.

Fig 15-38 shows the elevation pattern on 28.05 MHz for the beam sloped 10° from vertical and at 45° from vertical, with the feed point at 8 meters height, again compared with the beam as a flat top at 9.1 meters (30 feet). With a steeper vertical slope, the 10-meter elevation pattern has broken into two lobes, with the higher-angle lobe stronger than the desired low-angle lobe.

This demonstrates that it is

possible to be too high above ground for a vertically polarized antenna. Lowering the antenna so that the bottom wires are about 2.5 meters (8 feet) above ground (for safety reasons) restores the 10-meter elevation pattern without unduly compromising the 20-meter pattern.

Portable It Is

A winning feature of this antenna is that it is so simple to put up, take down, transport and store away until it is needed again. When I am finished using the antenna and it's time to move on, I just lower the array and roll the wire elements onto the 2 × 2s. I put a plastic bag over each end of the rolled-up array and tie the bag with string so that the wires don't come off the ends of the 2 × 2s. I then put it in the ski boot of a car, or in the back of a family van and away we go. At home, it takes very little space to store and it is always ready to go—No bother, no fuss.

Testimonial

How well does it work? It works very well. On location I use a bow and arrow to shoot a line over a tall tree and then pull one end of the array up as far as possible. For DX I aim for a height of 20 to 30 meters if possible. For the Canada Day, Field Day and Sweepstakes contests I aim for a height of about 15 meters. This antenna helped me to achieve First Place for Canada, in the 1997 ARRL November Sweepstakes CW Contest, QRP category.

The ability to quickly change direction 180° is a real bonus. Late in the 1997 ARRL SS CW contest with the antenna pointed east I tuned across KH6ND. He was the first pacific station I had heard during the contest and

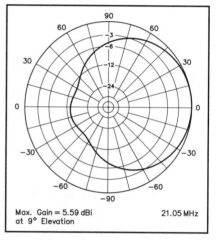

Fig 15-39—Azimuthal pattern for VE7CA Yagi tilted 10° from vertical on 15 meters.

obviously I needed to work him. After trying many times to break through the pileup and not succeeding, I flipped the antenna over to change the direction 180° and then worked him on my next call. **Fig 15-39** shows the azimuth pattern at 21.05 MHz for the beam mounted with a 10° slope from vertical. There is a very slight skewing of the azimuthal pattern because the slope away from purely vertical makes the antenna geometry asymmetrical.

VE7NSR, the North Shore Amateur Radio Club, has used this antenna sloped at about 45° for the last two years on 20 and 10 meters on Field Day with good success. The title photo shows the antenna attached to a tower during Field Day.

As they say, the proof is in the pudding. If you need a 20, 15 and 10-meter antenna with gain, this has to be one of the simplest antennas to build, and it will work every time!

A 3-Element Lightweight Monoband Yagi for 14 MHz

David Reid, PA3HBB, needed a portable beam antenna so he came up with an innovative design. See **Fig 15-40**. The following is from his article in July 2001 *QST*.

In preparation for the 2000 CQWW-CW contest for the PB6X Contest Group, I started looking at my homemade 2-element 20-meter beam. I decided that I needed more gain on 20 meters, along with a bit more front-to-back ratio (F/B). But the beam had to be light and it should have the following qualities:

- easy to handle with one or possibly two people
- lightweight—but sturdy enough to handle the winter weather (always bad during a contest) and be built/taken down many times during a year
- reliable construction
- full size—to meet the F/B ratio and the forward gain required
- the ability to dismantle it easily for storage—I am not in a position to keep my antennas permanently erected because I live in a rented property
- the ability to take the antenna into the field and on vacation

Finding the Right Materials

With these goals in mind, I started looking into possible designs and materials to make the beam. Having designed and built a lot of beams in the past, I knew from experience that 3-element all-metal construction was possible. But to keep the elements from drooping too much and, mainly, to keep the weight down (and thus, the diameter, thickness and weight of the main boom), I ruled this option out at an early stage. I did explore the possibility of using metal elements, and performed some experiments; all of these proved that I was not going to meet all of my design criteria.

I had recently been experimenting with fiberglass fishing poles for making verticals, single-element delta loops and dipoles. So, I had a few left lying around the shack. Each of these was 6 meters long and extremely lightweight.

Fig 15-40—The completed PA3HBB Yagi.

"Perfect!" I said. "I have my elements. Now I just have to work out a way to mount them on a boom."

Again, experience held the solution. I opted for a piece of angle material made from aluminum, which is bolted to the main boom with two zinc-plated bolts at right angles to the boom. The zinc-plated bolts are important because if you use stainless steel, it will corrode the aluminum if you live in an environment where the air often carries a substantial salt content (near the ocean, for example).

I had done experiments with gain, SWR and front-to-back ratio on the 2-meter band a few years ago, so I dug out my notes and then scaled the dimensions to 20 meters.

But because I was planning to use wire for the elements (instead of ¼-inch tubing), I knew the diameter-to-wavelength ratio of the elements was going to be higher than the 2-meter equivalent. This meant that my wire elements had to be longer than the scaled design. The question was, how much longer?

To solve this problem, I first constructed an exact model of just the driven element from the same material I had used in my original research on the

2-meter model. I then scaled this to 20 meters, but replaced the tubing with the #14 copper wire. I knew it would be too short—but I also knew that if I measured the resonant frequency of the 20-meter wire version I could calculate how much longer I needed to make the final driven element.

As the whole antenna design is scaled, I could calculate the percentage of the difference and apply this percentage to the other elements. The spacing between the elements was going to change so minimally that I decided not to alter these dimensions.

Now I had the dimensions for the three elements: reflector, driven element and director. The spacing was a direct scaling from the 2-meter model.

I calculated the weight and wind loading for the antenna and, to see if my calculations were in the ballpark, I compared them to some commercial monoband antennas. My results were very favorable. I am by no means a mathematician, so I always make sure that my calculations are in the same region as other antennas. Now to build the prototype...

Designing the Prototype

With the lightweight fishing rods as the elements, I decided the boom could be much lighter than a beam with all metal elements. The boom was calculated to be 16 feet, 3 inches long. I made it from three 6-foot, 6-inch lengths of 1-inch × 2-inch extruded aluminum channel stock. The three boom sections were overlapped by 20 inches and two zinc-plated bolts were used in each section to bolt (2-inch) sides together in an overlapping fashion. See **Fig 15-41**.

This made a strong boom that could be dismantled into its original three pieces whenever necessary. The

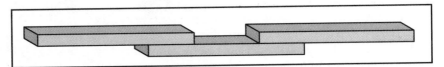

Fig 15-41—The boom sections.

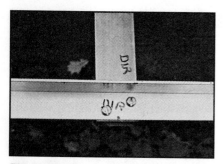

Fig 15-42—An angle section bolted to the boom.

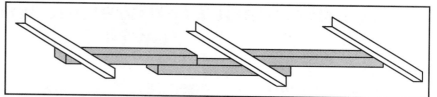

Fig 15-43—The boom and element brackets.

correct position of the elements was measured and marked on the boom and the three 3-foot, 3-inch pieces of angle aluminum were bolted to the boom sections at the appropriate places. These element bracket angles are held in place with two zinc-plated bolts each. See **Fig 15-42** and **Fig 15-43**.

The fishing rods were strapped to the angle material using three removable/adjustable zip-wraps per fishing rod. Once the elements were strapped to the angles, it was possible to determine the center of gravity of the beam in the middle of the garden and mark this on the boom (more about this later). See **Fig 15-44**.

A short piece of 2 × 2 lumber was used as a temporary stub mast mounting. This was bolted to the boom using four metal plates with bolts going all the way through the boom and stub. See **Fig 15-45**. (This was eventually replaced by two triangles of thick printed circuit board material.)

I raised my homemade mast and rested it on the fence surrounding my tennis court and then climbed a ladder with the antenna in one hand—it really is light and easy to handle—because the elements can stay telescoped while I am attaching the beam to the rotator. See **Fig 15-46**.

Having put the boom (with the telescoped elements) onto the rotator, I extended all of the fishing rods and friction-locked them in place. I extended the reflector first, then rotated the antenna through 180° and extended the director. Finally, I extended the driven-element rods.

The last step was to raise the mast to the vertical position. It all seemed too easy. No problems were encountered and there was no time when I felt unsafe

or unsteady on the ladder.

These experiments proved that it was possible to build the prototype mechanically, and it even looked like a real antenna. I left the antenna up for a week to see if it would suffer in the weather. We had some high winds and a lot of rain, but the antenna still stayed up and I was pleased when I took it down and found that all the parts were in perfect condition. It looked like I had a mechanical structure that would stand up for a lot more than just one weekend of heavy contesting.

The next step was to cut the wire elements, attach them to the fishing rods and put the whole antenna back up in the sky to see how it performs. Using the lengths I calculated earlier, I cut the #14 solid copper wire, marked the center point with tape and threaded it through the hoops on the fishing rods. I then taped the ends of the wire to the fishing rod so that tape at the center was sitting between the two rods at the centerline of the boom. Additionally, I secured the wire ends to each fishing rod with an extra zip-wrap fastener just to be sure they would stay in place.

In the prototype, the driven element was connected to the 50-Ω coaxial feed line through a 1:1 homemade

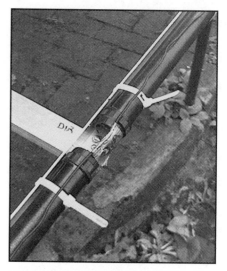

Fig 15-44—The antenna elements secured to the angle sections.

balun, which allowed me to test the resonance of the beam and determine the type of matching unit I required for the final antenna. A balun is generally necessary if you want your beam to have a directional pattern that is not distorted by the unbalanced feed line. However, it will also work without a balun. My preference is to use a balun on balanced antennas, but not on simple dipoles (or

Fig 15-45—Temporary plates for the boom-to-sub mast.

Fig 15-46—The author holds the finished antenna.

Fig 15-48—Here you can see the wires on the elements themselves.

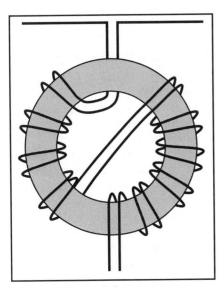

Fig 15-47—A diagram of the antenna balun.

low beams such as my 2-element 80-meter wire beam, which is only 10 meters (33 feet) above the ground).

I assembled the beam again and put it back up on the mast. I connected my MFJ-259B antenna analyzer to the coaxial cable and the resonance was measured at 14.030 MHz and the impedance was 34Ω. This was satisfactory. I could just use a 1:1 balun and still have an SWR of only 1.47:1. The 250-kHz 2:1 SWR bandwidth was about what I expected and it would certainly be sufficient for my needs as a CW-only antenna.

My first balun would not handle 400 W output, so a new one had to be built and tested. A 1:1.33 unun followed by a 1:1 balun would provide a better match and Jerry Sevick, W2FMI, has some interesting designs in his book *Building and Using Baluns and Ununs*. But, because I am looking for a simple, lightweight design, I opted for the higher SWR and a simple 1:1 balun; my

amplifier will easily load into 1.47:1. See **Fig 15-47**.

With my first balun still on the antenna, I decided to check out the properties of the beam by listening on 20 meters to stations in different parts of the world using my Elecraft K2 QRP rig and rotating the beam to record the pattern, directivity and front-to-back ratio. Well, it acted like a beam; the front-to-back ratio was consistently over 20 dB. I compared the results against my 2-element 20-meter antenna, which has a front-to-back of approximately 12 dB and the 3 element was always superior.

While the K2 was connected to the antenna, I could not resist calling CQ with the beam pointing Stateside. After a couple of calls I raised a few stations on the East Coast (while only running 3 W into the beam) and was getting 559 to 579 reports.

As far as forward gain goes, the antenna seemed to be quite a bit better than my 2-element antenna. Certainly I received better reports on the 3 element in every case.

Building the Antenna Yourself

If you'd like to duplicate my design, you'll be pleased to know that

it is a simple matter of drilling the holes in the correct places and bolting the boom sections together, the angle sections to the boom and the mast mounting plates in place. The last step is to clamp the fishing poles onto the angle sections and secure the antenna element wires to the poles. If you have never built a Yagi antenna before, you should know that the driven element is essentially a dipole, so the wire must be cut into two equal halves and attached at the center to the feed line (in this case, to the two wires from the balun). See **Fig 15-48**.

The only tools required are a drill (with the right size of drill bits for the bolts), and an adjustable wrench to tighten the bolts. No cutting or bending or folding is required, making building the antenna easy even for less experienced amateurs. It also has another advantage when on vacation or in the field—only one tool is required for assembly (an adjustable wrench). See the Bill of Materials in **Table 15-11** for a list of the necessary parts. The element dimensions are shown in **Table 15-12**. A drawing of the boom and element dimensions is available in **Fig 15-49**.

The fishing-pole supports for this antenna are a dielectric, so they actu-

Table 15-11
Bill of Materials

6—20-foot fishing rods. If you have difficulty locating suitable fishing rods, substitute six SD-20 antenna supports from WorldRadio, 2120 28th St, Sacramento, CA 95818; tel 916-457-3655.
3—aluminum rectangular box sections, 1´2 inches for the boom.
3—1.2×1.2-inch sections of angle material for the element brackets.
6—2-inch bolts for attaching the angle material to the boom.
4—3-inch bolts to hold the boom sections together.
4—4-inch bolts to attach the boom to the mast plates.
1—14×1/4-inch square printed circuit board for the boom-to-stub mast mounting plate.

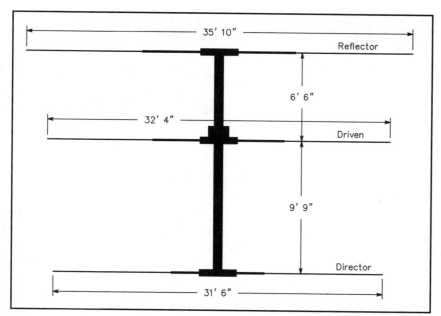

Fig 15-49—A drawing of the boom and element dimensions.

Reflector — 35' 10"
6' 6"
Driven — 32' 4"
9' 9"
Director — 31' 6"

to the boom. The driven element is placed at the end of this section of boom, 6 feet, 6 inches from the reflector (on the second section of the boom). The director is placed at the far end of the boom on the third section.

Finding the Center of Gravity

The next step was to find the center of gravity of the completed antenna. The boom and angle mounting brackets were ready for the elements (fishing poles) to be temporarily strapped in place. The antenna was assembled in the garden and I just picked up the beam and, using one hand, just kept moving my hand back and forth until the beam was stable and horizontal. When I found this point, I marked it as the beam center of gravity—the point where I wanted to fit the boom-to-mast clamps.

The Boom-to-Mast Clamp

There are several approaches you can use to secure the boom to the mast. One is shown in **Fig 15-50**. After several experiments with various materials, I wound up using plates made from printed circuit board material cut into triangles and bolted securely to the mast stub and the boom.

What Does it Weigh?

Traditionally, I weigh my antennas by putting the bathroom scales in the garden and, while holding the antenna, standing on the scales and recording the weight. Then I stand on the scales without the antenna and see the difference. With some quick subtraction I can determine the actual weight of the antenna. However, this method didn't work for this design—it was too light to measure the difference! So, I had to build a quick balance using a sawhorse and a long board, putting the beam on one end and weights on the other until it was stable and horizontal. According to my jury-rigged scale, the antenna only weighs 10 pounds!

Fig 15-50—One approach to securing the boom to the mast.

ally lower the resonant frequency of the elements taped to them. There may be some variation in the exact dielectric properties of different brands of poles, so the antenna elements may need to be changed a bit. The director and reflector should not be very critical, so you can cut those to the lengths shown in **Table 15-12**. The driven element will be a bit more critical, so it may be necessary to add about 6 inches to the lengths shown and prune the length of the driven element until the antenna is resonant in your favorite part of the band. As designed, the SWR may be 2:1 at the point of best resonance.

The Balun

The l-kW balun is made from a 2½-inch diameter ferrite toroid with a permeability of 40, wound with 10 bifilar turns of #12 copper wire (Fig 15-47). The wires are taped together first, then wound onto the core. The windings are crossed through the core at the 50% point (5 turns) to allow easy connection of the coax to one end and the driven element wires to the other. The whole balun is mounted in a suitable plastic box to keep it out of the weather.

The Spacing Between the Elements

The spacing for the elements is a direct scaling from my 2-meter model and it provides a reasonable front-to-back gain and forward gain as well as an acceptable SWR (2:1 or less) for the transmitter.

The angle section for the reflector is bolted to one end of the boom at 90°

Two-Element 40-Meter Switched Beam

Finally, for those of you who have the space and desire for something a bit more ambitious, this simple two-element wire antenna for 40 meters. This beam was described by Carrol Allen, AA2NN, *The ARRL Antenna Compendium, Vol 6*. Here's what AA2NN said.

Over the years I've seen a number of designs in amateur publications for three-element switched Yagis using remote relays to short out stubs or loading inductors to convert a reflector element into a director. Here is a simple, compact two-element switched beam for 40 meters that has an exceptional front-to-back ratio.

The antenna consist of two identical horizontal dipoles spaced 22 feet at a height of 50 to 60 feet, although other heights will work with some adjustments. The outer 9.5 feet ends of each dipole are bent toward each other to cover a rectangular area that is 46.25 feet by 22 feet. The ends of the dipoles are spaced 2 feet from each other. See **Fig 15-51**, which shows the physical layout of the antenna.

These are dimensions for 7.2 MHz, but you can rescale linearly for other frequencies. Bringing the ends close to each other increases the coupling between the dipoles so that the current in the parasitic reflector is almost equal to the current in the driven element, yielding a front-to-back ratio approaching 30 dB.

Two identical lengths of 75-Ω coax (Belden 9290) are run to the shack or to a remote selection relay. The length of the coax is selected to provide the required loading inductance for the non-driven element. To switch directions simply interchange the feed lines. The performance is similar to a phased two-element array but saves the expense and bother of a phasing network. Two 1:1 baluns are required on each dipole to isolate the feed lines from the elements. I use a shortened quarter-wave balun that I will describe later.

A length of transmission line less than a quarter wavelength will provide an inductive reactance when the far end is shorted. The required reactance for this antenna is about + 71 Ω. For 75-Ω

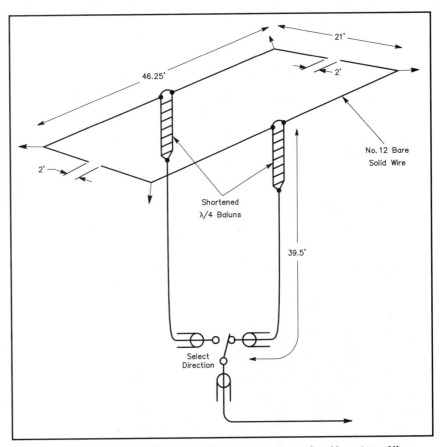

Fig 15-51—Layout of AA2NN's two-element wire beam for 40 meters. His beam is mounted 55 feet high. Details on the shortened λ/4 balun are shown in Fig 15-53 and Fig 15-54.

coax this would mean a length slightly less than $^1/_8$ of a wavelength. When the velocity factor is 0.78, as with Belden 9290, this would be only 12 feet 10 inches long. A cable this long would require some sort of structure that is almost as high as the dipoles themselves to support the remote selection relay.

The line length can be increased and still provide the required inductive reactance by adding another quarter wavelength and leaving the end open-circuited, or by adding a half wavelength and shorting the end. For Belden 9290 the other two lengths are 39.5 feet and 66.1 feet respectively. I chose the 39.5-foot length since this was a convenient length to reach into the attic of the house where the remote relay was located.

The longer lines have the disadvantage of having more loss and the reactance will vary more rapidly

with frequency, narrowing the antenna's bandwidth. The loss in the $^3/_8$-λ section introduces an equivalent series loss resistance of about 5 Ω. This only reduces the forward gain by about 0.34 dB. The $^5/_8$-λ line would add an additional 3 Ω.

Figs 15-52A and **B** show the computer-calculated elevation and azimuth patterns for this antenna, using W7EL's *EZNEC* software. Construction is very straightforward. I used #12 solid copper with the insulation removed for low visibility. Soft-drawn copper can be stretched by about 5% before measuring to reduce the amount of elongating with wind loading. For support I use 0.095-inch nylon Weed Whacker line over the top of four tall trees. The end spacers are also made from this line. Tying knots in this line is a little tricky—you should refer to any fishing book for information on tying knots in monofilament line. The

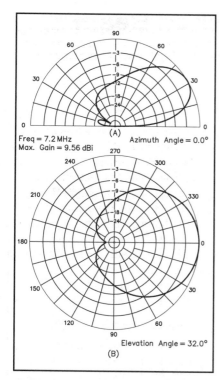

Fig 15-52—At A, elevation-plane response for AA2NN's two-element wire antenna at height of 55 feet over flat ground. Note the excellent front-to-back ratio of about 27 dB. At B, azimuth-plane response for antenna at an elevation angle of 32°.

corners are loops made by bending the antenna wire 270° around a ³/₁₆-inch diameter drill bit and soldering the wire to complete the closed loop. The corner loop is made to prevent slipping of the rope used to support the antenna. Note that a corner could have been made by twisting the wire into a loop at the corners, but I was concerned that this might induce stress failures.

The Shortened Quarter-Wave Balun

As mentioned earlier this antenna requires two 1:1 baluns to isolate the elements from the coax. While a toroidal or rod 1:1 balun will work fine, there is the question of the extra weight, especially if you are planning for high-power operation.

Fig 15-53A shows a familiar kind of λ/4 balun often used on VHF and UHF antennas. This would be 34 feet long on 40 meters and would be heavier than a ferrite-cored balun. The equivalent circuit of a λ/4 shorted transmission line is a parallel-resonant tuned circuit. The line length can be shortened considerably if the circuit is kept resonant by adding a parallel

capacitance across the inductance formed by the shorted open-wire line of the outer conductors of the two coaxes. See Fig 15-53B. Of course a discrete capacitor able to handle the voltage and current with 1500 W applied power is no lightweight either.

A simple solution is to use the capacitance of the non-feed line side of the balun to resonate the circuit. The exact length you end up with depends on the type of coax (capacitance per foot) and the spacing of the shields of the stub coaxes used to create the inductive part of the resonant circuit. I calculated the length for RG-6U first and then trimmed it to resonance using a grid-dip meter before connecting to a dipole. Changing the spacers' width will trim the resonant frequency, with wider spacing giving increased inductance and lowering the frequency. Being exactly resonant is not necessary, since the balun action is due to the symmetry. One other advantage of this type of balun is it actually improves the bandwidth of series-resonant antennas as it acts as a double-tuned circuit.

Fig 15-54 shows the completed balun. The center insulator is made from

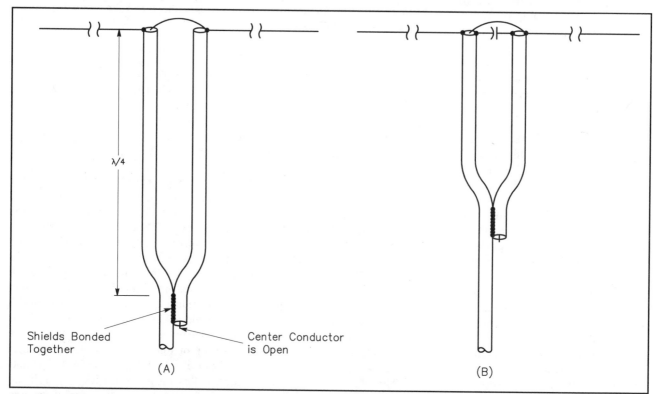

Fig 15-53—Development of the traditional λ/4 balun (at A) commonly used at VHF and the shortened λ/4 balun with a capacitor across it (at B) to tune it to parallel resonance.

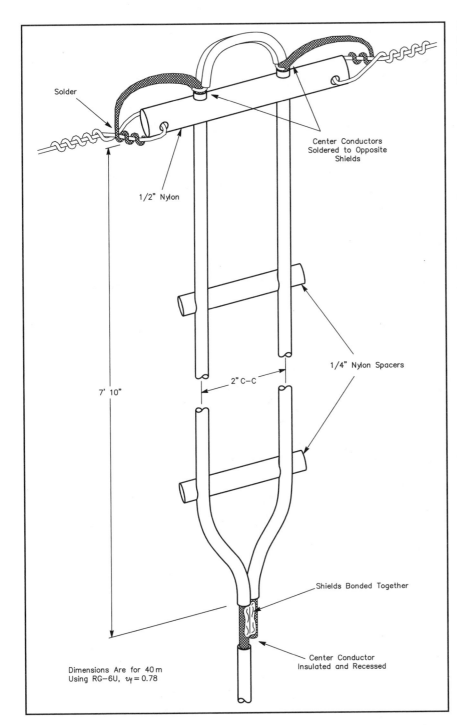

Fig 15-54—Diagram of AA2NN shortened λ/4 balun, which uses the capacitance of the non-fed portion on the right to tune the system to parallel resonance.

Solder

Center Conductors Soldered to Opposite Shields

1/2" Nylon

1/4" Nylon Spacers

7' 10"

2" C–C

Shields Bonded Together

Center Conductor Insulated and Recessed

Dimensions Are for 40 m
Using RG–6U, v_f = 0.78

$1/2$-inch nylon rod with two holes drilled for a snug fit to the coax shield after the insulation is stripped back. A couple of turns wrapped and soldered as shown prevent the coax from pulling out. After soldering all the joints I cover the ends and the bottom outer shield joint with coax seal to keep out water. The exposed braid is coated with liquid tape so that it doesn't act as a wick. The spacers can be made from any insulator—just as with open-wire line.

On-the-Air Performance

I installed this antenna oriented to fire east and west. This allowed me to work 40 meters at night, when the foreign broadcast AM stations were making the band unusable on a simple dipole or bi-directional W8JK antenna. Checks with stations in Australia confirmed the high front-to-back ratio predicted by *EZNEC*. Close-in stations did not exhibit this due to the high elevation angles involved. Being able to switch directions rapidly showed some interesting receive advantages. Many times signals could be heard more clearly by switching to the opposite direction due to a greater drop in noise or QRM. This was noticed mainly on close-in stations with high elevation angles.

This is a simple antenna. It doesn't take up much room and doesn't involve any expensive components. Probably the most expensive item would be the remote relay if you really wanted to use one.

16 Getting the Most Out of Your Antennas

You may have a top-of-the-line transceiver and the latest whiz-bang computer, with all the best Amateur Radio software. Nevertheless, you are the smartest, most intelligent thing in your ham shack. Please demonstrate your intelligence and practice Safety First!

Your first priority should be to protect persons. The second is to protect property. Never, ever compromise on these priorities. An entire chapter of *The ARRL Handbook* is devoted to safety issues and I suggest that you read—and heed—the advice given there.

Practice safety first and plan your projects and installations in advance. Think through each step. What tools and safety equipment will be needed? Think about what could go wrong and how you will deal with it if it does. If you're working with others, make sure that everyone understands the plan and the role that each person will play. (There should be only one "boss," particularly on tower jobs. Otherwise, you're going to have trouble.)

Observe the law and follow building and electrical codes. Be as diligent as you would if your life and well being depended on it. They do.

Station Performance

Antennas for most of us are not an end in themselves, but rather a means to an end. That end is communication via radio. In other words, antennas are merely a link in a chain. The best antenna in the world will do you no good if you have no radio to connect to it. Even then, you can't communicate on a dead band.

Let's call the measure of our ability to communicate *station performance*. (That's what we'll need to get the most out of our antennas.) There are three factors that will determine how well your station performs on a given day and in a given situation. These factors are: propagation, equipment and your skill. Let's consider them in turn.

Propagation

You have no control over propagation, but you can—and should learn to—exploit it. You can begin by reading about the topic. Both *The ARRL Handbook* and *The ARRL Antenna Book* have entire chapters devoted to propagation. In their current editions, these contain 24 and 38 pages respec-

tively. The sidebar describes what you might expect on the various bands.

Follow up your reading with on-the-air observation. This is important because as you spend time on the air, you will gain a *feel* for the bands. And as you build familiarity with *normal* conditions on your favorite bands, you'll be able to recognize and take advantage of propagation conditions on a given day.

I remember an incident that occurred in October 1974 that illustrates the good that can come from observation. I was living in Quito, Ecuador at the time and on the 12th and 13th had operated in the VK/ZL Contest. That weekend the 15-meter band had closed to the Pacific by 0200 UTC, and 20 meters was alive with signals. The VK/ZL Contest had been a fun warm-up for the CQWWDX Phone contest on the 26th and 27th. I got a late start (0200) on the 26th, and after a dozen contacts on 15, began to check the action on the other bands. At 0430, I went on 20 meters expecting to make a few contacts with Australia and New Zealand like I

had two weeks earlier. What I found were only a couple of weak stations from that part of the world. There wasn't much happening for me on 40 or 80, so I checked 15 again thinking that perhaps those weak signals on 20 were an indication of a higher MUF (maximum useable frequency). Indeed, the 15-meter band was open—wide open. In the next 90 minutes I worked the stations in Australia and New Zealand that I was looking for. I also worked 3 Malaysians, 2 Iranians, 2 Israelis, plus stations in Singapore, India, Laos and Ukraine among others. As the path lengthened, I worked a couple of Yugoslavians and even a fellow in the north end of Germany—very long path.

That incident not only illustrates the advantage of daily observation, it also shows the limitation of propagation predictions. Nobody's propagation predictions would have shown even the remotest possibility of that opening. It was discovered by those who were there on the band at the right time.

In other words, you should never

PROPAGATION SUMMARY, BY BAND

1.8-2.0 MHz (160 m)

Ground wave provides reliable communication out to 90 miles or during the day, when no other form of propagation is available. Long-distance paths are made at night via the F_2 layer. *Topband*, as 160-m is sometimes called, suffers from extreme daytime D-layer absorption.

At night, the D layer quickly disappears and worldwide 160-m communication becomes possible. Atmospheric and man-made noise limit propagation. Tropical and midlatitude thunderstorms cause high levels of static in summer, making winter evenings the best time to work DX at 1.8 MHz.

3.5-4.0 MHz (80 m)

Daytime absorption is significant, but not quite as extreme as at 1.8 MHz. Daytime communication range is typically limited to 250 miles by ground-wave and skywave propagation. At night, signals are often propagated halfway around the world. As at 1.8 MHz, atmospheric noise is a nuisance, making winter the most attractive season for the 80-m DXer.

7.0-7.3 MHz (40 m)

The popular 40-m band has a clearly defined skip zone during the day. During the day, a typical station can cover a radius of approximately 500 miles. At night, reliable worldwide communication is common on the 40-m band. Atmospheric noise is less troublesome than on 160 and 80 m, and 40-m DX signals are often of sufficient strength to override even high-level summer static. For these reasons, 40 m is the lowest-frequency amateur band considered reliable for DX communication in all seasons. Even during the lowest point in the solar cycle, 40 m may be open for world-wide DX throughout the night.

10.1-10.15 MHz (30 m)

The 30-m band is unique because it shares characteristics of both daytime and nighttime bands. Communication up to 1900 miles is typical during the daytime, and this extends halfway around the world via all-darkness paths. The band is generally open on a 24-hour basis, but during a solar minimum, the MUF on some DX paths may drop below 10 MHz at night.

Under these conditions, 30 m adopts the characteristics of the daytime bands at 14 MHz and higher. The 30-m band shows the least variation in conditions over the 11-year solar cycle, thus making it generally useful for long-distance communication anytime.

14.0-14.35 MHz (20 m)

The 20-m band is traditionally regarded as the amateurs' primary long-haul DX favorite. Regardless of the 11-year solar cycle, 20 m can be depended on for at least a few hours of worldwide propagation during the day. During solar maximum periods, 20 m will often stay open to distant locations throughout the night. Skip distance is usually appreciable and is always present to some degree. Atmospheric noise is not a serious consideration, even in the summer. Because of its popularity, 20 m tends to be very congested during the daylight hours.

18.068-18.168 MHz (17 m)

The 17-m band is similar to the 20-m band in many respects, but the effects of fluctuating solar activity on propagation are more pronounced. During the years of high solar activity, 17 m is reliable for daytime and early-evening long-range communication, often lasting well after sunset. During moderate years, the band may open only during daylight hours and close shortly after sunset. At solar minimum, 17 m will open to middle and equatorial latitudes, but only for short periods during midday on north-south paths.

21.0-21.45 MHz (15 m)

The 15-m band has long been considered a prime DX band during solar cycle maxima, but it is sensitive to changing solar activity. During peak years, 15 m is reliable for daytime DXing and will often stay open well into the night. During periods of moderate solar activity, 15 m is basically a daytime-only band, closing shortly after sunset. During solar minimum periods, 15 m may not open at all except for infrequent north-south transequatorial circuits.

24.89-24.99 MHz (12 m)

This band offers propagation that combines the best of the 10- and 15-m bands. Although 12 m is primarily a daytime band during low and moderate

---

rule out the importance of luck and of being there. To help me remember that, I have a sign hanging in my office that reads, "Luck is when preparation meets opportunity."

Finally, it's a good idea to have a reliable broadcast or beacon station to listen to. Six-meter operators learned long ago to listen to, and for, TV channel 2 carriers. They find them an excellent way to detect a band opening. It's certainly better than waiting to hear someone calling CQ. Once an opening is detected or suspected it's time to call CQ and to spread the word on the

Packetcluster and Internet.

If you listen on 21.455 MHz, you're apt to hear a low-power transmitter from HCJB in Ecuador. The strength of that signal will give you an idea of 15-meter propagation to South America. But what if you're interested in Europe or Africa? Good news. The Northern California DX Foundation and the IARU have teamed up to establish a worldwide network of beacon transmitters in the ham bands between 14.1 and 28.2 MHz. You can read about it on the Web at: **http://www.ncdxf.org/ beacon.htm** or see the sidebar for sys-

tem status as of early 2002.

Equipment

A fraction of a watt may be enough for you to make solid contacts through your local FM repeater. Depending on your antenna(s), it may also be enough power to make lots of DX contacts on the HF bands. A significant number of hams find their fun in QRP operating (running 5 W or less). Many of them use simple, home-built radios.

You can add a couple of S-units or so to your signal with a 100-W class transceiver. If you don't already own a sunspot years, it may stay open well after sunset during the solar maximum. During years of moderate solar activity, 12 m opens to the low and middle latitudes during the daytime hours, but it seldom remains open after sunset. Periods of low solar activity seldom cause this band to go completely dead, except at higher latitudes. Occasional daytime openings, especially in the lower latitudes, are likely over north-south paths. The main sporadic-E season on 24 MHz lasts from late spring through summer and short openings may be observed in mid-winter.

28.0-29.7 MHz (10 m)

The 10-m band is well known for extreme variations in characteristics and variety of propagation modes. During solar maxima, long-distance propagation is so efficient that very low power can produce loud signals halfway around the globe, even with modest equipment. Under these conditions, the band is usually open from sunrise to a few hours past sunset. During periods of moderate solar activity, 10 m usually opens only to low and transequatorial latitudes around noon. During the solar minimum, there may be no long-distance propagation at any time during the day or night.

Sporadic E is fairly common on 10 m, especially May through August, although it may appear at any time. *Short skip*, as it is sometimes called on the HF bands, has little relation to the solar cycle and occurs regardless of F-layer conditions. It provides single-hop communication from 190 to 2800 miles and farther. Ten meters is a transitional band in that it also shares some of the propagation modes more characteristic of VHF. Meteor scatter, aurora, auroral E and transequatorial spread-F provide the means of making contacts out to 1400 miles and farther, but these modes often go unnoticed at 28 MHz.

50-54 MHz (6 m)

The lowest amateur VHF band shares many of the characteristics of both lower and higher frequencies. In the absence of any favorable ionospheric propagation conditions, well-equipped 50-MHz stations work regularly over a radius of up to about 400 miles via tropospheric scatter, depending on terrain, power,

receiver capabilities and antenna.

During the peak of the 11-year sunspot cycle, worldwide 50-MHz DX is possible via the F_2 layer during daylight hours. Sporadic E is probably the most common and certainly the most popular form of propagation on the 6-m band. Single-hop E-skip openings may last many hours for contacts from 370 to 1400 miles, primarily during the spring and early summer. Multiple-hop sporadic E provides transcontinental contacts several times a year, and contacts between the US and South America, Europe and Japan via multiple-hop E-skip occur nearly every summer. Other types of E-layer ionospheric propagation can make 6 m an exciting band.

144-148 MHz (2 m)

Ionospheric effects are significantly reduced at 144 MHz, but they are far from absent. Sporadic E occurs as high as 144 MHz less than a tenth as often as at 50 MHz, but the usual maximum single-hop distance is the same, about 1400 miles. Other more exotic weak-signal modes such as auroral and meteor-scatter contacts are exploited by 2 m enthusiasts.

Tropospheric effects improve with increasing frequency, and 144 MHz is the lowest VHF band at which weather plays an important propagation role. Weather-induced enhancements may extend the normal 200- to 370-mile range of well-equipped stations to 500 miles and more, especially during the summer and early fall. Tropospheric ducting extends this range to 1200 miles and farther over the continent and at least to 2500 miles over some well-known all-water paths, such as that between California and Hawaii.

222-225 MHz (135 cm)

The 135-cm band shares many characteristics with the 2-m band. The normal working range of 222-MHz stations is nearly as good as comparably equipped 144-MHz stations.

420-450 MHz (70 cm)

Tropospheric propagation dominates the bands at UHF and higher. Well-equipped 432-MHz stations can expect to work over a radius of at least 200 miles in the absence of any propagation enhancement.

---

radio, this is probably a good level at which to start. When it gets boring (as in "too easy"), you can always lower the drive and try running 5 W.

Stepping all the way up to a legal-limit (1500-W) amplifier adds nearly two more S-units to your signal so *they* can hear you better, but it won't help you hear *them* any better. Also, when you increase your transmitter power, you dramatically increase the potential for interference to consumer devices, such as telephones and stereos.

One of the best things you can do with equipment to improve your station's

performance is to use multiple antennas. For example, if you use a vertical on 40 meters, you might want to put up a dipole as well. If you have one dipole, you might (if you can) add a second dipole—using different heights or different directions.

Skill

The operator's skill may be the most important factor in determining a station's performance. It doesn't matter if you're talking about getting message traffic to its destination, working a rare DX station or doing well in a contest; skill matters.

Operating ability is sharpened in the same way as any other ability is developed and improved. It takes coaching and practice.

You don't need to hire a personal trainer to build your operating skill. You can pick up tips from other hams and from publications (such as *The ARRL Operating Manual*). Observe what the best operators do on the air. Back in the 1960s when I was an aspiring contester, K8MFO helped me to improve my contesting techniques. Whenever Don and I heard him, we would both take a 20-minute break to listen to the smooth operating of Katashi

Nose, KH6IJ. I never heard an unruly pileup on Katashi—he seemed to always take control of the situation in a calm and competent manner. I learned a lot from listening to KH6IJ. You'll still find top-notch operators on the air today. Take time to listen to them. Try to copy the good things they do.

Practice means just doing it. If you want to handle traffic well, become a regular check-in on traffic nets. You will find it easier to handle messages and situations as you gain experience. When you're ready, volunteer to be a net control station.

Try your hand at operating contests. Start with some of the smaller events, such as state QSO parties. Don't be afraid. The guy on the other end wants to work you. If there is a large, unruly pileup, just keep tuning. You'll soon find a station to work.

What do contests offer?

- Concentrated activity—in a limited time span
- Round-the-clock operation—you'll hear stations at times they would not normally be active
- Short QSOs—no long waits
- Score counts—the other guy is trying to make as many QSOs as possible

This adds up to improved odds for you to make a QSO. Okay, it's not laid back. In fact, at times, it's in your face. Nevertheless, it's excellent training and can be great fun.

You can find contest information in *QST* or on the *ARRLWeb*: **http://www.arrl.org/contests/**. Speaking of the Web, Contesting.com at **http://www.contesting.com/** is dedicated to contesting and contesters. Even if your interest in contests is casual at best, you'll still find interesting stories of DXpeditions and operations.

NCDXF/IARU Beacon Transmission Schedule

The beacons transmit every three minutes, day and night. This table gives the minute and second of the start of the first transmission within the hour for each beacon on each frequency. A transmission consists of the callsign of the beacon sent at 22 words per minute followed by four one-second dashes. The callsign and the first dash are sent at 100 watts. The remaining dashes are sent at 10 watts, 1 watt and 0.1 watts.

Call	Location	14.100	18.110	21.150	24.930	28.200	Status
4U1UN	United Nations	00:00	00:10	00:20	00:30	00:40	OK
VE8AT	Canada	00:10	00:20	00:30	00:40	00:50	OK
W6WX	United States	00:20	00:30	00:40	00:50	01:00	OK
KH6WO	Hawaii	00:30	OFF	00:50	OFF	01:10	OK
ZL6B	New Zealand	00:40	00:50	01:00	01:10	01:20	OK
VK6RBP	Australia	00:50	01:00	01:10	01:20	01:30	OK
JA2IGY	Japan	01:00	01:10	01:20	01:30	01:40	OK
RR9O	Russia	01:10	01:20	01:30	01:40	01:50	May be garbled
VR2B	Hong Kong	01:20	01:30	01:40	01:50	02:00	Intermittent
4S7B	Sri Lanka	OFF	OFF	OFF	OFF	OFF	Moving
ZS6DN	South Africa	01:40	01:50	02:00	02:10	02:20	OK
5Z4B	Kenya	01:50	02:00	02:10	02:20	02:30	OK
4X6TU	Israel	02:00	02:10	02:20	02:30	02:40	OK
OH2B	Finland	02:10	02:20	02:30	02:40	02:50	OK
CS3B	Madeira	02:20	02:30	02:40	02:50	00:00	OK
LU4AA	Argentina	02:30	02:40	02:50	00:00	00:10	OK
OA4B	Peru	02:40	02:50	00:00	00:10	00:20	OK
YV5B	Venezuela	02:50	00:00	00:10	00:20	00:30	OK

The Formula for Fun

Fun is an *activity* that someone does for *enjoyment*. At least my dictionary indicates that activity and amusement (or enjoyment) are the factors that comprise fun. For me, Amateur Radio is fun. It is active, although not in the same way as scaling a sheer rock face or running a marathon. And the enjoyment is multifaceted. It feels great to build an antenna that works. That feeling is amplified when you use that antenna to contact a friend who is far away. I think you get the idea.

It doesn't take stacked monoband beams, full-feature transceivers and legal-limit amplifiers to have Amateur Radio fun. I remember a story that ran in *QST* many years ago that illustrates that truth with a twist. In the story our ham hero (main character) dies and goes to his final reward, where he is met by a guide to the afterlife. Once his guide learns that our hero is a ham, he's taken to an area to pick out his ham equipment. Everything he could possibly want was there, and he picked the top-of-the-line radio, amplifier, tower and beams. In the days that followed our hero works the rarest of the rare. He cuts through huge pileups in a single call and always get 59 reports. A month later, our hero is sad and feeling depressed when his guide appears and asks what's wrong. Our hero's response was to the effect that he was unhappy. Oh yes, he had enjoyed it in the beginning but after a while it was becoming boring to always win out in the pileups. Also, what was there left to do now that he had worked everything on the DXCC List? He concluded by saying that he thought that heaven would be better than this. His guide's response? "What make you think this is heaven?"

Okay, so you don't have to be the biggest and baddest to have fun. But what can a person do with only a modest station? Let me tell you about my friend Chip

Margelli, K7JA. In November 1993 Chip visited Pedro Piza Jr, NP4A, in Ponce, Puerto Rico; and while there, Chip operated the ARRL November CW Sweepstakes. His low-power (150-W class) entry won first place and set a new record in the process. (That record still stands as of spring 2002. His score would have put him in the top ten in the high-power category!) The secret weapon was Pedro's big antennas, right? Wrong! Chip had carried his AEA Isoloop antenna to Ponce in a suitcase. See **Fig 16-1**.

In Chapter 2, you read what Tom Schiller, N6BT, was able to do with just a light bulb for an antenna. Okay, what Tom did was extreme, but that's the point. How do you think Tom felt after he had worked all continents using that light-bulb antenna?

Here's another. Several years ago, Ed Hare, W1RFI, built a crystal-controlled transmitter using a 74LS00 low-power Schottky IC. That transmitter with about 100-mW (0.1-W) output was good enough for Ed to make 40-meter QSOs with nearby hams. In his lust for more power, Ed changed to a 74S00 IC and increased the voltage to get 250-mW output. He liked to brag that his final amplifier was a NAND gate. Then on a November weekend, Ed decided to do some operating.

Fig 16-1—This is the antenna that Chip, K7JA, used to set the low-power record in the CW version of the ARRL November Sweepstakes when he operated from Puerto Rico.

What he found on his crystal frequency was a fellow in South Carolina calling CQSS. To Ed's surprise, the guy answered his first call. Wow, South Carolina with a quarter watt! A bit later the frequency was clear, and Ed tried a few CQs and ended up working about a dozen states. The bug had bitten, and though it took a couple of years, Ed worked all 50 states with 250 mW. It took patience—in the case of Hawaii he spent hours answering a station's CQs before conditions were good enough to complete a Sweepstakes exchange. Then came Utah and finally with trembling hand he worked that final state—Alaska. Now for some folks that's a lot of work, but for Ed it was a rush!

These examples show that you don't need to run a lot of power or to use big antennas to have fun. Of course, I could tell you of others who have fun because they do use big antennas and because they do run the legal limit. One fellow is thrilled after breaking a personal record for most contest QSOs in a single hour. Another is ecstatic after having made a single contact with a celebrity (be it a US senator, a king, or an astronaut).

Fun then is doing active things that you enjoy and that bring you enjoyment. It *is* that simple. Find the fun and exploit it.

Resources

Sometimes a person needs a little more help. This section is provided to assist you in finding that help.

In Print

Do you receive *QST*? If so, you already know about the useful news and information that you'll find in its pages every month. If not, you should join ARRL. The reasons are explained on the page of this book titled **About the ARRL**.

If you want to know more about the theory of antennas and more about different and exotic types of antennas, you should purchase a copy of *The ARRL Antenna Book*. Not only will you get in-depth coverage of the theory, but you'll also receive the companion CD-ROM. On that CD you'll find software by the editor Dean Straw, N6BV. Two

of these are full-featured Windows programs: *YW* (Yagi for Windows) for analyzing monoband Yagis, and *TLW* (Transmission Line for Windows), a full-fledged transmission-line and antenna-tuner analysis program. One of my favorite programs from Dean is called *YT* (Yagi Terrain analysis), an HF terrain-analysis program that computes the effect of your local terrain by means of reflection and diffraction techniques. You also find a lot of propagation data and other useful programs on the disk. If you don't already have the latest edition of the *Antenna Book*, you ought to consider buying one.

For general Amateur Radio reference, it's impossible to beat *The ARRL Handbook*. The book is just a bit bigger than the *Antenna Book*, and it covers

every aspect of Amateur Radio. That means you won't find as many pages about antennas and related topics. Nevertheless, because of the breadth of coverage, you'll probably come to the conclusion that *The Handbook* is an essential part of your Amateur Radio library.

The ARRL Operating Manual is a useful reference for matters pertaining to operating. It's chock full of tables and tips. I keep my copy in the ham shack at my operating position.

People

Sometimes you can find a fellow ham in your neighborhood or town who is willing to help. Perhaps the best way to find such a person is through a local ham club. Ask other hams about clubs in your area. You can locate ARRL-affiliated clubs by contacting HQ or on the *ARRLWeb* at: **http://www.arrl.org/**. Click on "Clubs."

Computer and Online Resources

The premier place for hams online is the *ARRLWeb*. I won't try to describe it in depth here, because it is dynamic—changing everyday. What you will find is news, information and links to other Web pages. League members enjoy special privileges on the site. Check it out.

We've added a special section to the *ARRLWeb* with notes and *EZNEC* files just for you, as a reader of this book. You'll find this at: **http://www.arrl.org/notes/8624/**. These *EZNEC* files model some of the K8CH/N6BV

designs in *Simple and Fun Antennas for Hams*.

At **http://www.antennex.com/** you'll find articles and information about antennas. The content changes from time to time, so you'll want to regularly visit this site.

You can find articles, news, product reviews, classifieds, calendar and other resources on eHam.net at **http://www.eham.net/**.

Contesting.com at **http://www.contesting.com/** is geared toward hams who participate and enjoy contests. Even if that doesn't describe you, you'll want to visit this Web site often because of the mailing list archives that are there.

One of those lists is Tower Talk,

which is dedicated to antennas and related topics. You can find out more about this list at: **http://www.contesting.com/FAQ/towertalk**. The archive at Contesting.com will give you a chance to review past postings to Tower Talk. This list is very active. That means lots of messages and lively discussion. Some of the regulars are very knowledgeable and they provide excellent advice and insight. If you wish to subscribe, send a message with the word 'subscribe' only in the body of a message addressed to **towertalk-request@contesting.com**. If your subscribe was successful, you will receive an information message back automatically stating that you have been added to the list.

Your Help Needed

These final words are my personal message to you. Thank you for purchasing and reading *Simple and Fun Antennas for Hams*. Dean and I have done our best to bring you practical antenna

projects that work. Now we need to hear from you. How well have we met our goal? What could we do to improve this book? Send me e-mail at **k8ch@arrl.net**. Dean's address is **n6bv@arrl.org**. Share your opinions and ideas with HQ by filling out and returning the feedback form or by e-mail: **pubsfdbk@arrl.org**. Your communications are welcome.

FEEDBACK

Please use this form to give us your comments on this book and what you'd like to see in future editions, or e-mail us at **pubsfdbk@arrl.org** (publications feedback). If you use e-mail, please include your name, call, e-mail address and the book title, edition and printing in the body of your message. Also indicate whether or not you are an ARRL member.

Where did you purchase this book?
□ From ARRL directly   □ From an ARRL dealer

Is there a dealer who carries ARRL publications within:
□ 5 miles   □ 15 miles   □ 30 miles   of your location?   □ Not sure.

License class: _____

Name _____   ARRL member?   □ Yes □ No

_____   Call Sign _____

Daytime Phone   (   ) _____   Age _____

Address _____

City, State/Province, ZIP/Postal Code _____

If licensed, how long? _____

Other hobbies _____

_____

Occupation _____

For ARRL use only	SFAH
Edition	1 2 3 4 5 6 7 8 9 10 11 12
Printing	1 2 3 4 5 6 7 8 9 10 11 12

From _____

_____

_____

EDITOR, ARRL SIMPLE FUN ANTENNAS
AMERICAN RADIO RELAY LEAGUE
225 MAIN STREET
NEWINGTON CT 06111-1494

— — — — — — — — — — — — — — — please fold and tape — — — — — — — — — — — — — — —